FWB's Guide to Storage

FWB, Inc.
1555 Adams Drive
Menlo Park, California, USA 94025-1439

Phone and fax numbers

- Main number: 415-325-4FWB
- Technical Support fax number: 415-833-4662
- HammerFax™ number: 415-833-4683
- Marketing fax number: 415-833-4657
- Sales fax number: 415-833-4655

E-mail addresses

- AppleLink: FWB
- eWorld: FWB.INC
- America Online: FWBINC
- CompuServe: 71320,1034
- Internet: info@fwb.com
- FWB Web Page: http://www.fwb.com

MW00333251

FWB's Guide to Storage

Copyright Notice

Trademarks

Hard Disk ToolKit is a trademark of FWB, Inc. FWB, Hammer and SledgeHammer are registered trademarks of FWB, Inc.

All brand and product names are trademarks or registered trademarks of their respective holders.

Credits

This guide was written by Norman Fong with help from Steve Dalton, Bruce Dundas, Eric Herzog, Al Pierce, Stuart Saraquse, and Fred Swan. It was edited by Joan Carter with help from Allan Levite. Illustrations were produced by Deane Morris. The original version of this manual was written in 1991 by Leslie Feldman, Norman Fong, Kevin Kachadourian, Neil Strudwick, and Paul Worthington as part of FWB's *Hard Disk ToolKit* 1.x manual.

Dedication

This book is dedicated to my family and friends who put up with the long hours put into this effort. Kudos to those who enjoyed the original and inspired us to push the envelope once again five years later!

Preface

Thank you for purchasing FWB's Guide to Storage. We hope you will find this an informative guide to one of the most important components of your computer: your storage peripherals.

Most users never think twice about their drives until they cannot install a new program or save a file. Yet behind the drive letter or icon on your screen is a vast amount of technology representing millions of hours of research and development. Storage peripherals are another way technology has enabled users to dramatically increase their productivity.

This Guide is not meant to document each subject exhaustively, but to serve as a bridge between non-technical documentation on storage and the technical specifications that define the major standards and technologies. We will cover many of the most important storage-related technologies in detail.

Once you have read this Guide, if you are interested in deepening your understanding of storage technology, there are many fine books available today that focus on specific subjects, such as drive interfaces, jumper settings, and other specific storage technologies. Look in the Bibliography for additional relevant titles.

Please contact us if you have suggestions for additions to this Guide.

NORMAN FONG
President, FWB, Inc.

Table of Contents

List of Figures

List of Tables

1

Introduction

About This Guide

FWB's Guide to Storage is presented in seven sections:

- All About Drives
- All About SCSI (Small Computer System Interface)
- All About Serial SCSI
- Other Storage Interfaces
- All About Expansion Buses
- Storage Software
- Troubleshooting

Appendix, Glossary, Bibliography and Index information are included at the back of the book.

Overview of Chapters

This manual offers a foundation of information to help you take full advantage of the power of your storage peripherals and utility software. A brief overview of each chapter is provided below.

Chapter 2, All About Drives

Chapter 2 provides detailed information on the functioning of hard disk drives and other storage devices. If you are not knowledgeable about hard drives, read this chapter before changing any formatting options in your disk formatting software.

Chapter 3, All About SCSI

Chapter 3 describes the Small Computer System Interface (SCSI). Read; this chapter to discover how SCSI enables your computer to communicate with various peripherals, including drives.

Chapter 4, All About Serial SCSI

Chapter 4 describes the serial version of the Small Computer System Interface. Read this chapter to discover how Serial SCSI enables your computer to transfer data at rates not possible with normal parallel SCSI.

Chapter 5, Other Storage Interfaces

Chapter 5 describes the variety of storage interface technology available today, including IDE, Intelligent Drive Electronics interface. Read this chapter to boost your understanding of other storage interfaces.

Chapter 6, All About Expansion Buses

Chapter 6 describes the internal expansion buses of microcomputers. Read this chapter to develop your understanding of how buses extend your computer's speed and expandability.

Chapter 7, Storage Software

Chapter 7 describes the various categories of software designed to enhance the flexibility of your storage peripherals. Read this chapter to learn what types of utility software are available.

Chapter 8, Troubleshooting

Chapter 8 describes some typical problems with using storage peripherals and suggests solutions. Read this chapter to develop your knowledge of steps to take when things go wrong.

2

All About Drives

Overview

Hard disk drives, like most other storage devices, are named for their storage medium. There is an actual hard disk platter, or multiple platters, inside the mechanism. This is where data is stored and retrieved. A hard disk platter is about one-eighth of an inch thick. Its diameter varies.

See "Form Factor" on page 22 for more information on disk diameters.

Hard disk drives, or simply hard drives, are crucial parts of any computer system. They provide nonvolatile, online access to vast amounts of information, such as the software you purchase and the work you perform.

Nonvolatile memory means that data is not lost when the computer is turned off. This is in contrast to volatile memory, such as RAM, which forgets all stored data once the computer is turned off.

The central processing unit (CPU) executes programs that reside in volatile RAM, but those programs and corresponding data need to be loaded from disk. All data is lost when power is withdrawn from volatile RAM, but nonvolatile disk storage maintains its data after power loss. Next to the CPU and RAM, the hard disk is one of the most expensive pieces of hardware in your computer.

Storage Life

Compared to the computer's RAM (Random-Access Memory), which retains information only as long as the machine is running, hard drives do a much better job of preserving information:

- They have far greater capacity.
- They're cheaper.
  The cost of magnetic media (i.e., a hard drive) is much lower than the cost for silicon chips (i.e., RAM). This cost differential has been growing, making drive storage over 100 times cheaper per megabyte than RAM.

- They're far less subject to adverse environmental conditions.

  The hard disk media, that is the disk platter that data is stored on, is permanently encased in the drive and never contacts the drive's heads during normal use. The fact that the disk is neither exposed to air nor directly touched by the drive's heads minimizes the amount of degradation that naturally occurs over time.

If used and stored in accordance with the drive's recommendations, a hard disk drive could store data without loss for ten or more years. Yet no storage medium is truly permanent; all will eventually become degraded and lose information.

For a longer life, CD-ROM and other optical drives are the only storage media that may approach permanence. Current assessments anticipate that CDs will last for 100 years or more.

 See "Other Types of Storage Devices" on page 84 for more information on other types of media.

Capacity and Access

Most computer owners want greater storage capacity and faster data access than is offered by floppy disk drives. A computer can access data from a hard disk in 10 milliseconds (ms). A computer can access data from a floppy disk in 200 ms (average access time). Access from a hard disk is twenty times faster than access from a floppy. (They're both slowpokes compared to RAM, which can be accessed in 100 nanoseconds—200 times faster than a hard drive.)

A hard drive's storage media spins faster than a floppy's—5,400 revolutions per minute (RPM) or faster, compared to 360 RPM for floppy disks—and thus can access data more quickly. The disk in a hard disk drive, also known as the platter, spins constantly: It's always ready to do its job. A floppy motor turns on and off, which slows disk access and adds latency.

 Latency is the time it takes for the requested magnetic or optical disk track or sector to rotate to the correct position under the read/write heads of a disk drive. This is one of the factors that govern access speed.

 For more information on the mechanics of a hard drive, see "Anatomy of a hard drive" on page 8.

Most hard drives have data transfer rates that average from five to hundreds of megabits per second (Mb/s or millions of bits per second); floppy drives can transfer data only as fast as 0.2 to 0.4 Mb/s.

As of 1996, the storage limit on 5.25-inch hard disk drives is as much as 23 gigabytes (GB; one GB equals 1,000 MB). The 1996 storage limit on standard floppies is about 1.4 MB.

 The platter in a hard disk drive really is a hard disk; the medium is rigid, not flexible, and because its surface is dense, a large amount of data can be stored on it.

Before getting more deeply into the technology, let's explore some basic facts about hard drives.

It's somewhat like a record player

In several respects the operation of a hard drive is like a record player. A mechanism on the hard drive travels across the hard disk surface to read and transmit information similar to the way a tone arm on a record player travels across the surface of a record to provide audio.

Instead of a needle that detects bumps and pits in the record surface, disk drives have electromagnetic read/write heads that create and detect magnetic information on the surface of the disk platters. The read/write head of a hard drive is a tiny electromagnet at the end of an armature. The head is analogous to a record player's needle or stylus.

 An armature is the supporting framework for a drive head.

High-capacity drives have more than one platter. This is similar to having many records stacked on top of a turntable, with the following exceptions:

- A hard drive's "records"—disk platters—all rotate together.
- Most high-capacity drives have a separate armature for each platter.

Unlike a record player, the hard drive's "needle" does not come into contact with the disk. In fact, nothing should touch the platter. Most drives are virtually air tight so that not even dust particles can affect their operation. As the disk spins, it creates an air cushion upon which the read/write head floats. This air-cushion gap is much narrower than a speck of dust: only a couple microns tall (millionths of a meter).

Instead of plowing along physical grooves on a vinyl record and moving steadily inward, the read/write head follows tracks and moves in and out. These are the invisible magnetic "grooves" upon which data is physically stored. Instead of one continuous track, as you'd find on a vinyl record, tracks form distinct concentric circles that emanate from the center, or hub, of the platter out to the perimeter.

Information is sent as an electric current by the hard drive's controller to the controlling chips. This current passes through the magnetic read/write head, which magnetizes particles on the platter's tracks in binary on/off patterns, or bits—the standard building blocks of the digital language used by computers. The media stays magnetized when the power is turned off, just as a record holds a lasting impression after it is cast.

A Short History of Hard Drives

BH (before hard drives)

Storage for computers has existed since the early 1950s, when companies such as IBM stored data on what was known as "Drum Storage." These drives were shaped like drums, had heads that touched the platters, and held very little data.

 In 1956, a small group of IBM engineers developed the RAMAC 305. It stored 5 MB on 50 24-inch disks and had a 600 ms access time. It cost about $35,000 a year to lease. RAMAC is an acronym for Random Access Method of Accounting and Control. The RAMAC was the first storage device with random access to data.

The punch card was an early form of data storage for computers. Some mainframe computers still use 80-column punch cards. Binary data is encoded in the card using holes (or lack of holes) to represent ones and zeros (data bits). These principles were applied to punched paper tape, and later to magnetic tape, which held more data than could its paper counterpart. Instead of holes, magnetic tape used recorded magnetic signals in a fashion similar to audio tape recorders.

 The original Apple II and IBM PC had a port to which you could attach an audio tape recorder for data storage.

One disadvantage of all tape drives is that they access data relatively slowly. This is a limitation of their design. Most tape drive's read/write heads stand still while the tape is moved over it. To get information from two sectors at opposite ends of the tape, the drive must travel across the entire distance between them (this is known as sequential access). No matter how good the equipment, or how fast the motor, tape can wind only so fast before it snaps.

Disk drives are a great improvement. By using a spinning platter instead of winding tape, the media can move at far greater speeds. But the greatest advantage comes from putting the read/write head on an armature that can move across the platter to access the information "randomly." The head no longer has to travel down the length of the media but can cut across tracks of information to access what it needs directly.

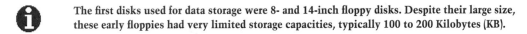

The first disks used for data storage were 8- and 14-inch floppy disks. Despite their large size, these early floppies had very limited storage capacities, typically 100 to 200 Kilobytes (KB).

The first true hard drive

IBM developed the first true hard drive technology in 1973. It was named the "Winchester 30/30," after the Winchester 30/30 rifle. The hard drive used two 30 MB disks, one fixed and one removable. The unit eventually got marketed as the model 3340.

The first widely available floppy drive was a 143 KB, 5.25-inch disk developed for the Apple II in 1979. To date, most hard drives are still manufactured by American firms, although companies from other countries are always trying to break into the market.

It wasn't until 10 years later, in 1983, that hard drives hit the mainstream with IBM's introduction of the PC XT. As technology improved, hard drives grew. Capacity doubled almost every 18 months. Price per megabyte dropped rapidly, from around $50 per megabyte to under $0.25 per megabyte.

Price per megabyte continues to drop at a rate of 10% or more per quarter.

The density of the magnetic material on the surface of the hard drive's disk platter increased, allowing storage of more bits of data on increasingly smaller areas. The read/write heads were made smaller and more sensitive so they could read a smaller magnetic domain. This made it possible to store even more bits per inch on the disk surface.

A magnetic domain is the space, or zone, on a magnetic disk that stores one bit of data.

The number of platters and heads have also increased. Some hard disk drives today have as many as ten platters, with two heads per platter—one reading/writing the top of the platter, the other the bottom.

Improvements in data encoding reduced the amount of platter space needed for mapping out the disk. Originally, encoding used half the space on each of the disks. Now, a multiple-platter hard drive using a dedicated servo head actuator can put all the encoding data on one side of one disk, freeing the remainder of the disks for storage of the user's information.

A head actuator is the physical device that moves the armature and thus the read/write head(s) across the surface of the platter. Servo information is used for guiding the head's positioning over data.

NOTE For more information on data encoding, see "Encoding" on page 26.

Mechanics

To understand a hard drive, you need to look at it from both a hardware and software perspective. Hardware is discussed below. Software is discussed in "Operations" on page 24.

Anatomy of a hard drive

Overview

A hard drive is a small box of magic. Its performance depends on the smooth interworking of its many components. Enclosed within a hard drive box are years of development in many areas:

- Computer software
- Electrical engineering
- Mechanical engineering
- Metallurgy

All these disciplines working together to create such a successful product is a great example of teamwork.

The hard drive's mechanics can be divided into two main functions:

- Moving the head so it is over the correct track
- Spinning the disk so the desired sectors pass under the head

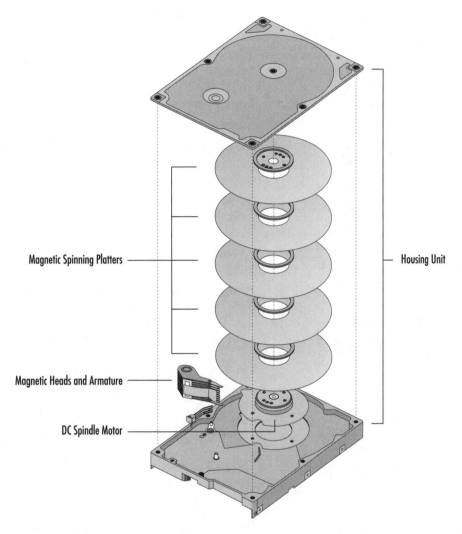

Magnetic Spinning Platters

Housing Unit

Magnetic Heads and Armature

DC Spindle Motor

Figure 1. *Exploded internal view of a hard drive*

Internal hard drive components include the following:

- Magnetic read/write head
- Magnetic spinning platter
- Power supply
- Specially designed electric DC motor to which the platters are attached

The DC motor is for spinning the spindle at a constant rate.

- Armature to which the read/write head is attached
- Atmospheric controls
- Vibration isolators
- Head actuator

Some of these have been touched upon in the preceding text and are illustrated in Figure 1, above.

On most drive mechanisms, jumper pins or DIP switches allow you to adjust the following settings:

- SCSI ID
- Terminator power
- Parity
- Wait spin
- Various diagnostics

These jumpers and DIP switches are located on the drive's controller.

 A drive controller is circuitry that provides the hardware interface between the disk drive and the computer, sending and receiving signals. It interprets the computer's signals and controls the operations of the disk drive.

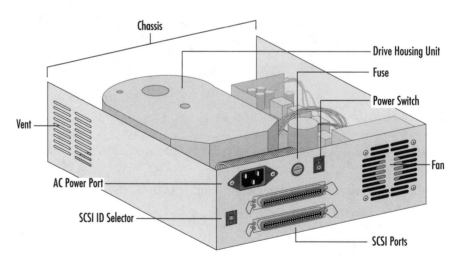

Figure 2. *Cross section of an external (enclosed) hard drive*

External components of a typical external hard drive include the following:

- Chassis (also called casing box or enclosure)
- LED indicating that power is on
- LED indicating when the drive is operating (on most but not all drives)
- Power switch
- AC power jack
- SCSI ports

Most external drives have two SCSI ports for connecting other SCSI peripherals.

- SCSI ID switch

Some drives require jumper pins or software to change the SCSI ID.

Head actuators

The read/write head is attached to an armature that is moved across the platter in precise incremental distances by mechanical devices called head actuators. The head actuator moves the head forward or back, not side to side. It uses the spinning of the platter in conjunction with the head's forward and backward movement to access off-center areas on a data track.

Read/write heads are designed to detect and create magnetic domains on the drive's platters. A magnetic domain is the area on a platter that contains one bit of data. Most heads consist of an iron core with 8 to 30 coil turns of wire banded around it. There is a gap in the core through which a magnetic field passes. The field is induced by the coil of wires wrapped around the iron core, depending on the direction current is flowing in the coil. Such heads are called inductive heads.

During the read operation, the head passes over a magnetic domain on the media; this causes the field to be inducted into the core and current to flow into the coil. During the write operation, the drive supplies the current to the coil causing a field to be induced onto the media.

The width of the head gap in the iron core determines to a great extent how dense data is on the disk. The wider the gap, the wider the tracks will be and the less dense the data will be on the disk. A smaller gap allows the head to fly closer to the platter, increasing reliability and data pickup. Gap width determines track density in tracks per inch.

You can calculate the number of tracks per inch by using the following formula (Figure 3):

$$\text{Tracks per inch (TPI)} = \frac{\text{Outer disk radius} - \text{Inner disk radius}}{\text{Track Width}}$$

Figure 3. *Formula for calculating tracks per inch*

Most modern drives have TPI in the 3000+ area. Most drives fly their heads mere microns above the platter (see Figure 4).

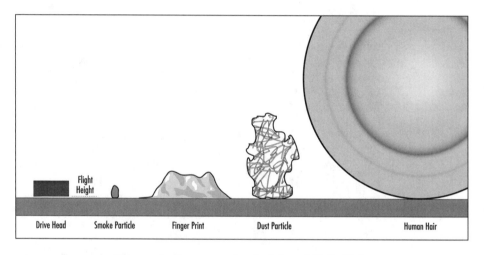

| Drive Head | Smoke Particle | Finger Print | Dust Particle | Human Hair |

Flight Height

Figure 4. *Comparative height of disk flight*

 The flight height of a modern drive head is equivalent to a jumbo jet flying at less than one inch above the ground.

The head disk assembly (HDA) must be sealed with very clean air inside. The HDA is not hermetically sealed; it needs air circulation to operate. But since the smallest particle would interfere with operation of the drive, most HDAs have absolute filters that prevent particles bigger than a certain size from contaminating the disk. These filters usually have a filtering ability of several tenths of a micron. At the same time, they allow outside air into the sealed area of the drive to equalize pressures and temperatures in accordance with changes in the computer's external environment.

Air is pulled into the drive by the centrifugal action of the platter and the spindle.

The head is mounted on a slider. The head/slider assembly is designed aerodynamically to enable it to fly across the disk surface on an air cushion created by the spinning disk.

A slider is a rigid block of material upon which a disk head is mounted. It provides lift, stability and mechanical strength to the head assembly. There are many types of sliders: A composite slider has a ceramic body and a thin core bonded with glass; a mini-composite slider is like a composite only 2/3 smaller; a monolithic slider is the oldest type of Winchester slider, made entirely of magnetic ferrite; a mini-monolithic slider is like a monolithic slider only 2/3 smaller; and a thin film slider, which is a silicon-based slider. In a thin film slider, the head, head core and coil are all built into the slider.

Heads are primarily made by a thin film process. The process is similar to making chips: a silicon substrate is doped and etched to form the slider. Hundreds of heads are created on a single wafer.

Some heads can record data longitudinally. This means that the magnetic field lines that move from the gap to the platter travel in a direction that is parallel to the platter surface and the track's length.

Other heads record data in a perpendicular or vertical method. In this case, regions of magnetic domains have their magnetism pointing up or down, into or out of the surface. This type of recording allows for greater data densities.

With inductive heads, the higher the bit density, the smaller the signals induced by these bits. The smaller the signal, the harder it is to measure reliably. This increases the need for a highly sensitive head, capable of accurately locating and reading the weaker signal.

Inductive heads have an iron core with 8 to 30 coil turns of wire banded around it. There is a gap in the core through which a magnetic field passes. The field is induced by the coil of wires wrapped around the iron core, depending on the direction current is flowing in the coil.

To address this problem, IBM developed the Magneto-Resistive (MR) head in the late 1980's. MR heads are thin conductive strips that detect magnetic domain transitions by measuring magnetic effects on the resistive element within the head. This element changes its resistance as its angle of magnetization changes. IBM first brought this technology to market in 1992. It made possible data densities of over 1000 megabits per square inch, a 10 to 25 percent improvement over previous technology. Second generation MR heads doubled densities to over 2000 megabits per square inch.

MR technology has two major limitations that have prevented it from being utilized by more than a few of the latest high-end drives:

- MR heads only read data; drives still need an inductive write head.
- They're expensive; MR heads are double the price of inductive heads.

The next head technology to supersede MR is giant magnetoresistance (GMR). It may permit magnetic recording in the tens of gigabits per square inch and data rates in the tens of megabytes per second. This new technology has sensitivity in the greater-than 3000 microvolt per micron of track width range. This should continue the 60 percent per year growth rate of data density.

Access time and seek time

Access time refers to the time it takes the read/write head to move back and forth in search of the appropriate platter and sector. Seek time is similar but involves finding a track rather than accessing data. The difference between the two is illustrated below.

Seek Time	+	Latency	+	Time to Read a Sector	=	Access Time
9 ms	+	6.7 ms	+	1 ms	=	16.7 ms

Figure 5. *Formula for determining access time*

Other relevant specifications are track-to-track seek time, which usually runs in the 2 ms range, and head switch time, which runs in the 1 ms range.

Heads and platters

In drives with more than one platter, the multiple armatures make up a comb-like structure whose "teeth"—the arms and heads—are interspersed with the platters. Most drives have two heads per armature (and thus per platter). In this scheme, one head is on top of the platter, the other below; data is written to and read from both sides. This allows the entire platter to fill with useful data. On drives with a dedicated servo positioning platter, the head for the servo platter is used to position the other heads.

 For more information on servo positioning, see "Servo positioning information" on page 17.

A drive with five platters would have 10 heads, with only one being used at any one time. There are special drives, such as the Seagate ST12450W, that utilize parallel transfers from two heads at the same time. This effectively doubles transfer rates but decreases data storage because sectors need to be half their size on each platter to form a normal 512 byte data sector.

Double actuators

A few drives feature two actuators, positioned at opposite sides of a disk. This design was first seen on Conner's Chinook in 1991. This scheme cuts in half the drive's latency time, which is the time it takes for the spinning platter to bring around the desired platter location to where the read/write head can access it. You could write with one head and read with another. But because reading and writing are not simultaneous in non-multitasking operations, this design—although costly—offers no performance improvement in those applications. It's typically cheaper to buy multiple drives.

For more information on latency, see "Spinning 'round" on page 20.

Actuator movement

There are two methods for head actuator movement:

- Stepper motor, a type of rotational pivot used in a floppy drive.
- Servo voice-coil actuator, which is a more efficient and accurate method.

Stepper motors

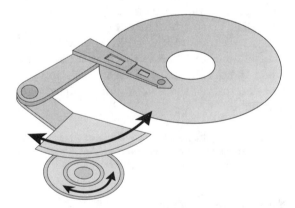

Figure 6. Stepper motor actuator

Stepper motors use a system somewhat like a car's transmission to convert an incremental rotary movement into linear travel. The motor rotates either direction a few degrees at a time. Connected to it is the stepper band, which converts that incremental rotary motion into linear movement, repositioning the armature and thus changing the read/write head's position over the platter. As the assembly ages, stepper motors will usually cause problems with

---

precision, known as head drift. This is due to the unadjustable mechanical nature of the motor. Stepper motors went out of use in the early 90's.

Servo voice coil actuators

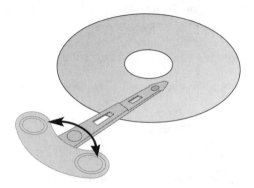

Figure 7. *Voice coil actuator*

Voice coils, or servos, work like common audio speakers. The sound of a loud-speaker is determined by the strength of the current pumped through its electromagnet, which pulls on a diaphragm connected to the speaker's cone. In a hard disk drive, the current passes through a voice-coil electromagnet that pulls the armature toward it. The armature is held back by a spring that provides a counter-force to the magnet and automatically moves the head back when the current is decreased. The strength of the current going to the voice coil determines the position of the head over the platter, making it infinitely adjustable.

 Servo control is the process used in disk and tape drives to regulate head positioning and seeking. It relies on "positioning data" that is either contained on a dedicated servo disk or embedded among data blocks on all disk surfaces.

Voice coil advantages

Voice coils provide an infinite degree of positioning control. This is superior to the stepper, whose accuracy is limited by its incremental rotational step. By moving the head in smaller increments, the voice coil actuator can take advantage of higher-density platters, which squeeze more tracks onto the same platter. They are also less susceptible to head drift. As the head assembly ages, the servo system can automatically compensate for the wear.

The voice coil system performs much faster than the old stepper motor. A large amount of current can be sent into the coils to push the head more quickly. With the stepper motor, the current is a fixed quantity.

Another characteristic of the voice-coil method—and another advantage it has over the stepper method—is that the head is usually "autoparking." Autoparking helps to prevent head crashes. Upon power loss, the heads are automatically pulled by the spring to a safe position on the disk—the landing or parking zone. Usually a capacitor is used to store extra charge, forcing the voice-coil to autopark onto the mechanical stop even if power is lost. Some stepper-motor drives come with an autoparking feature. This can be a function of the controller or part of the installation software.

Servo positioning information

The slightest fluctuation in the electric current can cause the head to wander away from the center of the track. To prevent this, servo data is embedded on the platter between the tracks in the form of magnetic bursts known as embedded servo or wedged servo. Wedged servo was the first attempt at embedding servo information on the platter. It placed a single burst of servo position information on each disk. Because there is only one burst, the drive would have to wait a full rotation to get the information, slowing performance. Others employed doubled embedded servos, placing servo information at the beginning and middle of the sector.

Later designed drives employed an embedded servo where multiple servo bursts are present on each track, each in front of a sector. This allowed for even greater accuracy. When sensors on the head sense that the bursts are too strong, the controller knows that the head is wandering from the center of the track and adjusts the current accordingly.

Embedded servo tracks take up space on the platter and reduce its data storage capacity. Some high-capacity, multiple-platter drives utilize a dedicated servo surface, in which one side of one of the platters contains only servo data, which is used to guide the head. The head for that surface is used solely for positioning. Others use embedded servo information encoded within a normal data platter. Because all heads are attached to the same actuator, all of the heads will be aligned and all other surfaces can be used for data.

Some drives employ a hybrid servo system where there are dedicated servo platters as well as embedded servo information on each of the other drive platters. This ensures that the drive can make precise positioning changes during read and write operations. The disadvantage is that a great deal of capacity is wasted.

Read/Write channel

After the read/write head is positioned over the data, a group of circuits known as the read/write channel actually transfers the data off the platter. These circuits read the sector header information to ensure that the data being read or written is the data that is desired. They also amplify signals to ensure they are strong enough to record information. These circuits must be extremely fast to handle the transitions between looking at sector information and reading or writing the data into the sector in the same rotation. These circuits are often the limiting factor in drive performance.

The Medium

Most platters are made of finely machined aluminum. Some are made of ceramic. Some are made of glass. Glass platters have been used in 1.8-inch drives. They allow 20 to 30 percent greater density than metal platters and offer a smoother, more rigid surface so heads can fly lower. Aluminum is preferred because it is strong and highly pliable. This is ideal for creating thin platters. Aluminum is also subject to very little expansion when it is heated.

A platter's structural integrity and weight are important, but what matters most is the coating applied to its surface.

For forty years, ferric oxide (FE_2O_3) coatings have been used as the primary medium for data storage. In recent years, a variant using cobalt-nickel alloys instead of pure ferric oxide has been used to improve densities and provide better reliability. If a floppy's surface looks rusty to you, it's because it's covered with rust-oxidized iron particles held in place with a binding agent (typically plastic). These are the particles that are magnetized by the magnetic head to represent the "on" or "off" patterns of data.

Magnetic recording is based on the fact that metals can be permanently magnetized by external magnetic fields. Areas saturated with magnetic charge are known as "domains." The magnetic head of the disk drive senses data by the amount of current induced in the head as it passes over the boundaries between domains and passes this on to read-channel electronics.

 A magnet is a metal that has been exposed to a magnetic field, causing the electrons in the metal to spin in a consistent direction. Electrons are theorized to spin in either a North-South or South-North orientation. Groups of atoms can be magnetized to align themselves in a particular direction.

Much more difficult, but more rewarding, is the application of a chrome-like covering found on most late-model, high-speed, high-capacity hard drives. A pure metal film is plated onto an aluminum platter, either by vapor deposition or sputtering. The thin-film media of a plated surface, as it's called, is one-tenth as thick as the standard oxide coating. Because this surface does not have a binding agent mixed in, the magnetic particles are packed much more tightly, allowing as many as 80,000 bits per inch. Oxide coatings allow only 20,000 bits per inch.

The future promises more innovations in data storage media, such as the glass platters that have recently been introduced in some 2.5-inch drives. Glass offers a smoother surface and better rigidity than aluminum or ceramic. It is very useful for platters that spin faster than the standard 3,600 RPM of the 1980's.

Spinning 'round

Platters are mounted on an axle called the spindle. A drive may contain more than one platter, yet all platters are mounted on a single spindle. The spindle usually rotates the disks in a counter-clockwise direction.

The spindle is turned by a brushless, direct-drive (no gears or belts), direct-current (DC) electric motor. This motor may be built into the spindle or may reside below it.

 The model that resides below the spindle is called a pancake motor because of its flat shape.

Depending on the specific drive, hard drive motors spin the disks at 3,600 RPM (which is typical), 5,400 RPM, or even 7,200 RPM. With higher spindle rates come higher noise and heat levels but also higher performance.

As noted in "Head actuators" on page 11, latency is the time it takes for a desired sector on the platter to pass underneath the head after head positioning is complete. For a platter spinning at the 7,200 RPM rate, average latency is 4.2 milliseconds. The faster the platter rotates, and the more read/write heads per platter, the smaller the latency and the better the performance.

Latency is one factor in data access time. Other factors that influence data access time include the following:

- Seek time

  Seek time is the time it takes for the read/write head to move back and forth before it locates the appropriate sector of information. Average seek time is the amount of time it takes to position the drive's heads on a randomly located place on the disk.

- Head switch time

  Head switch time is the time it takes to switch between any two read/write heads.

- Cylinder switch time

  Cylinder switch time is the amount of time it takes to move from one track to another.

The final factor in the access time equation is command overhead, which is the time needed for the computer's command to be interpreted and acted upon by the controller.

Thus, access time equals latency plus seek time plus command overhead. Some operations do not include command overhead time in the equation, while others add data transfer rates into the equation.

Head parking

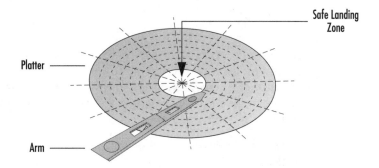

Figure 8. *Safe landing zone for head parking*

If the head were to physically contact the platter it could destroy data, perhaps even remove magnetic particles from its surface and cause irreparable damage.

While the platter is spinning, the read/write heads are kept off the platter by the air buffer the spinning creates. However, the head should be moved away from the data area of a platter when the hard drive is turned off. This process is called head parking. Portable and laptop computers also have a "sleep" mode that parks the head after a certain period of inactivity.

A head is parked when it is moved over an area on the platter that is used only as a "parking space" or "landing zone." This area is typically at the center of the platter near the spindle. Head parking avoids accidental contact of head and platter, and is particularly important if the drive is being moved.

Some drives park the heads in a position off the platters, preventing any chance of accidental contact from shock. Typically these drives also push a small wedge between the pairs of heads to keep them from slamming into each other.

However, head parking only *reduces* the chances of the head contacting the platter. To *eliminate* the possibility of accidental contact, many newer drives feature autolocking. Autolocking physically locks a parked head over the landing zone, preventing any movement.

Many drives that use a stepper actuator need utility software, often provided by the manufacturer, to tell the controller to park the head on computer power-down. This is obviously not as safe as an automatic device built into the drive itself. Some stepper actuator drives come with an autopark mechanism built into the controller.

Most hard disk drives manufactured since 1986 are autoparking.

Form Factor

Hard drives come in a variety of sizes, both in form factor and height. Form factor is a fancy way of referring to the platter's diameter. A hard drive with a form factor of 3.5 inches has one or more platters that are 3.5 inches in diameter. Standardized form factors allow drives to be installed on a wide variety of platforms with minimal changes.

The size of the entire housing unit, which also contains the mechanics and controller, is much larger than its form factor measurement. The housing unit or frame is the foundation to which all other parts are connected. This frame needs to be rigid so that components within the drive are not hurt on installation or during operation. Most frames are made from aluminum alloys.

Technological refinements in disk capacity have reduced the number of platters needed in high-capacity drives. Half-height models (1.625-inches tall for 5.25-inch drives) require fewer platters, and take up less vertical space in the casing. One-third-height, low-profile drives (1-inch tall for 2.5- and 3.5-inch drives) are readily available. Laptop computers that need high-capacity storage can take advantage of the compact size of 2.5-inch hard drives.

Among the more common hard drive sizes are full-height 5.25-inch drives with capacities of up to 23 GB; half-height 3.5-inch drives with capacities of up to 9 GB; one third-height 3.5-inch drives with capacities of up to 4 GB; and 2.5-inch drives with capacities of up to 2 GB. The trend has been to migrate most internal drives for Macintosh and PC to the 3.5 inch form-factor because of its price-per-megabyte advantages. Five-and-a-quarter-inch drives are used only for the highest capacity applications. Eight-inch drives are virtually extinct.

 The Macintosh II, Macintosh IIx, Macintosh IIfx and some older PCs were built to accommodate internal 5.25-inch half-height drives if a user wished to install one.

Smaller, 2.5-inch drives are gaining in popularity, primarily for laptops and notebooks. These 2.5-inch drives are available in a variety of heights from 19mm to 12.5mm. The most common size for external hard drives is

3.5 inches, although you can find 5.25-inch, 8-inch, and 14-inch drives in some mainframe or workstation applications.

Figure 9. *A 2.5-inch drive*

Drives are getting smaller

The trend in the computer marketplace is towards smaller and smaller drives. Higher densities make it possible to develop much smaller high-volume platters. Platters have gone from 14-inch to 8-inch to 5.25-inch to 3.5-inch to 2.5-inch. Even smaller 1.8-inch drives have been developed for use in personal digital assistant, palmtop, or laptop computers. The 1.8-inch drives typically come in a PCMCIA type II or III credit-card sized form-factor. Even smaller 1.3-inch drives were made at one time but proved unpopular. The reason the smaller form factor drives are not popular is usually cost. Cost per megabyte must be aggressive for consumers to move towards smaller sizes.

 PCMCIA stands for Personal Computer Memory Card International Association. It's a joint effort of various special interest groups aimed at setting a standard for memory cards used in PCs. PCMCIA cards add improved computer memory capacity or enhance connectivity to external networks and services.

Because storage capacity is the paramount concern of most users, the actual size of a drive is important to consider only when buying an internal drive—it has to fit inside the computer's casing. You are limited to a certain drive size that may not offer the capacity and performance you want. You should worry about the dimensions of a large external drive only if you have limited space or you want your computer system to be portable.

Look out for Bigfoot! In early 1996, Quantum Corporation announced the release of a low-cost, 5.25-inch form factor drive, called Bigfoot, that can be plugged into a bay used for a CD-ROM. The larger form factor is Quantum's way of dealing with the constant market demand for increased storage—up until Bigfoot, manufacturers increased storage by increasing areal density on a disk or adding more disks and heads. Quantum anticipates that Bigfoot will support only Fast ATA-2, spin at 3,600 RPM, and have a 15.5 ms access time.

In selecting a drive there are other considerations beyond the drive's physical dimensions. Smaller drives cost more per megabyte than full-size drives and, despite their denser platters, do not deliver better performance. Instead, they may sometimes prove to be both slower and less accurate, as the heads have to move more often and there is less room on the controller for a memory cache or other performance-enhancing options.

For more information on caching, see "Caching" on page 34.

Another disadvantage to internal drives is that they utilize the computer's own power supply. This may adversely affect the computer, particularly if it is a "loaded" machine. An external disk drive avoids this problem by utilizing its own power supply, allowing it to be easily moved from one computer to another.

An example of a "loaded" machine is a computer that has many internal devices and expansion cards, such as an accelerator or graphics card. These also consume power from the computer's internal transformer and generate heat, reducing the efficiency of the computer's overall operation.

Operations

Formatting

Before a hard drive can be written to, it must be formatted. Formatting's basic and critical function is to lay down tracks and sectors.

- Tracks are the invisible concentric circles of magnetic "grooves" within which data is physically stored on the platter.

- Sectors are subdivisions of tracks and are usually defined to contain exactly 4,096 bits of data (that is, 512 bytes times eight bits per byte).

  Besides the 512 bytes (or more) of data, a typical disk sector contains the following information:
  - Synchronization information
  - Sector header information
  - Sector header CRC (cyclic redundancy check)
  - Intrasector gap (separates the sector ID information from the data track. Data follows this gap.)
  - Error correcting code (ECC)
  - Intersector gap (separates the preceding sector from the next sector)

As you can see, there's a lot of information in a sector. The drive needs it for housekeeping. It is not accessible to the user. Some hard drive manufacturers factor these housekeeping bytes into total capacity, so the drive capacity available to the consumer is actually less than the stated capacity of the drive.

Formatting specifies alternate sectors, also called spares. The controller will utilize a spare while formatting when the read/write head encounters a bad, or corrupted, data block on the platter.

 Data blocks are the smallest chunk of memory accessed or transferred by the disk drive. They are usually 512 bytes, although they can be multiples of 512 bytes.

To support larger logical block sizes, drives automatically block and deblock physical sectors in the current block size. A data block allocated on the spare sector will correspond to the now unusable data block. The number of spares per track is configurable. It is possible to eliminate spares altogether. This frees up that sector for storage. We recommend one spare per track as a minimum. One spare is typically the default setting of a preformatted drive.

Drives usually keep a lookup table of spares in their local RAM, so the number of spares that can be handled is a fixed number limited by the size of this RAM.

By putting tracks and sectors in place, formatting sets up the hard drive's optimal organizational structure. It assigns logical data blocks to physical areas on the platter, skips over any defective areas it encounters, and keeps a grown defects list of the bad areas so that the controller knows not to write data to them.

 "Logical" is used to distinguish an abstract representation from a physical representation. Data is not physical; its representation is made physical via the read/write head magnetizing portions of the platter into recognizable patterns. For more information on logical blocks, logical units, and logical unit numbers, see Chapter 3, "All About SCSI."

Assigning logical blocks to physical sectors is done so that the drive's ability to access information can be maximized via interleaving, optimal block size, and other software configurable aspects of the hard drive's operation.

Interleaving is discussed in "Interleaving" on page 30.

Encoding

Once you have a fully functioning hard drive with all components cooperating, how does your computer store information on it? And how does it find and read this data after it is translated into magnetic patterns?

Information is not written as one contiguous stream in each track, but is broken up among sectors. The read/write head dips in and out of the sectors to read and write data as needed.

Encoding enables the head to read and write data on a moving target in fractions of a second, and to access that data again just as quickly. Encoding refers to two things:

- The protocol of laying down data as a sequence of on's and off's
- The process that lets the drive head constantly monitor its own position along a track

This definition of encoding as a process might be thought of as the digital equivalent of putting sprocket holes in a film strip. As the number of digital sprockets are tallied, an accurate measure of how far the head has moved may be determined by equating time with distance. This is possible because the speed of a platter's rotation is a known value. If one value—timing—is known, the crucial value—location—can also be determined.

Variable zone recording

The outer tracks of a platter are physically longer than the inner ones, and thus offer more real estate for data storage. In IDE and SCSI storage devices, controllers can take advantage of the outer tracks' greater storage capacity in a process called variable zone recording. This is possible because data is accessed at a high-level by specifying a block number and not a head, cylinder, sector.

In pre-IDE/SCSI drives, such as ST-506 drives, all tracks are typically assigned the same capacity.

With variable zone recording, tracks are grouped into zones. The tracks in each zone are allotted a specific number of sectors. The outer-zone tracks receive a higher number of sectors than the tracks in the inner zones. In addition to increasing the capacity of the platter, zone sectoring reduces access time and increases transfer rates because the head covers less ground to access the same amount of information on the platter.

The number of zones and the number of sectors per zone vary according to the size of the platter. Generally, drives with smaller form factors have fewer zones, but other considerations, including the type of media used and how it was formatted, also affect this. Variable zone recording keeps data density constant throughout the disk.

Encoding processes

On a platter spinning at 7,200 RPM, a read/write head has barely one-thousandth of a second to read one sector of information. At this speed, and with all this informational ground to cover, the head could easily lose its place. Encoding processes were developed to keep track of the head's location on the disk.

 More advanced encoding methods also allow for the recording of more data in the same amount of space.

Timing mechanisms correlate a platter's constant speed with the distance traveled to yield a precise calculation of the head's position over the platter.

Frequency Modulation (FM)

Frequency modulation was the first timing mechanism used. It needed every other magnetic domain to represent a clock pulse. This method had the disadvantage of using half of a disk's storage capacity just for the timing information.

Modified Frequency Modulation (MFM)

Modified frequency modulation solved this problem by moving the timing information onto a track all its own. During the original low-level formatting process of an MFM drive, the synchronization bytes—magnetic data that marks location and time—are added. Because it results in twice as much data storage as the original FM, MFM is also known as double-density recording.

Run Length Limited (RLL)

Run Length Limited (RLL) encoding scheme was borrowed from the world of mainframe computers to increase a drive's storage capacity beyond MFM.

As you might guess with a concept borrowed from mainframes, the theory behind RLL is more complicated than any normal computer user needs to know. Basically, it uses only a few selected optimal bit patterns, determined from magnetic flux changes in storage media.

RLL uses less disk space than MFM to store a bit. It actually uses smaller magnetic domains, or "bit cells." The read/write head of a specialized RLL controller can create bit cells one-third smaller than those used with MFM encoding. This requires a drive with a more accurate read/write head and higher density (or thinner) tracks. RLL also uses a special code that can read 16-bit patterns of information, rather than the eight bits used by MFM. Some MFM drives can directly use RLL encoding and controllers, but it is not advisable on older drives.

There are several types of RLL codes. The distinction among RLL codes is the number of zero bits that can be stored as a consecutive string before inserting a one bit.

 Bit is a contraction formed of "binary" and "digit." All computer information is represented as a unique combination of the binary digits 0 and 1, which are also called "ons" and "offs."

Under 2,7 RLL, from two to seven consecutive zero bits are allowed. This results in a 50 percent increase in drive capacity over standard MFM.

Under the 3,9 RLL technique, the run length of the zero string can range from three to nine. This method, also called Advanced Run Length Limited (ARLL), permits a 100 percent increase in drive capacity over standard MFM.

Data detection

Data is detected in hard drives typically with a technique known as peak detection. Peak detection has been used for data detection since the 1960s. It involves detecting data at high speeds by using a data-encoding method that spaces the signal during reads. The analog detection circuits can then scan each peak in series. The problem with this encoding scheme is that it generates a lot of overhead, slowing performance.

A newer technique is known as partial response maximum likelihood (PRML). This began to appear in drives in 1990. Instead of spacing out analog peaks as in peak detection, digital filtering is used to compensate for signal overlap. After filtering, the scheme identifies what are the likeliest sequence of data bits written to the media. This scheme still uses RLL encoding but can utilize advanced (0,4,4) encoding for greater density. The digital ones can take place without all the digital zero spacers. A 25 percent or better improvement in bit density can be achieved. Transfer rates increase by 25 to 50 percent. PRML causes larger errors, so error correction code needs to be longer (144-bit) and faster on these drives.

Error correction

Data stored on platters inevitably develops errors. Drive manufacturers have devised effective techniques that minimize the possibility of data loss. One of these techniques is error correcting codes (ECC), which store additional check information at the end of each data block. These extra bytes are used to verify the integrity of the block and to correct for minor errors.

Each company utilizes its own proprietary software technique. Many drives can correct for up to 22 bits with one error burst by using 11 bytes of ECC data. More advanced drives can correct even more bits. These ECC data bytes are read when using Read/Write Long commands on IDE and SCSI drives. All this error correction is transparent to the user and happens internally in the drive. Bits can be set in Mode Page 1 of SCSI drives, to alert the user to the fact that ECC was needed to correct data flaws.

 You can learn more about Mode pages in Chapter 3, "All About SCSI."

When you hear drives seeking the head hard (a hard seek usually makes a cha-chunking noise), it's probably because retries are occurring. Retries cause the head to seek back to track zero and retry the data access. A drive will try this multiple times. The number of times is defined in a SCSI drive's Mode Page 1 settings. If you hear the cha-chunking noise, you probably should back up all your data and test the drive's media for defects.

Interleaving

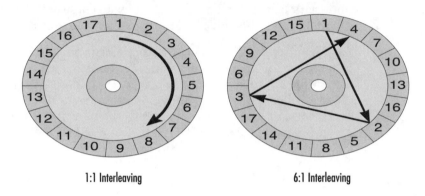

1:1 Interleaving   6:1 Interleaving

Figure 10. Examples of 1:1 and 6:1 Interleaving

The central processing unit (CPU) of some computers can't handle data as fast as the hard drive controller can access the data on the spinning platter. By the time the CPU digests the information that the head has just read from one sector and orders the head to access the next sector's information, that second sector on the spinning disk may have already passed by. To read it, the head must wait a full platter rotation for that sector to once again pass beneath it.

A hard drive's interleaving, set during low-level formatting, overcomes the CPU's slower response capability by matching data transfer rates between the read/write head and the Input/Output port of the computer.

Interleaving describes how sectors are arranged on the platter so that the head can read them in the fastest possible sequential order. The information allotted to ordered sectors does not follow the sectors' actual sequential numerical order. Information is placed on sectors that are not physically contiguous, so the head doesn't have to wait a full rotation for the sector it has missed to come by again.

On faster machines, a smaller interleave can be accommodated. Nowadays, a 1:1 interleave factor is fairly standard (Figure 10). A 1:1 interleave (actually contiguous sectors with no interleave) provides the fastest data access, but requires a fast computer (such as the Macintosh II family or newer or 80386/20, 80486 and faster).

On the Macintosh Plus or 8086 or 80286/6 machines, a 3:1 interleave factor is optimal. On the Macintosh SE or 80286/10 or faster machines, it's 2:1.

Interleaving to optimize performance became such a big issue on PCs that several programs such as SpinRite were written to re-interleave drives without losing data.

The optimal interleave is dependent on whether the drive has a track buffer. A track buffer stores the contents of an entire track that passes under a head even if the I/O request isn't for the entire range. Early ST506 and ESDI drives had track buffers on the controller card, while modern IDE and SCSI drives have them on the drive itself. A 1:1 interleave is supported on all computers for drives with track buffers. Most modern drives (those produced after 1994) actually ignore the interleave value specified during a format and always use 1:1.

Sector skew

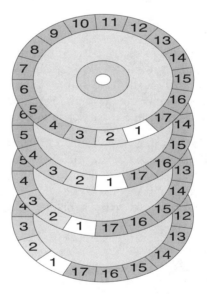

Figure 11. *Sector skew offset*

Sector skew optimizes the accessing and placing of information on adjacent tracks, in much the same way interleaving optimizes head movement within a track. It does this by taking into account the time it takes the head to move to another track and the distance a sector will travel in that time (due to the platter's rotational speed), and then offsetting the sector numbering on the next track.

Suppose the read/write head has just finished writing to the last sector on one track. Provided the interleave is set to a 1:1 optimum value, the head is ready to write to the first sector of the next track. If this takes too long on a revolution of the disk, the head will arrive too late in spite of the interleaving. To solve this, the numbering for the sectors of the next track is offset by one or more positions. This ensures that by the time the head travels to the track, the correct sector has not already passed.

Figure 11 shows a typical four-platter hard drive with a sector skew. Tracks are laid down in a cylindrical order on multi-platter hard drives. The first platter holds the first track, the second platter holds the next, and so on down the cylinder.

The concept can also be applied to a controller accessing another platter in the drive, with a different read/write head. The second platter would be skewed as many sectors as necessary to ensure that the proper sector is at the head when the controller is ready to access that platter. Only a few high-performance drives allow skew to be set by the user.

Transfer rates

Data transfer rates are determined by the density of the data encoded on the platter and how fast that data can be transferred to the host computer. The read channel on the head and the type of interface to the computer are the biggest factors limiting drive performance. Read channels are being improved, as are the links between read channels and the controller.

Data transfer rates are often communicated in megabytes or megabits per second. They are also communicated in megahertz or millions of bits per second. The sustained data transfer rate is typically the average rate at which the drive can transfer data. Most drives have differing densities depending where you are on the disk, so many transfer rate figures are variable.

A typical example of operational speeds and data density in 1995 is illustrated in Table 1:

Table 1. *Typical Operational Speeds and Data Density in 1995*

Category	Description
Speed	7200 rotations per minute (RPM) ÷ 60 seconds = 120 revolutions per second
Average Formatted Track Capacity	45,000 bytes
Average Sustained Data Transfer Rate	5.15 MB/s (more accurately from 4.16 to 6.59 MB/s)
To/From Host	20 MB/s burst (this is on a fast/wide SCSI-2 device)

A typical drive with 3200 tracks per inch has 36,352 to 57,856 bytes per track. It varies because of zoned bit recording. The sustained data transfer rate is not limited by the host interface. This is why striping multiple single drives in RAID 0 gains so much more performance.

See "What Is RAID?" on page 61 for details.

Transfer rates have not kept up with the fast pace set by CPU performance. This is illustrated in Table 2.

Table 2. *Comparison of Transfer Rates and CPU Speeds*

Year	Transfer Rates	CPU Performance
1984	1 MB/s (ST225N)	0.5 MIPS (68000, 8086)
1990	3 MB/s (3105S)	50 MIPS (68040, 80386)
1995	8 MB/s (ST12450W)	200 MIPS (604, Pentium Pro)

Disk performance appears to be improving at a rate of 20 to 30 percent a year. Conversely, CPU performance has improved 200 times in 11 years. The disk performance bottleneck has slowed total computer system performance.

Caching

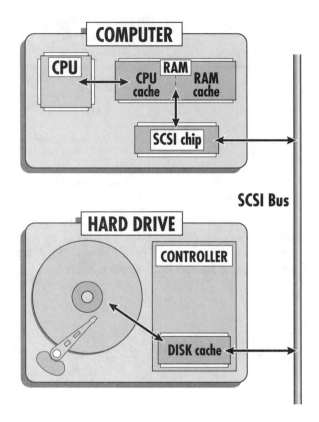

Figure 12. *Data flow in memory caches*

Caching is a popular method of accelerating operations by temporarily storing data on an intermediate medium that is faster than the source medium. Caching can improve the real performance of many diverse operations within the computer.

- Disks can be cached onto RAM.
- RAM can be cached onto cache memory.
- CD-ROM can be cached onto hard disks and/or RAM.

Disk caching minimizes overhead and access time while maximizing transfer rate in data retrieval by storing "popular," or likely to be used, information where it can be accessed quickly.

 Overhead is the operational delay incurred during command execution; the SCSI bus is the main culprit. When data is requested by the CPU, the request must go through the SCSI call chain,

---

wait for the bus, and wait for the drive's head to locate the data. Access time is seek time, plus latency, plus the time it takes the head to read a sector. For more information about the SCSI call chain, see Chapter 3, "All About SCSI."

By storing recently used data in a cache, a CPU request for this data will be served more quickly because it need not cause an actual transfer off the disk.

There are three common types of cache present in most computers:

- CPU cache resides on or near the CPU.
- Software disk cache resides in the CPU's RAM.
- Hard drive cache resides on the hard drive's controller board.

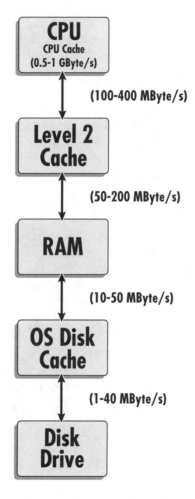

Figure 13. Data transfer rates increase the closer cache is to the CPU

The closer the information is to the CPU, the more quickly it can be accessed:

- Data stored in RAM is the closest (CPU and software disk cache).
- Data stored in the disk controller's RAM is farther away (hard disk's cache); access to the hard disk cache is slower than access to RAM cache, mostly due to data transfer on the SCSI bus.
- Data stored on the disk itself is the farthest away. In addition to the time needed to send the information on the SCSI bus, the access time and data transfer rates of the hard drive itself take a toll.

CPU cache

Cache in or external to the CPU can hold a part of a program or data so that it may be accessed quickly while the CPU is executing the program. CPU cache is fairly small because it is located in or near the CPU, where real estate is scarce and costs are high. CPU caches are constructed with expensive high-speed memory, so typically they are limited in size to about 4 to 256 KB.

 Cache that is external to the CPU is also known as Level 2 cache.

Most modern high-speed processors have secondary cache external to the CPU to speed up main memory performance. Level 2 caches range in size from 256 to 1024 KB. Typically they are constructed from high-performance sub-10 ns static cache RAM chips.

Software disk cache

Software disk cache, used for storing the most frequently accessed disk information, speeds data retrieval but limits the amount of RAM available for the program itself. Software disk cache on the computer is usually configurable. Typically it can be enabled/disabled and adjusted in size. It also can be increased through the installation of additional memory.

How much RAM you should set aside for the software disk cache depends on several considerations:

- How much RAM is available?
- How much is needed to run an application?
- What sort of application is being run?

Some programs make better use of a software disk cache than others. A word processing program loads files only as it needs them and repeatedly uses the data. Here, a software disk cache would almost certainly speed up data transfer. Spreadsheet programs usually load the entire spreadsheet at once, so a software disk cache is of little use.

The smallest software disk cache setting for System 7.5 on the Macintosh is 32 KB. If extra memory is available, set the RAM cache to a higher value. Apple has recommended 32 KB of cache per megabyte of RAM in the machine. The best way to find the optimum value is to run applications with the RAM cache at different settings. Start with 96 KB and increase it until performance is maximized. The optimum value will be the one that results in the fastest data access while maintaining enough RAM to run the program.

There is also a diminishing return with increasing cache size. As more and more memory is allocated for the cache, more and more overhead is required to maintain the cache. Applications such as digital video and color publishing stream large amounts of data, so set the software disk cache to a small number like 32 or 64 KB for these applications. Avoid virtual memory whenever possible.

Microsoft Windows for Workgroups 3.11 users should enable 32-bit file access, which handles disk caching for Windows. Users with at least 16 MB of RAM will be advised by the operating system to use 4 MB for a disk cache. Previous versions of Windows 3.1 utilize caching loaded by DOS's SMART-drive utility program. SMARTdrive is a real mode disk cache, so it does not greatly accelerate Windows operations. Windows 95 and NT automatically manage the size of the disk cache and dynamically size it depending on load.

 Windows 95 also lets you control read-ahead cache size.

Software disk caches help minimize IDE or SCSI bus traffic by servicing I/O requests within the computer itself.

Hard drive cache

Hard drive cache, located on the controller board, is used to store the most recently requested disk information or anticipated data. Although it is slower than RAM cache, it has the advantage of freeing up the computer's RAM for running programs. Hard disk cache is typically 256 KB to 1024 KB. Some drives have caches that have configurable parameters, including the following:

- Enable/disable
- Prefetch size
- Write cache enable
- Number of segments
  Disk caching uses one segment per cache entry, which prevents overwriting previously read data with a subsequent read.
- Buffer size (See "Track buffering" below.)

A segment is a logical division of a logical address space in a microprocessor. Segment lengths are variable according to, in this case, user definition.

Applications such as FWB's Hard Disk ToolKit can configure cache controls that are supported by most drives.

Track buffering

Track buffering takes advantage of the principle of locality. When data is requested from a particular sector, it is likely that the CPU will soon be asking for information located in adjacent sectors. In anticipation, the controller will read the entire track and store it in its RAM. This full track read-ahead buffer speeds up information retrieval for almost all applications, although there are exceptions. If an application uses many small data transfers from various locations on the platter, such as in database programs, having the controller read too far ahead may actually slow down the process; it will be reading and storing too much information that will never be requested by the program.

If a track buffer is not present, a program reading sequential sectors on the disk will have to wait an entire revolution for each successive sector access.

Prefetch

Prefetch is similar to buffering, except it can read ahead to the next track. These larger reads get more data ready for the CPU's next request, thus speeding up access time. The parameters controlling prefetch on many drives can be customized to maximize performance, including the number of sectors it will prefetch.

Applications such as FWB's Hard Disk ToolKit can set all configurable parameters that a specific drive supports.

Read caching

Read caching utilizes more RAM than track buffering, but it uses the RAM more efficiently. Usually there is enough RAM to store several tracks worth of data. Each time a disk request is made, the cache algorithm checks to see if it's in RAM cache. If the data is in RAM cache, it is returned right away. If the data is not in RAM cache, it is read from disk, copied to the cache, and transferred to the host. This continues until the cache is full. When it is full, there are different methods of selecting which data should be replaced with new data. Methods include:

- A random entry
- The least recently used

- The oldest entry

A variant to the read cache is the read ahead cache, where an entire track of data is read and stored in cache when a single sector of that track is requested. This allows all further transfers within the track to come from cache.

Write caching

In write caching, the controller transfers a write request to its own cache, tells the CPU that the task is complete, and then completes the write at a later time. This speeds operations because, ordinarily, the controller would not tell the CPU it had finished the command until it actually had, and the CPU would have to wait for notification before going on to the next command.

Write caching is a recent advance in improving disk performance. It holds great promise for speeding random small-chunk writes. For example, assume the following average times to complete a 4 KB random write:

Issuing the command (command overhead)	1 millisecond (ms)
Data transfer	1 ms
Seek time	14 ms
Latency	8.3 ms
Issuing a Command Complete message	1 ms
Total transfer time	25.3 ms

Figure 14. *Time it takes to complete a 4 KB random write*

With write caching, the CPU saves 22.3 ms by not being affected by latency and seek time. The total time spent is three ms. The downside is that information can be lost if there is a power off before data has been written to disk. Drivers should flush the cache when the computer is shutting down. An uninterruptible power supply (UPS) is vital when write caching is used.

 A UPS is an intermediary device connected to a power source and a computer. When there is a power failure, the UPS uses a battery and power circuits to produce the voltage required to keep the computer running. Depending upon the size of the battery and the power requirements of the computer, a UPS can last anywhere from a few minutes to several hours.

Multiple sectors of data could also be combined into a single write, saving lots of latency. Writes could also be sorting into ascending or descending order and performed in the fastest way possible.

A safer variation is the write-through cache, where data destined for the drive is written to the disk but also stored in the cache. If this data is needed again, it can be read from the cache instead of going to disk. This is often combined with read caching to accelerate disk performance.

Write caching is present in most modern hard drives and also in many operating systems. SMARTdrive 4.1 and newer, included with DOS 6, includes both read and write caching. Each of which can be configured or disabled.

Hardware caching controllers

Some vendors are offering hardware-based caching disk controllers that combine an IDE or SCSI interface with lots of RAM slots for cache. They can be very costly because you must populate them with expensive RAM. This RAM is dedicated to the controller and cannot be used by your applications. Disk caching is built into most operating systems, and an additional cache could get in the way. It is also very difficult to design a general cache algorithm that is good for a variety of uses. Cached data from RAM on the computer also arrives much faster than cached data stored on a caching disk controller expansion card.

RAM drives

The ultimate hard drive would be one made up entirely of instantly accessed RAM. The problems with this are that it would be prohibitively expensive, extremely volatile, and would need a back-up power source, such as a battery. There are many PCMCIA cards designed to store data by using nonvolatile flash memory chips. At one time, people believed that this type of storage would replace hard drives; but high cost prevented this. Flash memory costs about 50 times more than a typical 2.5-inch hard drive. The drives write data about five times slower than they read data. They are available only in very small capacities.

 For more information about PCMCIA cards, see Chapter 6, "All About Expansion Buses."

Thermal recalibration

Many hard drives need to recalibrate their heads every couple of minutes to compensate for heat buildup that causes components to expand and contract. This thermal recalibration (t-cal) doesn't affect the drive's normal operations but can adversely affect applications such as audio or video digitization and playback. T-cal can last hundreds of milliseconds. If a drive cannot service a request during a t-cal, a dropout of video or audio could occur.

An AV-ready drive needs to provide an uninterrupted sustained data transfer rate. Modern drives, or ones with an AV designation, are designed to overcome this limitation by using special algorithms to defer t-cal until there is no activity or by performing t-cal one head at a time. Drives with embedded servo also avoid the need for t-cal.

 Error-correction also causes AV problems. Handling error correction in the drive hardware helps avoid this.

Drivers

The final piece in the Operations puzzle is the device driver. The driver translates computer operating system requests into the SCSI or IDE commands that tell the drive how best to carry out the computer's orders.

 For more information about drivers, see "Device drivers" on page 181.

When Things Go Wrong

Despite all the excellent engineering that we've just described, hard drives can fail. When the drive stops working it's called a "crash." Although a crash can be the result of software problems, it may also be due to a mechanical problem in the drive itself. Keep in mind that the majority of failures are due to really minor glitches. A minor change in a disk sector could render your entire machine useless. When things go wrong, try not to assume the worst.

Common causes of failure are discussed below. Figure 15 provides an overview of the most frequent causes of system failure.

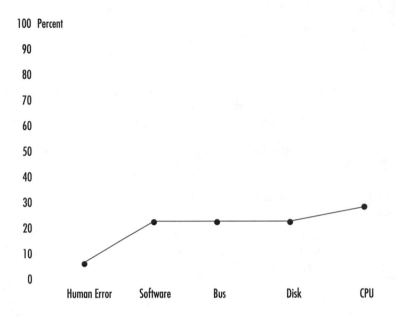

Figure 15. *Most frequent causes of system failure*

Software errors

In the case of software errors, the drive is still functioning and the data can probably be rescued using a file recovery program, such as Norton Utilities. The two most common causes of software errors are:

- Poorly written software
- Viruses

To reduce the number of possible causes for error, disable as much third-party hardware and software as possible. This will allow you and the various companies' technical support departments to diagnose the problem faster.

Many things can go wrong, but what's important is that you are alert to the warning signals. These include the following:

- Upon boot-up, the screen displays some sort of visual message, such as a blinking question mark or a Sad Mac (Macintosh), or a dialog box with an error message (Macintosh and PCs).

- Upon boot-up, the computer doesn't recognize a disk and asks if you want to initialize it or says the operating system is missing (Macintosh and PCs).

 Don't choose to initialize. This will wipe out all data, applications, and anything else you had stored on your hard drive.

- Upon boot-up, the disk does not mount, or crashes midway during boot (Macintosh and PCs).
- An application repeatedly crashes when launched (Macintosh and PCs).
- Opening a folder crashes the system (Macintosh and PCs).
- Copying a file crashes the system (Macintosh and PCs).
- Copying a file returns a write or read error (Macintosh and PCs).

Consult Chapter 8, "Troubleshooting," for some suggestions on what to do.

Hardware errors

Hardware crashes, or hard crashes, come in as many varieties as there are parts in the hard disk drive; four are the most common:

- Media errors
- Controller damage
- Head crashes
- Spindle failure

Media errors

Errors can result from bad sectors on the platter that are not successfully mapped out by the drive.

The disk will need to be tested to first find and then map out the bad blocks. If the corrupted information is in the directory, driver partition, or partition map, the drive will not know where to find the data stored on the platter. The disk will be unreadable and may have to be reformatted. Because there is limited physical damage to the platter or the hardware with media errors, much of the data is probably intact and can be recovered with a utility program.

Some formatting software such as FWB's Hard Disk ToolKit allows for configuring bad-block mapping and reallocation. Drives usually maintain a fixed number of spare sectors on each track. If these are all used up, then they look to a cylinder based spare. Operating systems such as DOS will map out bad sectors when they are high-level formatting a drive or running a utility such as SCANDISK.

If a bad block is encountered, is it often best to perform a full backup, then reformat the drive.

Look for programs that do a variety of tests to find disk problems. Sequential, data pattern, and butterfly tests are useful for finding media errors. Testing the RAM and controller on the drive are also useful tests.

Controller damage

Controller damage occurs when one of the controller's parts—such as a chip or capacitor—fails to perform. All the data is intact, and there is no damage to the platter. Possible causes include a voltage spike, which could blow out a chip, and environmental damage due to extreme heat or cold. You'll need to send the drive to the manufacturer for repair.

Head crashes

The typical, and most graphic, head-crash scenario is when platter wobble or a voltage drop causes the read/write head to contact the platter surface. Due to the platter's high speed and delicate surface, the head can plow through a lot of information very quickly. Several tracks could be destroyed in one crash. That data is lost forever. If the drive is still working, fragments of media can get between the head and the disk and cause further damage to the magnetic surface. If this happens, you need to replace the damaged head and platter. If you wish to recover the salvageable data, you would also need to pay for expensive data recovery.

Spindle failure

The spindle is a sealed unit with lubricated bearings. It should not need any maintenance, yet approximately 15 percent of hard drives eventually fail when friction-produced heat burns away the lubrication. (When a manufacturer uses the wrong lubricant, or too much of it, it is said to cause a "stiction" problem.) The bearings grind against the spindle and its casing; it can slow down, or seize up and lock in place. You may notice a grinding noise when the drive is running, or a failure to spin up when the drive is turned on. If the disks are intact, they can be removed in a "clean room" and installed in a functioning drive. This service is very expensive.

Stiction

Stiction is short for static friction. It happens when the heads of the drive are stuck to the platters of the drive. When you try to power up the drive, the heads cannot break free. Stiction is usually caused by improper lubricants on the drive platter.

Temperature problems

Some drives develop problems only after a certain interval of power-on time. This usually happens when there might be a fan cooling problem with the subsystem or when there is an unreliable part on the disk controller. Many modern drives spin at 7200 RPM or faster and utilize many watts of power. They usually need forced air cooling to keep their operating temperature within design guidelines.

Drives Don't Have to Die Quickly!

Saving data

The safest approach to saving your data is to rely on data duplication, rather than data recovery. This means having all your essential data backed up on another storage device, so that it's ready to be placed either on the damaged drive when it's up and running again, or on a replacement drive.

Copying files over to floppies is the most popular method of backing up data. It's a good method, but other more reliable, more automatic, faster, and—unfortunately—more expensive methods exist for those who are serious about protecting their data.

Some users have come to rely on tape drives to do incremental backups; that is, a software utility reads whatever information has been added to the hard drive during that work session, and copies it to a high-capacity, but slow, sequential access tape drive.

 See "Other Types of Storage Devices" on page 84 for more information.

Incremental backups only back up files that have been changed since the last backup, so they occur quickly, although the first backup must be a full backup. This technique can be used with a second hard drive or removable drive, either manually or with an automatic utility program.

Some users prefer differential backups. A differential backup is a combination of an initial full backup and subsequent backups of all files that have changed since the last full backup (not just the changed parts of those files). This allows for easier restoration of your drive to its original state.

Corporations typically have the means for centralized backup. They usually ask users to back up to a server or load a background agent that allows a central backup server to pull all the files that need to be backed up.

Whatever approach you take, try to automate the process so you do not have to remember to back up your data. You should back up as often as you feel comfortable. Most people back up at the end of every day, others back up once a week. Backup media should be stored in a safe place away from magnetic fields, liquids, smoke and high temperatures. Make sure you keep some backups off-site, so natural disasters cannot wipe out all of your data. Also make sure you test your backups by restoring some of your backed up files. Its shocking how many times bugs in backup software crop up.

Disk duplexing and disk mirroring

Disk duplexing and disk mirroring were developed to provide automatic backup for network servers—computers that store data for a large group of connected PCs. But the techniques are applicable to single-user data safety as well. Both methods are expensive because twice the number of drives is required to obtain the same capacity.

Disk duplexing

Disk duplexing, as its name suggests, is using one drive to duplicate the read/write moves of another. This creates an identical copy of the original. This is accomplished through a dedicated set-up that has two drives and two separate drive interfaces and host adapters, each with its own power supply. Because the host computer has two separate SCSI ports—the standard port and usually a card-based controller board—there is minimal reduction in system performance. Data is both read from and written to both drives. When reading, the data from the two drives may be compared to verify data integrity. If the main drive or controller fails for any reason, the second is activated automatically, and the user is notified of the failure. Using duplexed drives, in effect, puts one's data eggs into two baskets.

Disk mirroring

In disk mirroring a single disk controller is connected to two drives. All controller activity is performed twice; first to one drive, then the other. If one drive fails, the other one takes over. Because data is read from one drive but written to both, there is no reduction of performance during read operations and about a 50 percent reduction during write operations. With mirroring, in contrast to duplexing, if the host adapter fails, the system will go down.

You still need to maintain backups when doing mirroring. You need to protect against theft, fire or software problems.

RAID, or Redundant Array of Independent Disks

RAID takes the concept of duplication one step further by linking together a number of drives. This technique has been developed at five different levels, most of which use a "check disk," which keeps information about the other drives so that data can be reconstructed in the event of drive failure.

For detailed information on RAID, see "What Is RAID?" on page 61.

But When You Gotta Go ...

Unlike other parts of the computer, hard drives have many moving parts, making them more susceptible to failure. Other components that fail often in computers are the fan and the power supply. Those components fail because they include moving parts and are forced to operate at high temperatures. Unfortunately, all disks will eventually die—it's only a matter of time. New techniques, such as Self-Monitoring, Analysis and Reporting Technology (SMART), help to predict when a drive is likely to die. It does this by watching for tell-tale signs, such as many recoverable errors, many retries or slowing perfor-mance.

Physical damage is expensive to repair, so practice basic maintenance and be aware of what can damage your drive. Drive failure can result from a number of easily-preventable factors.

Preventative measures

The following are preventative measures you can take to prolong the life of your drive:

Table 3. *Prolonging Disk Life and Maintaining Data Integrity*

Measure	Explanation
Backup	You must religiously back up the contents of your drive onto another storage medium, be it floppies, tape or optical. This will insure you against loss of data due to hard disk crashes, accidental erasure, errant software or hardware, or viruses. Think about it this way: if your drive died today, would you be able to reconstruct its contents? Make sure you test some of your backups to ensure they are restorable.
Utility Software	In addition to backup software, you should own a disk recovery tool to repair disk problems. Most of these recovery packages also include useful utilities to mirror directories, optimize your drive and undelete files. It's also handy to have a low-level disk utility program that can test data, such as FWB's Hard Disk ToolKit. Virus eradication software is also a very useful product.
Emergency Boot Disk	Make an alternate bootable floppy, hard drive, or CD-ROM that you can use for startup in case your primary drive is damaged. Try to place important utility programs such as disk recovery tools and hard drive utilities on this emergency disk.
Dust Control	One of the most important aspects of your drive's environment is dust control. A fleck of dust in the wrong place—even smoke particles—can crash your drive. Keep the area your drive occupies relatively dust-free, so no dust can block its air flow.
Surge Suppressor	Power spikes or surges can be minimized by a surge suppressor, a device that smooths the current sent to your drive and that will, when properly fused, shield it and the controller from a killer voltage spike. Voltage irregularities are commonplace—every time a refrigerator or other large electrical device comes on or off, for example—so a surge suppressor is a necessity.
UPS	You may wish to consider acquiring a UPS, or uninterruptible power supply, to allow you precious time to back-up your data in the event of a power outage. A typical UPS supplies 1,200 watts of power and should buy your system 30 minutes of time.
On/Off Policy	Some people think that turning your drive off at every opportunity will help prolong its life. That is a tough call: switching drives on and off causes more wear and tear; a drive draws the most current during spin-up, and the motor is under the greatest stress at that time. We think this is a good rule of thumb for most systems: shut it down if it's going to be unused for more than a couple of hours. Also don't power down then power up the drive right away. Give the drive a minute to settle. Make sure there is no disk activity when you shut down your computer.

Table 3. *Prolonging Disk Life and Maintaining Data Integrity (Continued)*

Measure	Explanation
Temperature Control	A good flow of air is crucial to avoid overheating the computer's or external drive's power supply. Because the components of hard drives operate at very small tolerances, it doesn't take much of a shift in temperature to throw things off kilter. To make matters worse, because the hard drive is a sealed unit, when heated it acts like a pressure cooker. To compensate for temperature changes, drives have auto-compensators that regularly conduct seek tests and adjust the movements of the head actuators accordingly. Be sure to keep your drive operating in a temperate environment: Most hard drives are rated for operation between 50° and 122° Fahrenheit, eight and 80 percent relative humidity, and −1,000 and 10,000 feet altitude.
Drive Placement	Hard drives are designed to operate in certain physical orientations, and upside down is not one of them. A drive operated upside down will get "used to" this orientation and may not work properly when righted. Most drives can be operated sideways, but should not have the power supply situated below the drive; otherwise, the drive could get "cooked" by the power supply.

Data recovery

If your hard disk has a serious hardware crash and you need to recover data, you will need to send your drive to a place that can perform data recovery. These firms perform a variety of services. They can try replacing the controller card on the drive to see if there was a part that was damaged. This usually fixes 75 percent of the failures.

If there is a mechanical failure, they can open up the drive in a Class 100 clean room and attempt to repair any head, spindle or platter damage. Be prepared to spend lots of money on these repairs. It's far cheaper to keep frequent backups.

Defragmentation

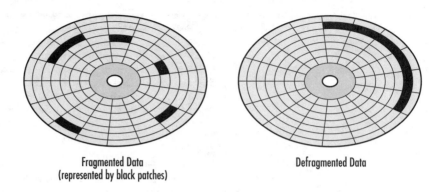

Fragmented Data
(represented by black patches)

Defragmented Data

Figure 16. Fragmented and defragmented disks.

A simple method to reduce some of the wear on the read/write head and actuator is to defragment the drive. This will also help the drive achieve its maximum performance potential.

When a computer writes to a platter, it begins writing to the first available location. If it runs out of space before it runs out of data, it moves to the next available location, which may not be on a contiguous block. Spreading a file across non-contiguous blocks is called file fragmentation.

When a drive head reads a fragmented file, it has to jump about the platter to locate and deliver the fragmented data. The extra movement of the heads increases wear on the drive's components.

Fragmentation is not very apparent when a drive is new or freshly formatted. It gets worse over time as the head grabs whatever sector space is available. When new applications are installed on the drive, they may start out in a fragmented state because the drive was already fragmented. It only gets worse from here. If your hard drive is taking longer to load an application or read a file, or if the status light goes on and off instead of staying on, your drive is probably overly fragmented.

There are two ways to defragment a drive. The first is with a dedicated optimizer. These software utilities can reorganize files on the drive and put them in contiguous sectors. The second method involves copying the contents of your hard drive onto a second, essentially empty (although formatted) hard drive, and then recopying the files back onto your hard drive. Either method will defragment your drive, thus reducing the work of the read/write head and actuator, and optimizing its access time.

Although defragmentation programs are not destructive, be sure to back up all data before you defragment. As with any operation that writes data to the disk, various factors—such as a power surge or outage—could corrupt the data.

Need a New Drive?

Once you become familiar with all the capabilities a drive can have, you may find that the limitations of your present hard drive have been brought into sharp focus. What should you look for in a new drive?

Indicators of durability and reliability

Most sales literature that discusses the attributes of a disk drive will include at least these three indicators of durability and reliability:

- Mean Time Between Failure (MTBF)
- Mean Time to Repair (MTTR)
- Shock Ratings

Mean Time Between Failures (MTBF)

Start with the drive's MTBF rating. This vendor-supplied specification indicates how long a drive should last. MTBF ratings can range up to 1 million hours or more. It is important to understand the meaning of this rating when purchasing drives. The drive holds all your data, so you really want to purchase one that is reliable.

An MTBF rating of 50,000 hours indicates that half (or the mean) of the drives with that rating will fail within 50,000 hours, or 5.7 years.

$$\frac{50{,}000 \text{ hours}}{24 \text{ hours a day} \times 365 \text{ days a year}} = 5.7 \text{ years}$$

Figure 17. Interpretation of the MTBF rating

A 100,000 hour MTBF drive **should** last twice as long! Approximately eight percent of drives fail each year. After one year, 92 percent are still operating; after two years, 84 percent are still running, and so on. MTBF ratings of one million hours are not uncommon; however, this does not actually mean the drive will run for over 100 years.

MTBF is determined by running only a couple of thousand hours of tests on a representative population of drives in an optimal environment and then extrapolating the results. "Corrected" for the real world, MTBFs would drop about 35 percent. Rarely do MTBF ratings include power cycling, access testing and variations in temperature. If they did, we would still be waiting for a rating on most drives now on the market. However, the testing is rigorous—punishing shocks, temperature extremes, constant read/write operations—and it pushes the drives well beyond what they will likely encounter in a lifetime of use. MTBF ratings are typically geared for office conditions. A dust-free, environmentally controlled "clean room" can increase MTBF ratings by 100,000 hours or more.

MTBF ratings are not standardized; manufacturers use different methods for establishing ratings. They have mainly been used for marketing purposes. MTBF ratings should serve only as a guideline.

Here are three ways to calculate MTBF; all result in different ratings:

1. Combined Life Expectancy

    Combined life expectancy utilizes the combined life expectancy of all the parts used to make a drive. It relies primarily on Mil Spec 217 or the BellCore publication. This method does not include head disk failures. This is the most conservative method, generating MTBFs in the 30,000 to 50,000 range. It was in use in the early days but has since been abandoned.

2. Field Rate of Return (FRR)

$$\text{MTBF} = (\text{No. of drives shipped per month} \times \text{Power-on hours per month}) \div \text{Drives that fail per month}$$

Figure 18. *Formula for determining MTBF by Field Rate of Return*

This only relates to the failure rate of the installed base, not the average life span of each drive. An MTBF of 1,000,000 means that out of 10,000 drives, you can expect one drive to fail every 100 hours:

$$1,000,000 \text{ MTBF} = (10,000 \text{ drives} \times 100 \text{ hours}) \div 1 \text{ failure}$$

Figure 19. *Interpretation of the MTBF rating based on FRR*

3. On-Going Reliability Tests (ORT)

   Manufacturer's randomly select drives at the plant and test them. ORT is useful in combination with combined life expectancy and FRR to determine MTBF ratings on older drives.

The bottom line is the warranty on the drive. The longer the warranty, the more confident the vendor is in the reliability of the drive.

Mean Time To Repair (MTTR)

Mean Time to Repair is a vendor-supplied figure for the average length of time a typical repair would take for that drive. If a drive had been repaired five times over the period of a year and the times involved in repair were two, one, one, three and three hours respectively, the MTTR for that device would be two hours (10 hours ÷ 5 repairs = 2 hours). It is intended to indicate the modularity of the drive and the quality of its parts.

Shock ratings

Shock ratings are a way of comparing the overall ruggedness of a drive. Unlike the MTBF ratings, which are extrapolated predictions, shock ratings are the result of actual tests and are therefore considered much more accurate and reliable. Shock ratings are measured in g's; a g is equivalent to the pull of earth's gravity. The average rating for hard drives is from 5 to 20 g's when operating. Drives in the 1.8-inch form factor have operating shock ratings in the 200 g's range. 200 g's equates to a drop of only one foot. Bernoulli drives shine in this area: they are rated at over 1,000 g's due to the use of flexible disks. Bernoulli's are useful for portable and laptop computers. Newer drives include shock sensors that shut down the drive when acceleration is sensed.

 For more information on Bernoulli drives, see "Bernoulli drives" on page 89.

Other statistics to consider

An average seek time of less than 10 milliseconds (ms) is respectably fast. Sub-12 ms is typical.

The sustained data transfer rate should be at least 5 MB/s, or at least as fast as your computer can handle. Vendors like to promote their drive's "burst" data transfer rate (10 MB/s up to 100 MB/s). This is the fastest that data can be moved at one instance under optimal conditions, which means data transferred from cache. Sustained rate is the average data transfer rate over time (5 MB/s is average; 100 MB/s is high). Sustained data transfer rate includes burst from the cache (optimal) and cross-cylinder accesses (suboptimal).

If you are a real speed demon, invest in an add-on SCSI accelerator and RAID to improve throughput. High-end applications, such as color publishing and digital video, demand the fastest throughput available. Raw, uncompressed, full-frame, 60 field per second video requires 27 MB/s, while manipulating 100 MB color scans requires as much performance as possible. More performance equals better video quality (less compression) or more jobs performed per hour.

Make sure your drive's cabling interface will accommodate the future expandability you will need.

Capacity

Choose a drive with a high formatted capacity. Hundreds of megabytes isn't very much anymore, considering the size of today's popular applications and files. Many operating systems alone require 50 MB of space. An office suite of applications may require an additional 100 MB. Utilities and games could require another 100 MB. Graphic programs can generate individual files that are hundreds of MB. One minute of high-quality digital video can occupy 200 MB. One minute of CD-quality audio occupies 10 MB.

Technology is bringing down the price of higher capacity drives. You may be surprised at the price difference between two adjacent capacity models. Get 50 percent more capacity than you think you need; you'll use it sooner than you think.

Keep in mind that most drive manufacturers measure megabytes in millions of bytes (1,000,000 bytes instead of 2^{20} = 1,048,576 bytes). Capacities are increased by five percent from this fact alone. On a 1000 MB drive, the difference is 48 MB. Operating systems do not measure capacity this way, so your operating system probably displays the capacity of the drive to be less than what you thought the drive holds.

Other considerations

Get a drive with a voice-coil actuator. It provides superior head positioning, and automatic parking for added safety. Also, the drive should accept what are called step pulses. (Ironically, this is even more crucial for voice-coil actuators than for stepper motors.) A step pulse moves the head one track over, and speeds access time by quickly positioning the head over the correct track.

Consider SCSI-3 drives rather than SCSI-2 drives to take advantage of vendor's implementations of current and imminent improvements. You will need a SCSI-3 compatible controller or host.

 NOTE

Read Chapter 3, "All About SCSI," for more information.

Consider a drive with advanced RAM caching features. Write caching—featured on several drives—is a tremendous advance in caching technology.

Trends in Hard Drives

Smaller platters

As the density of hard disks and the sensitivity of read/write heads has increased, hard drives have gotten physically smaller. The gap between the read/write heads and the platter is getting narrower. Because of this, the magnetic flux has a shorter distance to travel and the magnetic domain on the disk can be smaller. This results in more bits per inch on each track.

 Magnetic flux is the magnetic exchange between the read/write head and the platter. Magnetic flux allows the head to write and read data.

Improvements in servo data recording and head movement are allowing for disks with even more tracks per inch. One GB, 2.5-inch drives combine 6,000 tracks per inch and over 100,000 bits per inch to produce densities of more than 1600 MB per square inch. Disk size (referred to as its form factor) has gone from 8 inches to 5.25 inches to 3.5 inches. Disks as small as 2.5 inches and 1.8 inches are now in use, typically in laptop and notebook-size computers. The 3.5-inch drive has replaced the older 5.25-inch as the industry standard.

 See "Anatomy of a hard drive" on page 8 for more information.

In general, the larger the drive (in dimension, not capacity) the greater the speed. The smaller the drive, the lower the cost and the power consumption. But note that currently the 3.5-inch drive seems to represent the price break. It offers the lowest cost when figured on a per-megabyte basis. Surprisingly, drives smaller than 3.5 inches are more expensive than larger drives, but may assume the price-break position in the near future.

Shorter drives

Computers are getting smaller. Desktops have become laptops which have become notebooks. Real estate is now becoming a significant concern; the insides of these boxes are getting cramped. Third-height drives, standing one inch tall, are currently the most popular. Not only do they fit into a smaller computer, but two half-height drives can be installed in the space where one full-height drive (1.6 inches tall) used to fit in a desktop computer. For extremely tight casing requirements—such as for laptop and notebook computers—17 mm height drives (2.5-inch form factor) have been developed.

Although the smaller drives are currently more expensive per megabyte, the prices are sure to come down as their sales and use increase.

Faster, smaller controllers

The controller chip sets of newer drives (the "brains" of the controller) are composed of fewer and faster integrated circuits, providing greater processing power at higher operating frequencies while requiring less physical space in the drive itself. Most 16-bit based controllers utilize either the Intel 80186 family of microcontrollers or the Motorola 6811 family. Most drive vendors stay with a particular processor family to ensure firmware compatibility. With the emergence of high-speed serial SCSI, vendors are forced to move to faster 32-bit processors and 32-bit memory subsystems. The chip sets on newer 2.5-inch and smaller drives incorporate variable zone recording and dedicated servo capabilities to increase disk density and capacity. Advanced semiconductor technology such as multichip-module (MCM) and chip-on-board (COB) packaging allows multiple unpackaged chips to be placed in tight areas.

 See "Anatomy of a hard drive" on page 8 and "Encoding" on page 26 for more information. For a discussion of chips, see "SCSI Integrated Circuits (Chips)" on page 125.

Despite these advances, the space limitations of smaller controllers means that there is less room for the sophisticated circuits, such as large caches, that are supported by larger drives. These functions may have to be relocated to the computer.

Connector size is slow to change

Strange as it seems, the shrinking disk size may be limited by the hard drive's connectors. A standard 50-pin SCSI connector measures 2.69 inches wide and 0.25 inches thick. It is already a challenge fitting these connectors on smaller drives.

 For more information, see "Physical connections" on page 140.

A solution is to use high-density "D-sub" connectors, as defined in the SCSI-3 specification. These connectors pack the pins more tightly, and measure a trim 1.44 inches wide and a quarter-inch thick. Another solution, already in limited practice, is to reduce the number of pins on the connector. This is possible because many of the pins are connected to ground wires, and in practice not all the ground wires may be needed. Forty-pin arrangements are used for 2.5-inch drives.

Eighty-pin SCA connectors are also gaining in acceptance. These support fast and wide SCSI-2 and include power and spindle synchronization and reduce the amount of cabling required. These are good for disk array applications where drives have to be hot-swapped and less cabling is desired.

"SCA" stands for single connector attachment. It is a high-density connector that carries every type of signal passed along a SCSI bus, including SCSI ID, LED and spindle synchronization information. It is particularly suitable for hot-swapping—removing and inserting removable drives while the system is powered on—due to its timed pins. Timed pins allow for removing power first and ground last when a drive is disconnected, and attaching ground first and power last when a drive is plugged in.

Faster, lighter heads and actuators

The read/write heads on hard drives are becoming smaller and lighter. The lower the mass of the head and actuator, the more easily and quickly it can be moved across the disk. Unfortunately, if a head and actuator are too small and light, they will be unstable. These components may soon reach their physical limits.

Force equals mass times acceleration. The faster the head moves, the greater the force exerted on it. If the head is made any lighter, it will break apart.

For this reason, advances in seek time performance—the time it takes the head to physically arrive at the location where it can read and write data—will be minimal. Some drives increase seek performance by "short-stroking" a higher capacity drive. Basically it means using only half of a higher capacity drive to achieve faster seek times by requiring the drive to seek across only half the platter. Overall, seek time has only improved from about 16.5 to 8 ms in the last ten years, while processor speeds have increased about 1000 times. The laws of physics start to get in the way of reducing seek times any further. It is clear that storage systems have become a limiting factor in increasing a computer system's performance.

The next areas for advancements in the performance of hard drives will include the following:

- Increased medium rotation rate
- Larger caches
- Higher densities
- Faster and wider transfer rates
- More drive intelligence

Green drives

Of increasing importance is the need to produce environmentally correct products. Environmental concerns have already resulted in the development of hard drives that support a low-power sleep mode. Some drives even have a deep sleep mode where everything is turned off. Newer drives are coming out that require 3V instead of 5V. In Europe, there are laws that require this. In the US there is a standard, known as Energy Star, that specifies power management in the computer. In effect, power management means that the drive will spin down after a certain amount of inactivity. The EPA estimates that a system that powers down during inactivity could save the user $70 to $90 a year. Obviously, energy consumption is extremely important to portable computing users.

You'll want to balance your power management configuration with your desire to prevent wear-and-tear on your drive. See "On/Off Policy" in Table 3 on page 48.

All digital drives

Drives are becoming more digitally oriented every year. Older drives possessed many analog components. Newer drives include:

- Digital read channels
- Digital servo control
- Digital spindle control
- Digital processors

Going all digital makes drives more programmable. It permits a finer degree of control over the specific physical interface variables. Some drives even go further by adding low-cost digital signal processors (DSP) to perform mathematical functions faster.

Holographic memory

After decades of research, the first holographic memory system appeared in 1995. Holographic memory is a variation of conventional holography. Two laser beams are focused in the system at different angles and optically interfere on a light-sensitive film. One beam carries the data, which can be either a representation of the digital data stream or a pictorial image. By using a scanner to change the angle or position of the other beam, multiple views of the image are recorded. Thousands of these holograms can be recorded on a single piece of film.

The advantage to holographic recording is that a large quantity of data is stored in parallel in an image, making for very high data transfer rates. The first system from Holoplex, the $10,000 HM-100, retrieved 26 MB/s. Future versions promise to be up to 10 times faster and up to 100 times larger in storage capacity.

Large volumes

Whatever type of drive you pick, you can be assured that you are among many people needing lots of capacity. About 90 million hard drives were produced in 1995 (Table 4).

Table 4. *Worldwide Volume of Drives*

	1995	1996 (est.)	1997 (est.)	1998 (est.)
500 MB–1 GB	36.3 M	32.8 M	25 M	20 M
1 GB–2 GB	15.5 M	32.5 M	41 M	20 M
All capacities	90 M	118 M	140 M	160 M

Drive capacity will continue to grow, doubling in size every 18 months—a 60 percent annual rate of increase. Previously, capacity had increased 30 percent a year. Drive product life cycles are about 9 months. Current and predicted high-capacity drives are illustrated in Table 5.

Table 5. *Current and Future Capacities of 3.5-inch Drives*

1995	1996 (est.)	1997 (est.)	1998 (est.)	1999 (est.)
8 GB	16 GB	24 GB	32 GB	40 GB

The amount of storage needed on an average server will continue to grow, as illustrated in Table 6.

Table 6. *Amount of Storage on an Average Server*

1995	1996 (est.)	1997 (est.)	1998 (est.)	1999 (est.)	2000 (est.)
8 GB	20 GB	50 GB	125 GB	300 GB	500 GB

Storage will continue to become more affordable due to improved technology and ongoing price wars. Table 7 illustrates the historical and predicted cost per megabyte of storage space.

Table 7. *Historical and Predicted Cost per MB*

1980	1990	1995	2000 (est.)
$30/MB	$10/MB	$0.25/MB	$0.05/MB

Consolidation has pared down the number of drive companies. Ten to twelve percent per quarter decreases are typical.

Drives will continue to become faster, as illustrated in Table 8.

Table 8. *Escalation of Typical Drive Speeds in RPM*

1990	1995	2000 (est.)
3600	7200	10,800

What Is RAID?

RAID stands for Redundant Array of Independent Disks. It was developed at the University of California at Berkeley in the mid-1980s. It was designed to provide greater practical performance, capacity and reliability by properly coordinating the read/write activities among a series of linked drives. It addressed the topic of how to organize several small disks to make them behave and appear as one large drive. RAID was built upon existing technology rather than developed as a radical new product.

RAID originally stood for redundant array of inexpensive drives because the drives used were not that expensive. Later it changed to independent disks. Although these systems were inexpensive considering their capacity and data security features, they were more expensive than single drive solutions because they contained more advanced software and hardware technology.

RAID provides an alternative to SLED (Single Large Expensive Drives) as a high-capacity, high-performance storage method with the added benefit of data protection. Most RAID systems implement the latest versions of SCSI and serial SCSI to maximize data transfer rates. RAIDs typically provide very fast sustained transfer rates by greatly reducing latency and seek time. This could increase performance by up to 25 percent.

RAID is not a substitute for backup. Data could be destroyed by accidental erasure or viruses, and lost forever if you're not backing up regularly. RAID simply ensures the storage array will remain highly available.

RAIDs are used almost exclusively by high-end users who need very large, very fast and very reliable data storage systems. The application is often mission critical, where losing any data would cost thousands of dollars. RAID technology is typically used for the following applications:

- File-servers
- Database servers
- High-end users of digital video and color publishing applications

RAID has become an important area of storage. Businesses have adopted RAID for its reliability and its performance aspects. The RAID market has been growing at about 30 percent per year. Sales in 1994 totaled about $3.5 billion. They are projected to double to $7 billion in 1997.

What to look for

RAID's key aspects include the following:

- Availability
- Reliability

- Capacity
- Expandability
- Performance
- Manageability
- Cost

Different RAID levels offer varying amounts of fault-tolerance. Some levels do not offer increased reliability. Different RAID levels are expandable in different ways. Some require the addition of only one drive, while others require the addition of two to five drives at a time. Performance varies with each RAID level. It is important to define the intended application and related performance requirements to make a match with the appropriate RAID level. RAID can be very expensive. The application must justify the need for a RAID subsystem.

Specific features

Table 9 lists some features of RAID subsystems:

Table 9. *Features of RAID Subsystems*

Feature	Explanation
Parity	RAID systems that include parity allow the system to continue to run if one of the drives has failed. Parity is a data transmission system in which the number of "1" bits must add up to an odd (odd parity) or even (even parity) number. SCSI uses odd parity. This means the sum of all ones in a byte plus its parity bit will always be odd.
Caching	Some RAID controllers, especially ones for levels 3, 4, and 5, have RAM that is used for prefetching data or for write caching. Write caching helps alleviate the penalty paid for writing in some of the higher RAID levels. More sophisticated write caching includes battery backup that can maintain data for hours in case of a power loss. Some have a mirrored cache for redundancy.
Hot Spare	Some RAID subsystems include extra drives that are fully spun up but will be used only if one of the other drives fails.
Warm Spare	Other RAID systems require the system to go off-line but not power-down in order to replace components such as drives.
Multiple Hosts	Some RAID subsystems allow multiple host adapters or computers to be hooked up at the same time.
Redundant Controllers	Some RAID subsystems include two RAID controllers. Should one fail, the other takes over automatically. Some systems have both controllers active; others have one active and one in standby mode.

Table 9. Features of RAID Subsystems (Continued)

Feature	Explanation
Hot Swappable Drives	Various RAID subsystems include drives in canisters, shuttles or carriers that can be removed and plugged in while the system is running (see Figure 20).

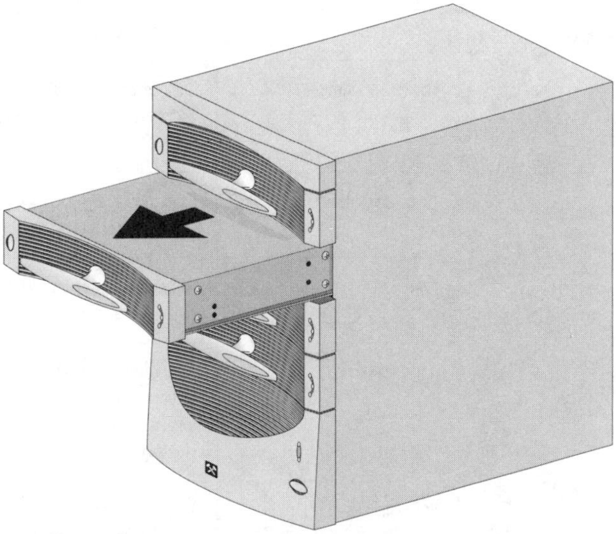

Figure 20. FWB's SledgeHammer•Pro Removable

Feature	Explanation
Hot Swappable Power Supplies	Power supplies on some RAID subsystems can be hot swapped and load shared. Load sharing means that when both power supplies are operable, they share the load of supplying power to the system. If one should fail, the other assumes the full load. Hot swap capability allows you to swap out the inoperable power supply with an operable spare while the system continues to run. This setup gives you N+1 fault tolerance (where N is the number of power supplies required by the system and 1 is the spare). Hot swappable power supplies should be used in conjunction with uninterrupted power supplies and power conditioners to ensure a continuous flow of power during swaps.

Figure 21. Hot-swappable power supply

Feature	Explanation
Redundant fans	Some subsystems include multiple fans. Should one fan fail, the others will cool the system. Fans should be monitored to detect overheating caused by failures.

Table 9. *Features of RAID Subsystems (Continued)*

Feature	Explanation
Setup Software	RAID subsystems can be setup by one of the following: • Graphical setup software • LCD front panels • Serial terminal based connections
Monitoring Software	More advanced RAID subsystems include monitoring software to check the status of the subsystem across the network. Some also include automatic notification of changes in the array's status through pager, SNMP (simple network management protocol; used with TCP/IP), or e-mail.
Configurable Rebuild	Some RAID subsystems allow the rate of the rebuilding of data to be configured. This allows it to be tuned to the amount of user activity.
Ranks	Some RAID subsystems allow you to construct multiple groups of disks into RAID sub-units. Each rank could have a different RAID configuration but be controlled by the same controller.
Active Backplane	More advanced RAID subsystems allow you to hot plug drives. The only way this can happen is with an active backplane that you plug drives into. The backplane provides drives with power and data connections even when they are pulled or plugged in on the fly. Without an active backplane, plugging in a drive while the system is operating could kill the SCSI bus.
Drive Channels	The more channels to the drives in a RAID system, the greater the fault tolerance and the faster the performance. Drive channels are not made equal. Some offer much faster performance than others.
XOR Engine	RAID 4 and 5 systems need to generate parity through the use of an XOR routine. The XOR routine is designed to create information that allows a RAID to be recovered in the event of a failure. Higher end RAID subsystems include a custom XOR hardware engine that speeds up generation of parity. Others rely on an on-board processor to do the XOR calculation. For more information on XOR, see "RAID and Fault Tolerance" on page 73.

Spindle synchronization is a feature available on some RAID systems (mostly RAID 3). The spindles of all drives in the RAID are synchronized so that they spin in unison, not just at the same speed. Each platter of each drive will be in precisely the right position relative to the other drives. This nearly eliminates latency, because the head on drive B will be over the appropriate sector of its platter just as the head on drive A finishes reading from or writing to the appropriate sector on its platter.

RAID Levels—Overview

RAID subsystems differ from each other in the variety of features offered and in the variety of disk and data storage configurations available. The primary factors that define the RAID level of a subsystem are:

- The way data is written to the disk array
- Whether there is some form of data redundancy
- Whether and how the array is expandable

There are six standard RAID levels: RAID level zero through RAID level five. Table 10, below, provides an overview of those, plus RAID level 6.

Table 10. Comparison of Common RAID Levels

RAID Level	Common Name	Description	Disks Required	Data Reliability	Data Transfer Capacity	Maximum I/O Rate
0	Disk Striping	Data distributed across the disks in the array. No redundant information provided.	at least 2	Lower than single disk.	Very high.	Very high for both read and write.
1	Mirroring	All data is replicated on a matching disk.	2, 4, 6…	Higher than RAID Level 2, 3, 4, 5, lower than 6.	Higher than single disk for read; similar to single disk for write.	Up to twice that of a single disk for read; similar to single disk for write.
2	–	Data protected by a Hamming Code (a type of error tracking algorithm). Redundant info is distributed across m disks (see next column).	n + m	Much higher than single disk, comparable to RAID level 3, 4, 5.	Highest of all listed alternatives.	Up to twice that of a single disk.
3	RAID Level 3; Parallel Transfer Disks with Parity	Each data sector is subdivided and distributed across all data disks. Redundant info normally stored on a dedicated parity disk.	n + 1	Much higher than a single disk; comparable to RAID Level 2, 4, or 5.	Highest of all listed alternatives.	Up to twice that of a single disk.
4	–	Data sectors are distributed as with disk striping. Redundant information is stored on a dedicated parity disk.	n + 1	Much higher than a single disk; comparable to RAID Level 2, 3, or 5.	Similar to disk striping for read, significantly lower than single disk for write.	Similar to disk striping for read, significantly lower than single disk for write.
5	RAID Level 5	Data sectors are distributed as with disk striping. Redundant information is interspersed with user data.	n + 1	Much higher than a single disk; comparable to RAID Level 2, 3, or 4.	Similar to disk striping for read, significantly lower than single disk for write.	Similar to disk striping for read, generally lower than single disk for write.
6	RAID Level 6	As RAID Level 5, but with additional independently computed redundant information.	n + 2	Highest of all listed alternatives.	Similar to disk striping for read, significantly lower than RAID Level 5 for write.	Similar to disk striping for read, significantly lower than RAID Level 5 for write.

RAID Level 0

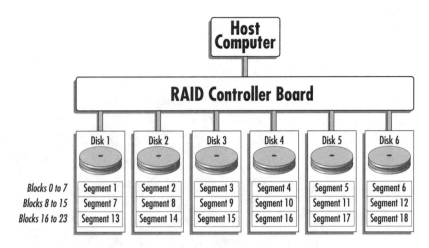

Figure 22. *Six-drive, level 0 RAID*

RAID level 0, also known as data striping, is an array of drives transferring data in parallel. The data is spread out among the drives one segment at a time.

 A segment is a predetermined number of blocks.

Level 0 provides higher performance while remaining transparent to the user. Because there is no redundancy, the capacity of the array is equal to the sum of the capacities of the drives used. For example, if you have six 1 GB drives striped, you have virtually a single 6 GB volume.

No redundancy also means no parity for error recovery over and above that provided by a normal drive.

Figure 23. *RAID 0 array*

Level 0 is easy to expand by adding one extra drive at a time. Generally, more drives equals more performance. Performance increases until the bus is saturated, in which case more buses could be used. Striping two drives generally increases performance about 1.8 times the performance of a single drive. A drive that achieved 10 MB/s on its own would perform at about 18 MB/s arrayed with a like mechanism. The smaller performance gain from doubling is due to command and disconnect overhead. The maximum bandwidth of the bus must accommodate these transfer rates. In this example, the bus would have to accommodate a burst transfer rate of at least 20 MB/s. Without the security of data redundancy, you must avoid potential data loss problems due to inadequate bandwidth.

RAID level 0 is quite popular with users of digital video, image processing and color publishing applications where the highest performance is very important. Broadcast quality compressed video requires about 12 MB/s sustained data transfer rate, far more than a typical single drive could offer.

 The lack of data redundancy makes level 0 unsuitable for mission-critical applications.

The RAID controller board at level zero is generally a SCSI host adapter that came with or was added to the computer.

RAID 0 also has been implemented with removable drives, such as Winchester cartridge or magneto optical, allowing a fast drive to have the additional benefit of unlimited capacity.

RAID Level 1

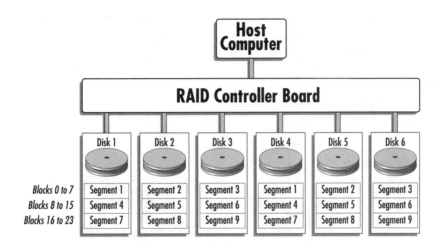

Figure 24. *Six-drive, level 1 RAID*

RAID level 1 is basic disk mirroring. It offers only a little extra performance and security over that of a single drive. With RAID level 1, the data written to one drive is written at the same time to a second drive. If one drive fails, the mirror of its data exists on the other drive. Because of this redundancy, the usable storage capacity of level 1 is half the total capacity of the drives used. This makes it an expensive solution. Drives must be added two at a time to expand capacity.

The RAID controller board used for level 1 is generally a SCSI host adapter that came with or was added to the computer.

RAID Level 2

RAID level 2 is a patented architecture of Thinking Machines, Inc. It uses sector bit interleaved data and multiple, dedicated parity disks. Data is interleaved across drives, so less overall storage space is required for data back-up. The parity disks avoid the cost of the duplicate-disk structure required for data mirroring by RAID level 1.

NOTE

For more information on interleaving, see "Interleaving" on page 30.

In RAID level 2, all of the array disks are synchronized, so that all disks must be accessed in parallel. This is good for supercomputer applications that require large file transfers at high bandwidth. It is not good for applications that call for many small reads and writes.

Another disadvantage is that it is not possible to simply add another drive. Level 2 is set up with a fixed number of drives, each reading a fixed number of data bits from each drive. Adding another drive would entail redesigning the system.

RAID Level 3

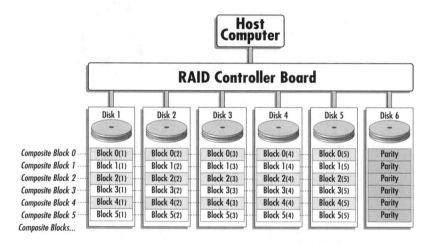

Figure 25. *Level 3 RAID*

RAID level 3 is an array of disk drives that transfer data in parallel, while one redundant drive functions as the parity check disk. Data is interleaved at the byte level. A single block requires a transfer from every drive. Together they work as one virtual disk.

RAID level 3 is also known as parallel disk array, or bit or byte-based striping with parity.

Level 3 is noted for fast data transfer rates of large files such as in graphic applications and digital video. However it is even slower than a single drive on small transfers. Level 3 has higher performance over a single drive as well as increased reliability.

 With level 3, if a data drive fails, the controller rebuilds the data on the fly, using a combination of the data on the other drives and the parity drive.

More of the disk space is usable for data than in Level 1. From 83 to 90 percent is available, depending on the number of drives in the array. However, the parity check disk still makes it 10 to 20 percent more costly than using an equal number of single drives. With RAID level 3, it's easy to add extra drives to expand capacity.

The RAID controller board at level 3 is generally a stand-alone SCSI-SCSI disk array controller board that resides in the storage subsystem.

RAID Level 4

RAID level 4 utilizes an independent disk array, meaning the drives don't function in parallel. With RAID 4, data follows independent paths to the individual drives. Data is striped across the drives in units of blocks. One drive is dedicated to parity. This method spreads data across many disks, providing higher performance. Writing is slow because reads from drives must be done to calculate parity information. Level 4 is noted for fast data transfer rates of large files such as in graphic applications and digital video.

The RAID controller board at level 4 is generally a stand-alone SCSI-SCSI disk array controller board that resides in the storage subsystem.

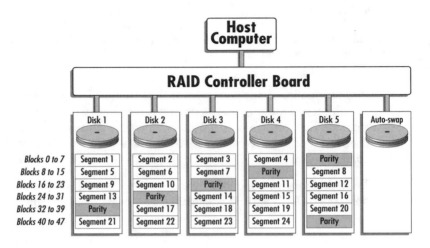

Figure 26. *Level 5 RAID*

RAID level 5, the independent disk array, provides the highest data security. It is similar to level 3 except:

- Parity and data are spread over the disks.
- More than one drive can be written to concurrently.
- It's faster when transferring small data blocks.

RAID level 5 is slower than level 3 on larger transfers and when writing data. An eight-drive system can write to four drives at the same time. No dedicated check disk is needed at level five, as the parity information is spread over the entire array. Performance and data rates are higher than a single drive. Writing is slow because reads from drives must be done to calculate parity information. Spindle synchronization is optional on level 5 arrays.

It's easy to add drives to level 5. This level requires at least three drives. Ten to twenty percent of capacity is used for parity overhead. Under RAID level 5, data lost on a failed drive can be reconstructed on a spare drive.

The RAID controller board at level 5 is generally a stand-alone SCSI-SCSI disk array controller board that resides in the storage subsystem.

Level 5 is great for file-servers, database servers and internet servers. However, it doesn't provide the performance that video and publishing applications need.

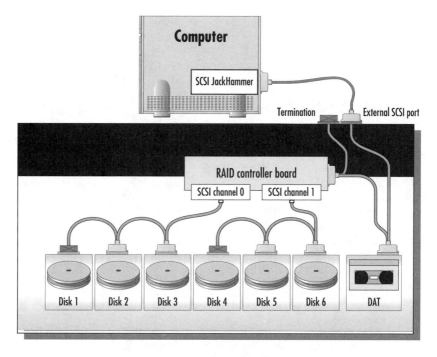

Figure 27. *Fault tolerant RAID*

Fault tolerance is the ability of a system to continue operating even when one (or more) of its component parts have failed. The following is an example of how FWB's SledgeHammer•FT, RAID Level 5 and XOR work together:

"FT" is an acronym for Fault Tolerant. "XOR" stands for "exclusive or," a function of Boolean logic used in creating parity data.

Assume that a SledgeHammer•FT disk array with six disk mechanisms has been set up according to FWB default settings—Disks One through Five are initialized for RAID 5 and are considered member drives; Disk Six has been allocated as the auto-swap unit.

Suppose now that a 2 MB data file is saved from the host computer to the RAID system. The file is first received by the RAID controller board, whose functions include the creation of parity data and the management of all I/O operations to the six disk mechanisms.

The RAID controller board creates an additional 500 KB of parity data from the original 2 MB of file data, and interleaves all data in segments across all member drives.

 A 2 MB file consists of 500 segments of data with an additional 125 segments of parity data.

The file data and parity data are saved to the five RAID level 5 member drives of the RAID system in the following fashion:

- Segment 1 is written to block addresses 0–7 on Disk One.
- Segment 2 is written to block addresses 0–7 on Disk Two.
- Segment 3 is written to block addresses 0–7 on Disk Three.
- Segment 4 is written to block addresses 0–7 on Disk Four.

The information written to block addresses 0–7 on Disks One, Two, Three and Four is processed through an XOR algorithm to create parity data (also one segment in size). This parity data is written to block addresses 0–7 on Disk Five.

- Segment 5 is written to block addresses 8-15 on Disk One.
- Segment 6 is written to block addresses 8-15 on Disk Two.
- Segment 7 is written to block addresses 8-15 on Disk Three.

Parity data is created from the same information written to block addresses 8–15 on Disks One, Two, Three and Five, and is written to block addresses 8–15 on Disk Four. Segment 8 is written to block addresses 8–15 on Disk Five. This process is repeated until all 500 data file segments and its 125 parity segments are interleaved equally among member drives.

For this example, assume that Disk One fails. The data that was stored on Disk One is automatically rebuilt, segment by segment, from the information stored on the remaining disks. The first segment is rebuilt by taking the data from block addresses 0–7 on Disks Two, Three, and Four and the parity information from block addresses 0–7 on Disk 5 and processing them in an XOR algorithm. The resulting segment of data is an exact duplicate of what was stored on block addresses 0–7 on Disk One. It is written to block addresses 0–7 on Disk Six.

This process is repeated until all the data that was on Disk One is rebuilt onto Disk Six. The lost parity information that was on Disk One is also rebuilt by processing the data on the remaining four member disks through the XOR algorithm.

When the rebuild is complete, Disk Six's role has been transformed from auto-swap drive to an active member drive in the RAID 5 array. During or after the rebuild process, Disk One may be pulled from the RAID system. A replacement drive canister may be inserted during or after the rebuild process (this is known as a hot-swap). The RAID controller board automatically allocates the replacement drive canister as the auto-swap unit.

RAID 5 in detail

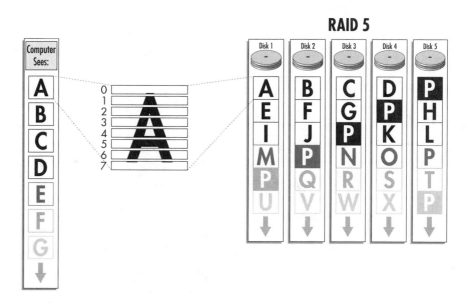

Figure 28. *Data organization in RAID level 5*

RAID 5 is a data organization method for multiple storage devices. It includes some extra redundant data for data recovery in the event of failure of one of the storage devices. From the host's perspective, a RAID 5 array appears to be one very large storage device.

Individual storage device sectors are first grouped into equal sized segments. In Figure 28, each lettered box represents a segment made up of eight sectors. Each sector in a segment contains a sequential piece of the image of a letter.

Data is striped from storage device to storage device in sequence by segments. From the host's perspective, the first sequence of sectors would be stored on the first storage device in the first segment. Following sectors would be stored in first segments on subsequent storage devices. The host, however, has no knowledge of the size of the actual segments. In the example illustrated in Figure 28, we have five storage devices. The host sees the images of the letters stored in each of the segments on each of the storage devices in sequence.

For each stripe or set of segments on the storage devices with the same sequence of sectors, one of these segments will contain parity instead of data. This is repeated on subsequent segments with the same sequence of sectors on the storage devices. The position of the parity segment is rotated with each stripe so that no one storage device becomes a bottleneck for access to parity information.

Parity information is generated by comparing the data from one disk to the data from another, bit-by-bit, across all data disks of an array, using the mathematical Boolean function "exclusive or" (XOR). The XOR function sets a parity bit to 1 if and only if either of the compared data bits is 1, but not both (Figure 29).

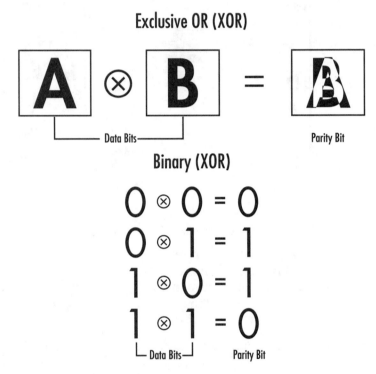

Figure 29. *Boolean function exclusive (XOR)*

 The symbol "⊗" is the logical symbol for "XOR."

XOR is similar to addition or subtraction, except that it never has carryover. In addition and subtraction, you can determine a missing element in an equation by using simple algebra (Figure 30).

$$12 + 28 + X - 6 = 81$$
$$34 + X = 81$$
$$X = 81 - 34$$
$$X = 47$$

Figure 30. *Using algebra to reconstruct a missing element*

Imagine that the missing element represents lost data due to failure. With XOR, the lost data can be reconstructed. Since the data and parity segments are fixed in size, you cannot use simple addition or subtraction because any carryover amounts would jeopardize a fixed value. To overcome the carryover problem, XOR is used.

Parity information is constructed by XORing each data segment in a stripe with every other data segment. The result is a parity segment.

RAID 5 XOR

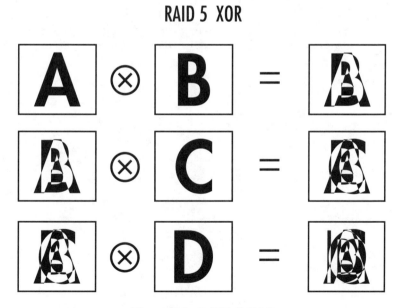

Figure 31. *RAID 5 XOR*

RAID 5 Failure Example

Assume you have a five-drive RAID 5 array with one of the drives acting as the parity drive. The parity drive has a transformed version of data from the other four drives. This configuration is represented below in Figure 32.

RAID 5

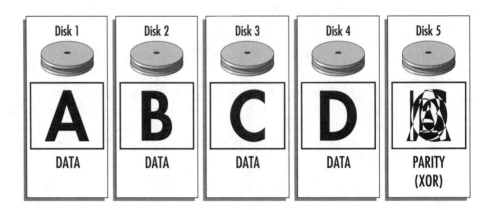

Figure 32. *RAID 5 with one parity drive*

With RAID 5, data blocks representing the sequence ABCDEF… are striped across all five drives, with parity information rotated through each drive.

Drive Three fails, but since the RAID is operating at level 5, the unit can continue operating on the fly by reconstructing the data for Drive Three with the parity drive.

RAID 5 Failure

Figure 33. *RAID 5 with failure of disk C*

To reconstruct the data on the failed drive, data on the remaining drives is XORed together to create the original data (Figure 34).

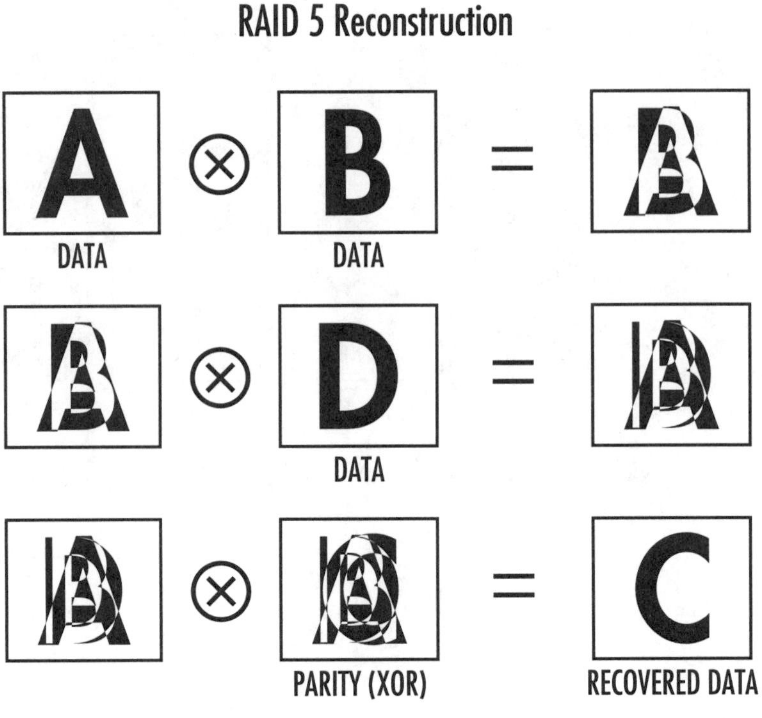

RAID 5 Reconstruction

Figure 34. *RAID 5 reconstruction*

Up to two disks can fail

After the failure of Disk One, Disk One's contents were automatically rebuilt to the online spare, Disk Six. Disk One (drive canister #1 in drive bay #1) is removed, and after contacting your vendor for an RMA number, it should be returned for service. The RAID system still provides optimal performance at this point, as it still has five member drives to stripe data across. Although the level of fault tolerance has been diminished, it is not eliminated.

Now suppose that Disk Three (drive canister #3 in drive bay #3) fails. The RAID system remains operational, even though only four drives are on-line. Performance will suffer at this point because the RAID controller board has to use the XOR algorithm to recreate the lost data segments on-the-fly for each read and write command it receives, rather than service the requests directly.

Increasing fault tolerance

Fault tolerance can be increased by purchasing a seventh drive canister for use as an emergency spare. When the seventh drive canister is inserted into the drive bay of a removed failed drive, the RAID controller board automatically allocates it for use as the online spare.

Other RAID Levels

Some vendors have created additional RAID levels that are proprietary or non-standard. Some of these have been adopted by the RAID Advisory Board as a standard. Several examples of non-standard or proprietary RAID levels are listed below in Table 11.

Table 11. *Other RAID Levels and Devices*

RAID Level	Description
RAID 6	This level is an enhanced version of RAID 5 that includes two sets of parity data rather than one (RAID Advisory Board definition).
RAID 0+1 or 10	This is a combination of RAID 0 and 1. Basically, drives are striped together like RAID 0, then mirrored onto another set of drives like RAID 1. Some companies have called this RAID 6.
AutoRAID	Developed by Hewlett-Packard in 1995, this technology automatically switches between RAID 0, 1 and 5, depending on how the array is accessed. This system is easy to expand.
Tape Arrays	RAID 0, 1 and 3 have been implemented using tape drives. RAID 0 allows tapes to be striped for maximum backup performance. RAID 1 allows 2 copies of a tape to be made at one time, preventing data loss due to media failure or loss. RAID 3 allows for enhanced backup performance but also redundancy if one tape is lost.
Removable Arrays	RAID 0 and 1 have been implemented using removable drives such as optical, SyQuest or Jaz drives. This allows performance to be maximized or fault tolerance to be achieved. Because the media offers infinite storage capacities, projects can be archived and transported easily.

 Some enterprises are marketing layered—or "RAID on RAID"—products as RAID 10, RAID 53 and RAID 77.

Hardware-Based Disk Arrays

The drives of a hardware-based disk array are connected to a RAID controller board installed inside the disk array chassis. The host computer recognizes the RAID controller board as the SCSI storage device, and not the drives connected to it. Read and write commands sent from the computer are processed by the RAID controller board, which in turn sends the appropriate read and write commands to the drives. Overall performance is enhanced when RAID management tasks are executed by a processor on a controller board, because the host computer is freed from input/output overhead, and the disk array itself is freed from the host computer's server and application loads. These arrays are sometimes known as SCSI-SCSI array controllers.

Bus-Based Hardware Disk Arrays

Bus-based hardware disk arrays are controlled by a RAID host adapter that resides in the computer. These are typically PCI-based boards that include multiple SCSI channels to drives and a RISC-based processor. The advantage to these is that there is a direct, high-speed connection to the host bus. These generally outperform platform-independent arrays and cost half as much. This type of controller typically requires a PC with many drive bays or an active hot-swappable backplane. The disadvantage of this type of array is that it is platform-specific.

Software-Based Disk Arrays

The drives of a software-based disk array are connected directly to the host computer and its SCSI bus(es). The member drives may be connected in a variety of methods, such as the dual SCSI bus setup of a Quadra 900/950 or Power Macintosh 8100/8500/9500, or they can be daisy-chained onto a single SCSI accelerator card such as the SCSI JackHammer. Regardless, it is the host computer and software drivers that manage the read and write commands to the member disks of a software array. Although software-based arrays are not as versatile as hardware-based arrays, they are much simpler and less expensive.

Specialized RAID software, such as FWB's RAID ToolKit™, performs the setup of the software-based disk array, initializing each of the member drives with a RAID driver. During general RAID usage, the member drive's RAID driver tells the host computer's system software how to read and write data to it. This will differ depending on whether the disk array volume has been initialized for RAID 0 (striping), RAID 1 (mirroring) or standard HFS usage.

HFS stands for Hierarchical File System. It is used by the Apple Macintosh for storing files and folders on a hard disk.

SAF-TE

SAF-TE stands for SCSI Accessed Fault-Tolerant Enclosures. This specification, started by Conner, was designed to address the need for a standard method of communicating with fault-tolerant enclosures. It defined a set of SCSI commands used to check the status of fans, power supplies and temperature. A small computer with its own SCSI ID essentially monitors the enclosure and tells the computer how it's doing. Other standards for enclosure monitoring include I^2C and AEMI.

RAID Advisory Board (RAB)

The RAID Advisory Board is an association of suppliers and consumers of RAID-related products. It was formed for the following reasons:

- Promote RAID and related technologies
- Write test plans
- Measure performance
- Stimulate standardization efforts
- Share resources among members
- Help grow the RAID industry

You can contact them at 507-931-0967 for more information.

Other Types of Storage Devices

Hard disk drives are not your only option when choosing a storage device. Table 12 provides an overview of many alternatives currently available.

Table 12. *Overview of Other Types of Storage Devices*

Device	Description
Removable Drive	A hard drive and its entire head assembly in a rigid cartridge module that plugs into a "mother" unit. (See page 85.)
Removable Cartridge Drive	One or more hard drive platters in a self-contained rigid case that can be removed from the main drive unit. (See page 86.)
Zip Drive	A drive with a 3.5" cartridge containing a flexible disk that spins within a cushion of filtered air. (See page 88.)
Bernoulli Drive	A drive with a 5.25" cartridge containing a flexible disk that spins within a cushion of filtered air. (See page 89.)
Magneto-Optical Drive	MO devices use a high-powered laser to write to the disc and a low-powered laser, which does not heat the disc significantly, to read the disc. (See page 90.)
Phase Change Optical Drive	The surface coating of phase change media can be changed from an amorphous to a crystalline state, depending on how much it is heated by a laser. (See page 91.)
Floptical Drive	Floptical drives marry optical and magnetic technology. The servo data is perforated into the disk. The magnetic data is located between these optical grooves. (See page 92.)
CD-ROM Drive	CD-ROM drives use laser beams to read CDs. (See page 93.)
CD-Recordable (CD-R) Drive	A high-intensity laser beam changes a dye in the surface coating of the disc to reflect the low-intensity read laser in the same way that a pit would on a CD-ROM. (See page 97.)
WORM Drive	Write-Once Read-Many. Some WORM drives prevent over-writing or erasing data through a series of software flags and special data bits. Others change the physical properties of the media in a way that cannot be undone. (See page 105.)
CD-ROM Erasable Drive	A new standard proposed to create a rewritable compact disc. (See page 106).
Jukebox	A large chassis contains multiple optical cartridges, tapes, or CD-ROM discs that get shuffled around by a mechanical device. (See page 107.)
Digital Versatile Disc (DVD) Drive	DVD is a new standard that provides for up to 4.7 GB of storage on a 120-mm CD-ROM-sized optical disc. (See page 108.)
Tape Drives (DAT and DLT)	Tape Drives use magnetic recording tape to store data in a fashion similar to audio tape recorders, only the information is usually stored in digital form. (See page 110.)

Alternative storage devices are discussed in greater detail below.

Removable drives

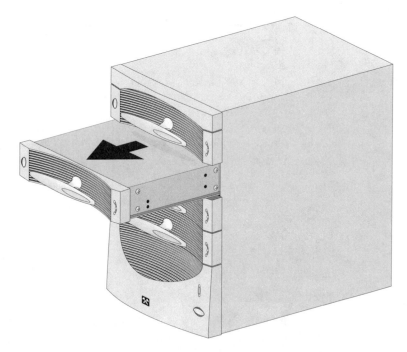

Figure 35. *FWB's SledgeHammer• Pro Removable drive*

Removable drives, also known as canister drives, combine the capacity of a hard drive with the convenience of carrying or storing multiple units. A removable drive is essentially a hard drive and its entire head assembly in a rigid cartridge module that plugs into a "mother" unit. The removable part contains the platter and read/write head. The mother unit contains a power supply and may contain a hard drive controller for communicating with the computer.

 Do not confuse removable drives with removable media drives. See page 86.

Table 13. *Advantages/Disadvantages of Removable Drives*

Advantages	Disadvantages
• High capacity (up to tens of gigabytes) of individual drive and infinite storage capability with multiple drives. • Performance is equivalent to a regular hard drive. • Arrays can be created. • Data can be moved quickly from station to station. • Cartridge modules are made of sturdy construction (although they are still hard drives and should be handled as carefully).	• High cost. • Limited compatibility due to unique manufacturer designs. • Limited number of offerings compared with other types of drives. • They are subject to wear and tear from repeated insertions into the controller (mother) unit. Removable drives are not as sturdy as fixed drives, since they are portable and subject to damage in transit. • Less shock resistant than other types of storage.

Removable cartridge drives

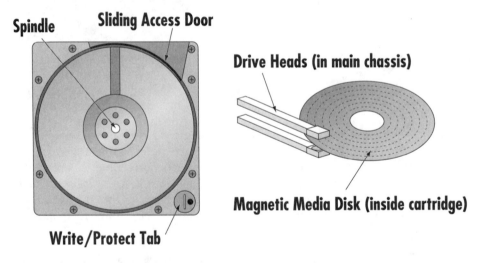

Figure 36. *Removable hard cartridge system*

Removable cartridge drives are devices with one or more hard drive platters in a self-contained rigid case that can be removed from the main drive unit. When the cartridge is inserted into the chassis unit, a door in the cartridge opens automatically. The read/write heads in the chassis unit are moved over the spinning platter(s) inside the cartridge and float on a cushion of air, just as in most fixed hard drives. When the cartridge is removed:

- The heads withdraw.
- The opening to the platters closes.
- The cartridge is ejected from the drive unit.

Removable cartridge drives are great for capacity-intensive activities. They are very popular among desktop publishing, graphic design, and multimedia gurus because they're easily transportable, can be used instead of hard drives, and have a wide customer base, making them excellent transportable media for jobs going to service bureaus.

The most popular base mechanisms are manufactured by SyQuest Inc. and Iomega. These companies use various designs that have certain similarities.

Iomega and SyQuest disks are not interchangeable.

SyQuest Inc. has been making cartridges for a number of years and is considered fairly reliable. They offer both 3.5" and 5.25" disk versions that vary in capacity, compatibility and performance. SyQuest also has a 1.8-inch PCM-CIA-based removable drive.

PCMCIA stands for Personal Computer Memory Card International Association. It's a joint effort of various special interest groups aimed at setting a standard for memory cards used in PCs. PCMCIA cards add improved computer memory capacity or enhance connectivity to external networks and services.

Iomega Jaz platters, while newer to the market, incorporate a few design features that could be an improvement over the original design of the SyQuest units, particularly in keeping dust away from the platter surface. The initial Jaz drive accommodates Jaz media in 540 MB and 1 GB capacities, making it a great medium for storing large data files.

There are other manufacturers of similar systems. However, there are no formal international standards for media interchange on drives of this type.

Therefore, it is not possible to mix the media of one manufacturer with the drive of another.

Table 14. *Advantages/Disadvantages of Removable Cartridge Drives*

Advantages	Disadvantages
• As fast as most hard disk drives. • Some cartridges are relatively inexpensive. • Theoretically infinite storage capabilities. • Wide installed base.	• Cartridges can be used only in a single manufacturer's drive unit. • The possibility of dust and other corrupting particles entering through the cartridge's opening increases with extensive use, making reliability somewhat lower than a fixed hard drive. • Relatively low shock rating. • Cartridges hold a limited amount of data. • Questionable future compatibility.

Zip drives

Zip drives are 3.5-inch removable media drives that work on a principle somewhat similar to Bernoulli drives (see page 89) and are made by the same manufacturer, Iomega. They offer about one-tenth the capacity per cartridge of Jaz drives, but still enough capacity for many users.

 Like the Zip and Bernoulli drives, Jaz drives are manufactured by Iomega.

They are also substantially slower than Jaz drives, but substantially less expensive as well. With their sub-$200 price point, they become affordable to all users.

Table 15. *Advantages/Disadvantages of Zip Drives*

Advantages	Disadvantages
• Enough capacity to accommodate a wide range of user needs. • Inexpensive.	• Slower than Jaz drives. • Less capacity than Jaz drives.

Bernoulli drives

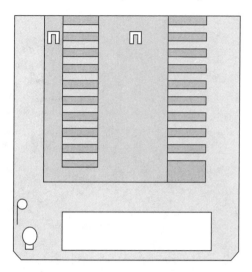

Figure 37. *Bernoulli cartridge*

Bernoulli drives use 5.25″ cartridges containing a flexible disk that spins within a cushion of filtered air. The drives get their name from a phenomenon called the Bernoulli effect. The Bernoulli effect is observed when the velocity of a fluid over a surface is increased and the pressure of that fluid on the surface decreases. In the instance of Bernoulli drives, the fluid involved is air. The reduced air pressure draws the disk toward the read/write head. If a dust particle somehow enters the filter between the head and the platter, the platter's flexibility allows room for the particle to escape; the filtered air blows it away.

Table 16. *Advantages/Disadvantages of Bernoulli Drives*

Advantages	Disadvantages
• Flexing capability apparently makes the drive almost immune to a head crash (a Bernoulli drive has a shock rating of 1,000 g's). • They have a similar capacity as SyQuest units. • They have high reliability ratings (MTBF). • They have reasonably high marks for speed and data security. • Cartridges are relatively cheap. • They have theoretically infinite storage capability.	• Slightly slower speed performance than SyQuest. • More expensive hardware than SyQuest. • Small installed base. • Limited capacity per cartridge. • Only one vendor.

Magneto-optical drives

Figure 38. *Magneto-optical drive and optical cartridge*

Magneto-optical (erasable and multifunction optical) drives use 3.5- or 5.25-inch cartridges that look like and have similar capacities to some WORM cartridges (write-once, read-many; see page 105). The difference in MO technology is that data can be stored, retrieved, manipulated or deleted, over and over (write-many, read-many).

The recording surface of the MO disc is similar to other typical magnetic drives except that it is covered with a protective polymer coating in addition to the protective cartridge. The magnetic particles are also somewhat different in that they consist of metals with relatively low coercivity at room temperature. This means that in order for their magnetic polarity to be switched, the particle must be heated to a high temperature—in this case about 400°F.

Writing is done in two passes:

1. On the first pass (the erase pass), the laser heats the particles that represent those data bits that need to be changed, while the magnetic head sets their polarity to the "0" position.

2. On the second pass, the polarity of the magnet is reversed while the laser heats up only those particles that need to represent "1s."

A low-powered laser, which does not heat the disk significantly, is used to read the disk, taking advantage of the Kerr effect.

 The Kerr effect states that when a polarized light is reflected off a metal surface in a magnetic field, the polarity of the light is rotated clockwise or counterclockwise, depending on the field's polarity. The drive detects this rotation and interprets it as data.

Future optical drives will handle direct overwrite, significantly improving performance. LIMM-DOW (light intensity modulation method direct over-write) allows data to be written in a single pass. This new method of writing requires new drives and media.

The magneto-optical disc is sturdier than other magnetic media. The magnetic particles do not deteriorate or fade as quickly. Information is recorded in a special translucent material that looks like audio compact discs.

There are both 5.25-inch and 3.5-inch ISO magneto-optical drives. These have slightly faster transfer rates, spin rates and seek times than Bernoulli drives because there is less real estate to navigate, but they hold less data. The media are also less expensive than hard drives.

3.5-inch magneto-optical drives appeared first with 128 MB of capacity. Later in 1994, versions with 230 MB appeared. Sometime in 1996, a 650 MB version should be introduced, and in late 1997 a 1.3 GB version.

5.25-inch magneto-optical drives appeared first with 650 MB of capacity. Later in 1994, versions with 1.3 GB appeared. Sometime in 1996, a 2.6 MB version will be introduced, and in late 1997 a 5.2 GB version. By the year 2000, 5.25 magneto-optical drives should be approaching a 10 GB capacity.

Some vendors have created proprietary standards with varying capacities and success rates. Beware of these products when looking for a new drive. Industry-standard support allows for backwards compatibility and lower operating costs not always found in proprietary standard products.

Table 17. *Advantages/Disadvantages of Magneto-Optical Drives*

Advantages	Disadvantages
• Very high capacity (up to several gigabytes). • Reliable storage medium; stable up to 30 years. • Impervious to heat (up to 300° Fahrenheit). • Not affected by magnetic sources. • Impervious to dust. • ISO standard media. • Most higher capacity drives read/write smaller capacity cartridges.	• Highest cost. • Slow compared to magnetic media drives. • Non-standardization among manufacturers (incompatibility between manufacturers is very possible). • Spin rate is usually less than 3,600 RPM, increasing latency. • Writing is done in multiple passes, so it is slower than reading.

Phase change optical drives

Phase change optical drives, like magneto-optical drives, change the physical nature of the disk to record data, but phase change drives write in one pass instead of the two passes necessary for magneto-optical drives. Phase change drives use a medium in which the data-storing material can be changed from an amorphous to a crystalline state, depending on how much it is heated by a laser. At a lower level, the laser heats the media to the point where it becomes crystalline (if it is already crystalline, it remains so). At a higher level, the laser melts the media, which returns to the amorphous state when it cools. The reflectivity of the crystalline spots is different than that of the amorphous ones. The disk is read using a low-level laser, similar to ones used on magneto-optical drives.

Table 18. *Advantages/Disadvantages of Phase Change Optical Drives*

Advantages	Disadvantages
• By writing in a single pass, phase change drives provide all the advantages of magneto-optical drives plus the added speed resulting from one pass writing, which makes it almost twice as fast.	• The repeated heating of the media wears it down and so limits its life. • The disks for some phase change drives are rated at 100,000 read/write cycles, while magneto-optical drives are rated at 1,000,000 cycles. • Very expensive hardware (more than MO). • Slow seek times. • No ISO standard. • Very small installed base.

Floptical drives

Floptical drives marry optical and magnetic technology. The floptical media follows standard, high-density DD and HD, 3.5-inch floppy diskette technology. As with optical discs, the servo data is perforated into the disk and then used by an optical system to position the read/write head. The magnetic data is located between these optical servo grooves. The embedded servo is indelible. It cannot be destroyed or corrupted. It allows the head to follow the eccentricities of the media. This increases track density from typically 135 tracks per inch to over 1,000. Formatted capacity is usually between 20 and 100 MB, compared to a standard floppy's 1.44 MB.

The read/write heads have two different head gaps:

• A narrow gap for use with high density floptical disks.
• A wide gap for use with standard floppy disks.

The drive senses which type of disk has been inserted and automatically uses the appropriate head gap and servo system. This is a low-end product that may replace current floppy drives but not hard drives.

In 1996, Compaq and 3M released information about an LS-120 floptical disk. It has 120 MB capacity, 500 KB/s data transfer rate, 70 millisecond average seek time, rotational speed of 720 RPM, and track density of 2490 tpi.

Table 19. *Advantages/Disadvantages of Floptical Drives*

Advantages	Disadvantages
• Higher densities than standard floppy disks. • Compatibility with standard DD and HD 3.5 floppy disks. • High capacities when used with floptical discs.	• Slower than hard drives (135 ms seek time compared to less than 20 ms for Winchester-type drives). • Disk media is subject to wear. • At present, floptical drives are about two and a half times more expensive than standard floppy drives. • Media not that sturdy compared to Bernoulli. • Slow start/stop times.

CD-ROM drives

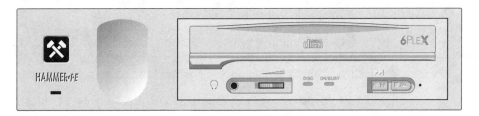

Figure 39. *FWB's 6Plex CD-ROM drive*

CD-ROM (Compact Disc, Read-Only Memory) drives use laser beams to read compact discs (CDs). A CD is a combination of a reflective aluminum platter, a polycarbonate layer stamped with microscopic pits and lands, and a clear lacquer coating, which protects both the stamped polycarbonate (data side) and the aluminum platter (label side).

A pit or land represents an "on" value in binary code; the transition between them signifies "off." The laser beam in a CD-ROM drive shines through the polycarbonate coating, bounces off the surface of the aluminum platter, and returns to be interpreted. The label side could get scratched and, depending upon the severity of the scratch, the disk could still be read. If the side with the pits got scratched, it is more likely that the disk could no longer be read. It would depend on the depth, length and location of the scratch. CDs should have a shelf life of about 50 years.

Data is arranged on the 650 MB disc in data blocks of 2048 bytes. Each block has 304 additional bytes for error correction and overhead. This allows for an error rate of one per 10^{13} bytes, which is extremely low.

 BLER is an acronym for block error rate. BLER is a measurement of how many errors are detected in the error correction code (ECC) blocks on media. BLER is usually expressed in numbers of errors per second. Different CDs have different BLERs. This is attributable both to quality of manufacturing and care taken with handling. BLER can increase from scratches, finger prints and environmental degradation.

Drive performance is measured in terms of data transfer rate and access time. The basic transfer rate of a CD-ROM is 150 KB/s. Drives faster than this basic speed are designated double-speed, quad-speed, or xxxx-speed drives. A quad-speed drive transfers data at approximately 600 KB/s. The current limit of CD-ROM technology appears to be around 10x, due to mechanical and economic constraints.

Drive performance varies depending on the location of data on the disc. Single-speed drives run at 200 RPM at the outside edge and 500 RPM at the inside. Access time is measured the same way as hard disks. Access time for CD-ROM drives is in the hundreds of milliseconds, making these devices 20 to 40 times slower than a hard disk.

To speed up loading, most CD-ROM drives have RAM caches on board. Performance can be furthered by third-party software, such as FWB's CD-ROM ToolKit, which you can use to extend caching.

CD-ROM drives are available in both IDE and SCSI interfaces. Because the devices are so slow, IDE is a perfect low-cost interface for these drives.

Data is structured in one of several data formats named after colored books such as Orange Book, Yellow Book, and so on.

 See "Compact Disc Recordable drives (CD-R)" on page 97 for more detail on disc format standards.

There are also several file system formats used on CD-ROMs. The most common file system formats for CD-ROM are ISO 9660 for PC or cross-platform CDs, and HFS for Macintosh CDs. Table 20 lists common CD-ROM file system formats and describes some pros and cons for each.

Table 20. *Pros and Cons of CD-ROM File System Formats*

File System	Pros	Cons
HFS (Hierarchical File System)	Standard Macintosh interface.	Not usable on most non-Macintosh operating systems.

Table 20. *Pros and Cons of CD-ROM File System Formats (Continued)*

File System	Pros	Cons
ISO 9660 Level 1	Usable with almost all computer operating systems.	• Maximum file name length is eight characters with a three-character extension. • Directory nesting is limited to eight total characters. Defining a file in a directory or path is limited to 256 characters.
ISO 9660 Levels 2 and 3	• Provides ISO compatibility. • File name can be up to 30 characters, including three-character extension.	• Directory nesting is limited to eight total characters. • Defining a file in a directory or path is limited to 256 characters.
Rock-Ridge	• Provides versatile file naming. • Based on ISO 9660 Level 2.	Supported almost solely in Unix environments.
Hybrid	• Compatible with almost all operating systems. • Provides HFS support on Macintosh, ISO for non-Macintosh systems.	• Limits disc capacity slightly due to duplicated directories. • Requires extra set-up time.
Generic	Allows exact duplication of a device or volume, including partitions unusable in the native OS.	• Features are not often needed. • Requires special driver to mount.
Generic XA	Same as Generic, but in XA (Extended Architecture).	• Features are not often needed. • Less widely supported than Generic.
CDRFS	• Provides support for packet-written discs. • Necessary driver is freely available.	• Not ISO "standard," but ISO "compatible." • Requires separate driver or OS support.
CD-UDF	• "Universal" file system. • Extensible to non-CD media. • Provides packet support.	• Not ISO "standard," but ISO "compatible." • Requires separate driver or OS support.

CDs are a standard way to publish large amounts of information, such as databases, directories, and graphics and font libraries for desktop publishing and multimedia uses. The cost to stamp out a CD-ROM has fallen below $1.00 when done in large quantities.

Common stereo audio CD players, while based on the same laser-etched pits technology, use different electronics than CD-ROM drives. They cannot be used as a data storage device for the computer. However, computer CD-ROM drives can also play audio CDs.

There are many CD-ROM drives on the market, sometimes making it difficult to chose the model that will best suit your needs. Table 21 lists some of the features you should look for when you shop for a CD-ROM drive.

Table 21. *Features to Look for in CD-ROM Drives*

Feature	Why You Want This
Multiple Platters	Some drives can hold 4, 7, or many more CD-ROMs at one time and switch between them on the fly.
Digital Audio Extraction	Some CD-ROM drives can transfer digital audio from a compact disc to the computer for saving into files.
PhotoCD Compatibility	Some drives are incompatible with the Kodak PhotoCD format.
Multisession Compatibility	Some CD-ROM drives cannot read CD-ROM's that have multiple sessions on them.
Tray vs. Caddy Loading	Different CD-ROM drives load the disk differently. Some use a caddy; others have a tray onto which you place the CD.
CD-Extra Support	Some CD-ROM drives cannot read audio disks with data tracks.

In 1994, 22 million CD-ROM drives shipped. Approximately 33 million were shipped in 1995, making CD-ROM drives commonplace on virtually all new shipping computers.

Table 22. *Advantages/Disadvantages of CD-ROM Drives*

Advantages	Disadvantages
• It is a standard format supported by all personal and workstation computers. • Inexpensive hardware and media. • Wide availability of titles.	• Slow access time. • The drives are read-only.

Compact Disc Recordable drives (CD-R)

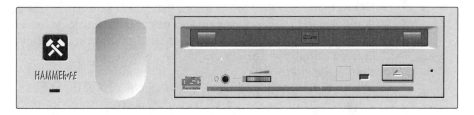

Figure 40. *FWB's CD-ROM recorder*

The desktop CD-Recordable drive (CD-R) market is relatively new. The viability of CD-R technology has resulted from a combination of factors:

- Technical refinements
- Material cost reductions
- Growth in the installed base of CD-ROM readers

This technological evolution is bringing about a revolution within many areas of personal computer usage, including:

- Electronic publishing
- Multimedia
- Imaging and archiving

This revolution along with continued reductions in price are going to lead to one of the steepest growth curves ever experienced by a data storage product. We are at the beginning of a huge opportunity for those who will manufacture, resell, integrate or use CD-R technology.

CD-Recordable (CD-R) has been the longest anticipated and perhaps most frequently requested data storage technology of the past ten years. Shortly after audio CDs were introduced in 1983, users began requesting a means to record their own audio mixes to CDs. When CD-ROM was introduced for computer data distribution in 1984, demand for writing to CD formats on the desktop increased further. Rewritable magneto-optical drives were released in 1987 and one of the most common end-user questions became, "Why can't this drive read and write CD-ROM discs?"

Finally, the pricing, feature set and software support of CD-R drives has reached the point where it is practical, affordable, and easy for a typical end-user to create a CD-ROM disc on their personal computer. This capability, coupled with explosive growth of the installed base of CD-ROM readers over the past three years, ensures the CD-R drive market huge growth for many years to come. Analyst reports consistently position CD-R as the fastest growing segment of the data storage market.

CD-Recordable is an international standard sometimes referred to as "Orange Book, Part II." This standard defines the technology by which CDs will be written—by means of laser rather than stamping—so that the discs may be created quickly with relatively low investment by the creator. It also ensures that those discs will conform to the standards created for each disc format (such as audio disc and CD-i) and will thus be compatible with all drives and software designed to use CDs of that format. Because of this standard, it is possible for anyone with a fairly decent personal computer to choose a CD-R drive and media from more than 15 manufacturers, buy off-the-shelf software, and create a CD that is readable by any CD-ROM reader in the world.

For more information on standards, see Table 23 on page 101.

Standardization also sets up competitive situations where all manufacturers find themselves on a level playing field, assured of a broad potential market. This in turn leads to steadily decreasing costs, improvements in performance, and disciplined market growth.

The typical CD or CD-ROM disc is created at a factory or "mastering facility" on a piece of equipment called a stamper. Stampers are capable of producing large volumes of discs very quickly. But there are disadvantages, too: stamping is analogous to paper printing on a large scale. The equipment is specialized and very expensive. It is designed for high-volume reproduction with a relatively long and costly set-up process. Trained personnel are required to operate and set-up the equipment. The whole process is cost-effective only when a large quantity of discs is required. Such a process requires that the disc's author:

- Send data off-site to the mastering facility.
- Wait for set-up.
- Wait for creation of a check disc.
- Wait for the check disc to be shipped.
- Review the check disc.
- Provide approval.
- Reship the check disc to the manufacturer.

Finally, a few days after approval, the discs are produced and shipped back to the author. This process requires considerable preparation, involves numerous possibilities for delay, and introduces additional costs, such as shipping and handling.

CD-R technology moves CD mastering onto the Desktop. Just as the Macintosh computer and laser printers revolutionized the paper publishing world with Desktop Publishing, personal computers and CD-R solutions will radically change electronic publishing by decreasing costs and time-to-market while increasing flexibility. Mastering can be done on-site, to a Desktop, from creation to testing. Stamping will remain very important, and will even grow, because those facilities will still be required for mass duplication of discs.

CD-R media is similar, but not identical to, a "normal" CD or CD-ROM disc. Both media use a polycarbonate substrate, covered by one or more other layers, all of which are encased in a protective layer of lacquer. Normal CDs have only one additional layer, a reflective aluminum layer that is sandwiched between the substrate and the protective coating. CD-R discs also have a dye layer that lies between the substrate and the reflective layer. Most CD-R discs use gold for the reflective layer because of its higher reflectivity, resistance to corrosion and greater ability to protect the dye.

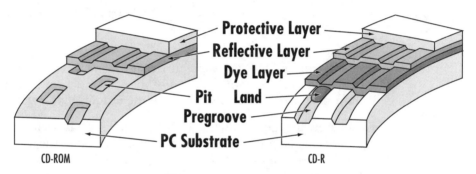

Figure 41. *Comparison of CD-ROM and CD-R media*

On a conventional CD the data, represented digitally by 1s and 0s, are recorded as pits and lands (flat spots) in the pre-grooves of the media. On a CD-R disc, rather than a physical pit or depression in the groove, a dye is used to change the reflection of the laser in the same way that a pit would. This dye is activated by a laser beam of a somewhat higher intensity than that used to read data. The use of this dye allows discs created by a laser to be just as readable on conventional CD readers as discs created by a stamper.

Two types of dye are used in CD-R media:

- Cyanine
- Phthalocyanine

The proponents of phthalocyanine claim that media using that dye has a longer shelf life based on extended life testing. On the other hand, some proponents of cyanine dye claim that it is more tolerant of CD-R drives whose lasers are on the edge of being within specified ratings. To date, no conclusive impartial tests have been published on this topic. In reality, the actual chemical formulation of the dyes and other coatings varies somewhat with each manufacturer. Some media are clearly superior to others. CD recorders and readers should work equally well with either dye. However, some recorders do seem to work better with one manufacturer's media than another. When in doubt, use only the media recommended by the drive manufacturer.

CD-R discs come in three capacities, 650 MB, 550 MB and 150 MB. Because they can also be used to record audio data, the capacity is sometimes described in minutes: 74, 63 or 18.

It is very important that the underside or recording surface of CD-R discs not be touched, scratched or contaminated in any way until after the disc is completely recorded. Oil, grease and other contaminants can prevent data from being written accurately to the disc. After the disc has been written, it can be treated like any normal CD.

 You can identify the recording side of a CD-R disc because it should have no label or printing on it.

Currently, most CD-R drives require that the media be put into caddies. In the future, most mechanisms will probably change to tray loading. But, in the meantime, make sure that you have some caddies if you want to write CDs.

Fortunately for the user, while CD-R technology has been growing in popularity, CD-R media prices have been shrinking. In 1993, the street price for a single blank disc was at least $20. In 1995 was $10. The price will likely drop to about $5 in 1996.

CD-Recordable drives are very similar to CD readers. In fact, many recorders are based substantially on manufacturers' reader mechanisms. However, the differences are both important and complex. The primary differences include:

- The laser diode
- The electronics
- The firmware

Unlike CD readers, recorders need a laser diode that is capable of emitting beams of two different intensities. The read beam is the same as that of CD-ROM readers. The write beam is more powerful since it is used to create a chemical reaction rather than just a reflection. Other circuitry that allows the drive to receive incoming data and perform error correction is also necessary. CD-R drives need larger RAM buffers to prevent data underruns and firmware that supports all of these new features.

Virtually all CD-R drives use a SCSI interface. SCSI offers a good combination of performance, software features and versatility, plug-and-play installation and relatively low cost. At some point, when new methods of writing limit the requirements for maintaining consistent transfer rates, CD-R drives will appear with other interfaces, such as ATAPI.

For more information on ATAPI, see Chapter 5, "Other Storage Interfaces."

There are many different formats for compact discs. Many of these formats are also international standards. As mentioned above, these standards are often named for the color of the book in which their specifications are published. Table 23 lists CD formats and standards with an explanation of their applications.

Table 23. *Overview of CD Formats and Standards*

CD Format	General Information	Standard
CD-DA	Compact Disc Digital Audio. The format used for conventional audio CDs. It is readable on all audio CD players and most CD-ROM readers as well as a wide variety of other multimedia devices.	Red Book
CD-ROM	Compact Disc Read-Only Memory. The format used for almost all CD-ROM applications. It is readable on all CD-ROM drives and some multimedia devices. (See page 93.)	Yellow Book
CD-ROM XA	CD-ROM Extended Architecture. A seldom-used CD format that allows for the interleaving of data, audio, video and graphics for smoother playback of multimedia content. It is only readable on XA-ready (i.e. XA compatible drives). Most—but not all—readers sold after 1991 are XA-ready.	Yellow Book
CD-i	CD interactive. Used for some home entertainment systems. Philips, which developed the standard, has been the most vocal proponent of this technology. Like CD-G, many readers support the format but there are few computers or applications that allow the discs to be used.	Green Book
CD Bridge	This format is used for Kodak Photo CDs and Video CDs. Many readers support the format but it has not yet become important globally. Software support and demand for discs in these formats is still somewhat immature. The standard for PhotoCD was created and is enforced by Kodak. Standards are proposed, but not in place.	Proposed: White Book Blue Book (see CD-Extra)
CD-G	CD Graphics. The format used for Karaoke CDs. The format is readable on a variety of devices, but most of them are consumer audio components. While the discs may be readable on CD-ROM drives, special software, such as FWB's CD-ROM ToolKit™, is required to see the graphics.	White Book

Table 23. *Overview of CD Formats and Standards (Continued)*

CD Format	General Information	Standard
CD-R	CD-Recordable. The format used for CDs that can be written to.	Orange Book, Part II
CD-Extra	A new standard for combining audio and data on a disc in such a way that the audio may be played on any consumer CD player, while both the audio and the data can be enjoyed on a computer with a compatible CD-ROM drive. This standard is very new and many CD-ROM and CD-R drives do not support it.	Blue Book

There are several different methods of writing to a CD-R disc. The method to use depends on the following criteria:

- What the drive supports
- The application for which the disc it is being created
- The audience it is intended to reach

What follows is a description of the various methods of writing to a CD-R disc.

Disc-at-Once

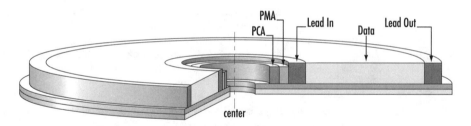

Figure 42. *Order of information on a DAO CD*

Disc-at-once, also known as uninterrupted write and DAO, is a writing method in which the entire disc is written in one uninterrupted session. Data cannot be added to the disc later. A DAO disc is Red and Yellow Book compliant. DAO is 100 percent compatible with all CD-ROM drives. It is used for creating final discs for electronic publishing, audio and any other application where complete compatibility is crucial.

 A session is defined as a group of data containing a Lead In area, a Data area and a Lead Out area. A session can be recorded in one sitting or can be recorded incrementally, depending on the formatting software's capability. Each session carries about 15 MB of overhead for the Lead In and Lead Out areas.

Incremental

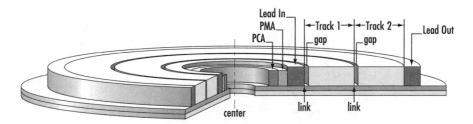

Figure 43. *Order of information on an incremental CD*

Incremental recording is a method in which data can be added to a CD-R disc in segments. There may be, but does not have to be, interruptions in the data flow between segments. Data can be added using track-at-once (TAO) or packet writing and single session or multisession recording. These discs are Orange Book compliant.

See below for more information on TAO, Packet and single- or multisession recording.

Track-at-Once

With track-at-once (TAO), the user can copy one track of data at a time to a CD-R disc. Up to—but no more than—99 tracks of data can be stored on a disc, space permitting. TAO recording can be used with either single-session or multisession recording. The finalized disc is 100 percent backward compatible.

A track is a logical group of data, not a physical track.

Packet

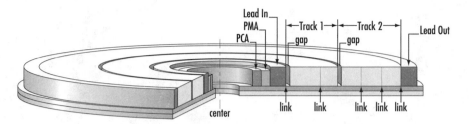

Figure 44. *Order of information on a packet CD*

The user can copy a packet of data at a time to a CD-R disc. Like a track, a packet is a logical group of data. However, while a disc can hold no more than 99 tracks, it can hold up to 1,000 packets, space permitting.

About 20 percent of each packet is overhead space. This method can be used in single-session or multisession recording. It eliminates buffer underrun problems—where the source of data supply is unable to keep pace with the CD-R device's recording speed—allowing reliable recording from slow sources. It also lessens the need for a dedicated source or buffer drive.

Packet writing is still undergoing standardization and is not yet widely supported. The compatibility of packet-written CDs will not be known until the standard is complete. It is fairly certain, however, that packet writing will not be well-suited for writing audio discs.

Multisession

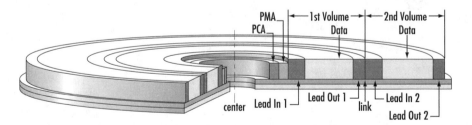

Figure 45. *Order of information on a multisession CD*

A multisession disc is a CD-R disc containing more than one session. Each session carries 15 MB of overhead for the Lead In and Lead Out areas. A multisession-capable writer is necessary for writing to the disc. A multisession capable reader is necessary for reading the disc, although the first session can be read by any CD-ROM drive.

 A session is one, contiguous, spiraling string of data written to, or stamped into, a disc. There may be more than one session on a disc. A track is a portion, possibly all, of a session. A session may contain many tracks, but a track may not contain a session.

An audio CD will have several tracks that are stamped into the disc as one, contiguous, spiraling string of audio data—the silence between tracks is data that makes no sound. If a conventional CD contains digital and audio data, it is stamped with at least two tracks in one session, that is one, contiguous, spiraling string of data: first the digital data, then some silent data, and the audio data in the rest.

If a CD is made with two sessions, the boundary between the sessions also forms a boundary between tracks. The two sessions are recorded as two, contiguous, spiraling strings of data, one following the other. The boundary between the sessions is not soundless data in this case, but a small bit of smooth, unmarred, CD surface. The sessions are physically separate.

Multivolume/Multisession

Multivolume/multisession is a format where each session appears as a separate volume of data. On a PC, different volumes can be displayed as different drive letters. On a Mac, different volumes can be displayed as different icons. This is the most common type of multisession disc.

Kodak® Multisession

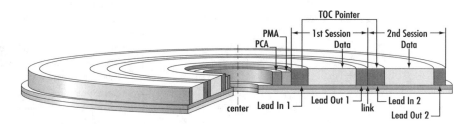

Figure 46. *Order of information on a Kodak multisession CD*

Kodak multisession is a format where all sessions appear as one unique volume. On a PC, the disc can be displayed as one drive letter regardless of how many sessions are on the disc. On a Mac, the disc can be displayed as one volume icon.

WORM drives

WORM stands for "write-once read-many." There are many different types of WORM drives. They come in various form factors, with various media formulations. They use a number of different writing techniques. Examples of

WORM drives include 12-inch platter drives from companies such as Sony and Hitachi, multifunction magneto-optical drives from many different manufacturers, phase change optical drives designed by Panasonic, and the currently popular CD-Recordable drives.

Some WORM drives, including many multifunction drives, prevent over-writing or erasing data through a series of software flags and special data bits that tell the firmware of the drive not to write to certain data blocks. Others, such as the 12-inch drives and CD-R, are ablative—meaning the writing process changes the physical properties of the media in a way that cannot be undone.

 One meaning of ablation is reduction or dissipation, as by melting. The "ablative" in "ablative WORM" refers to the creation of permanent pits in the media surface.

Ablative WORM is the ultimate archive device, because the information is written physically and therefore is less prone to incidental data loss from things such as magnetism and viruses. The primary benefit, however, is that the data cannot be tampered with. Ablative WORM media is an excellent choice for storing legal, medical and other important documents.

Table 24. *Advantages/Disadvantages of WORM Drives*

Advantages	Disadvantages
• Good archiving material; disks can last up to 100 years. • High capacity—from 650MB for CD-R up to 15GB for a 12" platter.	• Historically expensive media and unit, CD-R is an exception to this. • As the name suggests, once data is written, it is there for good, occupying disk space. • Slow access time relative to hard discs. • Aside from CD-R, there are few standards and little cartridge interchangeability. • Incompatibility.

CD-ROM Erasable drives

CD-ROM Erasable (CD-E) is a new proposed standard for creating a rewritable compact disc. Unlike CD-R, the discs can be reused many times. CD-E uses a special drive and media to provide erasability. CD-E discs can be read in many CD-ROM drives, starting with the 1996 models. However, they cannot be read in older CD-ROM drives because they reflect less light than the discs shipping now.

 On October 25, 1995, Philips announced the release of the first draft of Orange Book, Part III. Version 1.0, which contains the CD-Erasable specification, was set to follow in the first quarter of 1996. According to the specification, CD-E discs will be readable in CD-ROM drives, readable and writable in CD-R drives, and readable, writable and rewritable in CD-E drives. CD-E drives will be capable of reading all existing disc formats. Ricoh has developed a CD-E media that uses an aluminum reflective layer, rather than the gold of CD-R. Additionally, it saves data by using phase change technology. For more information on phase change technology, see "Phase change optical drives" on page 91.

Jukeboxes

Jukeboxes are set up in a fashion similar to the music machines often found in restaurants and bars. A large chassis contains multiple optical cartridges, tapes or CD-ROM discs that get shuffled around by a mechanical device. A particular platter is fetched and moved to the enclosed drive when the data on that cartridge has been requested.

Jukeboxes have differing capacity for the number of drives in the unit and number of disks supported. The more drives in the unit, the faster data can be accessed and the more data can be accessed by multiple users at one time.

Table 25. *Advantages/Disadvantages of Jukeboxes*

Advantages	Disadvantages
• Massive amounts of storage possible, usually many gigabytes. • Suitable for networked computers and large operations that need centralized archival storage.	• High hardware costs and possibly high maintenance costs. • More moving parts to wear out, so more things can go wrong. • Slow when going from one cartridge another.

Digital Versatile Disc drives

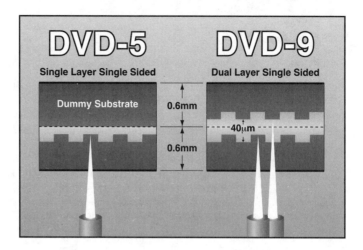

Figure 47. *Comparison of single- and dual-layer DVDs*

Digital Versatile Disc (DVD) is a new standard designed to be the successor to the CD-ROM and to the VHS video cassette. The DVD standard was first announced in 1995. At that time CD-ROM's 650 MB capacity was becoming a barrier. Due to advances in multimedia, programs were growing beyond the capacity of a single CD-ROM disc. VHS, with its costly cartridge, terrible picture quality, and slow duplication times, has been looking for a successor for a while.

This new standard provides for up to 4.7 GB of storage on a 120-mm, CD-ROM-size optical disk (DVD-5). In the consumer format, DVD-VIDEO, it has room for up to 133 minutes of high-quality, 500-line MPEG-2, compressed video with AC-3 Dolby Digital surround sound. The format achieves this capacity boost by using a smaller dot pitch allowing it to use a shorter wavelength red laser (650/635 nanometers).

DVD discs use two bonded 0.6 mm substrates, reducing the distance between the disc surface and the physical pits. Lasers don't have to penetrate as far as on CD-ROM's, so pits can be more finely positioned. Also with two substrates, a separate layer could be added. It would be read by a different lens, allowing for increased capacity.

Other parts of the specification call for a dual layer disk, DVD-9, with up to 8.5 GB of capacity. Also specified are dual-sided flippable disks, DVD-10 and DVD-18, with capacities up to 9.4 and 17 GB. Write-once DVD versions, known as DVD-R, are disks with up to 3.8 GB in capacity. DVD-RAM specifies a rewritable version that provides more than 2.6 GB per side utilizing phase change technology. When used as a CD-ROM, DVD is called DVD-ROM.

DVD-ROM may utilize the Universal Disk Format (UDF), ISO 13346 standard for formatting of data on the disks. This standard has been spearheaded by the Optical Storage Technology Association (OSTA). This would allow disks to be read/written on any platform, ensuring full data interchange.

Most DVD products will be backward compatible with current CD-ROM discs because they include two separate optical pickup lenses. Initial drives should be about twice the price of current CD-ROM or CD Players. Future versions should rapidly fall in price.

Because the DVD disc is higher density, it offers a basic quad speed transfer rate of 1.35 MB/s, equivalent to a 9x CD-ROM drive. The system's peak data rate is 10 Mb/s with an average sustained data rate of 4.94 Mb/s for each side.

When used in consumer applications, this type of disc provides for up to 100 minutes of D-1 quality digital video with Dolby AC-3 digital surround sound. Movies can now be stamped out quickly and cheaply. DVD disks can be manufactured using very few changes to current CD production techniques.

DVD products should be on the market in late 1996.

Tape drives

Figure 48. *FWB's DAT and DAT autoloader tape drives*

Tape Drives use magnetic recording tape to store data in a fashion similar to audio tape recorders, only the information is usually stored in digital form. The primary difference between the different types of tape drives is their capacity and the type of tape cartridge they use (such as 4 mm digital audio tape, 8 mm tape, quarter inch tape [QIC], Travan and half-inch DLT).

 Travan is a subset of the mini-cartridge format QIC (quarter-inch cartridge). At .315 inches, Travan tape is slightly wider than standard QIC. It allows a 750 foot tape length, which translates to larger capacity—up to 10 GB for proposed TR-5—and data transfer rates up to 1.2 MB/s.

Most tape drives include a compression feature that compresses data written to (or decompresses data read from) the tape drive on-the-fly. Compression ratios range from 4:1 for spreadsheets, to 2.4:1 for text files, to 1.3:1 for graphics files. The amount of compression you get depends on your data set.

The most common tape drives are the low-cost QIC tape drives with almost 80 percent of the market. These QIC drives are very popular on PCs. Next is the 4 mm DAT drive with about 15 percent market share, with the remainder in the 8 mm and DLT markets.

Digital Data Storage (DDS)

DDS is a high-performance, high-capacity, streaming tape device designed for use on mid-range and high-end computing systems. They are used for local and network backups or archiving. They allow you to back up a larger data capacity at a higher speed than many other types of tape drives.

Digital Data Storage (DDS) is a standard format for 4 mm tapes using helical scan recording. It was developed by Hewlett-Packard and Sony. Originally developed to replace the audio cassette, DDS has found homes in both pro-audio and computer areas.

- The first generation standard is DDS-1 (or simply DDS).
- Data compression was added to DDS-1 to produce the DDS-DC standard.
- Further enhancements, notably narrower tracks and thinner tape, led to DDS-2, the third generation. DDS-2 provides twice the capacity of DDS-1.

DDS-3 will appear in 1996, offering higher capacity and faster data transfer rates due to the use of PRML read/write channels and a higher density metal particle MP++ tape.

 PRML stands for partial-response maximum-likelihood. It is a technique used by a read/write head in a drive mechanism for detecting data. Instead of spacing out analog peaks as in peak detection, digital filtering is used to compensate for signal overlap. After filtering, the scheme identifies what are the likeliest sequence of data bits written to the media.

Table 26. *Comparison of Features of DDS-1, 2 and 3*

Feature	DDS-1	DDS-2	DDS-3
Tape Length	60 or 90 m	120 m	125 m
Native Capacity	1.3 or 2 GB	4 GB	12 GB
Compressed Cap	2.6 - 4 GB	4 - 8 GB	12 - 24 GB
Channel	8,10 mod	8,10 mod	PRML

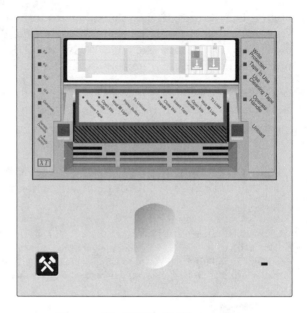

Figure 49. *FWB's DLT tape drive*

DLT is a high performance, high capacity, streaming cartridge tape device. FWB's hammerDLT is a 5.25-inch form factor, half-inch tape drive used for data backup or archiving. The design includes:

- A dual-channel read/write head
- Digital Lempel-Ziv (DLZ) high-efficiency data compression
- A tape mark directory for maximum data throughput and minimum data access time

DLT allows you to back up a higher data capacity at a higher speed than other personal computer-oriented tape products. When operating in non-compressed mode, the drives have a maximum sustained transfer rate of 1.5 MB/s. When operating in compressed mode, the maximum transfer rate is 3 MB/s write and 3.5 MB/s read.

Capacities range all the up to 40 GB on a single tape in compressed mode.

Table 27. *Advantages/Disadvantages of Tape Drives*

Advantages	Disadvantages
• Tape drives are, to date, the most inexpensive way to back up data. • Multiple cartridges can increase the capacity of a tape drive. • Transfer rates up to 100 MB/min. and beyond are possible.	• Due to their slow access speed and sequential access, they are inappropriate for continual, on the fly, primary data storage. • Not a very reliable medium over the long term. It is subject to warping and shrinking due to natural elements.

All About SCSI

Overview

Chapter 3 begins with SCSI background and basics, skims the surface of SCSI's technical waters—occasionally diving a bit deeper into computer-specific surf—and finally deposits you firmly at the shores of information beyond and outside the SCSI scope.

If you're unfamiliar with SCSI, you'll want to read Chapter 3 from beginning to end. Even SCSI gurus will benefit from this refresher. You'll get the most out of it if you've already read through Chapter 2, "All About Drives."

SCSI Is: Simple ...

Storage products need a way to connect and communicate with the rest of the computer. SCSI has emerged as a very popular method of interfacing storage products to a personal computer. SCSI, pronounced "scuzzy," stands for Small Computer System Interface. It is a standard specification that defines how computers and their peripherals communicate with each other. SCSI is perhaps best known as the interface for Apple Macintosh hard disk drives.

In June 1986 SCSI-1 was adopted as an American National Standard by the American National Standards Institute (ANSI). It qualified as ANSI standard X3.131-1986.

 ANSI is a private, nonprofit membership organization that performs two functions:

- It coordinates the United States' voluntary consensus standards system.
- It approves American National Standards.

ANSI ensures that a single set of non-conflicting American National Standards are developed by ANSI-accredited standards-developers, and that all interests concerned have the opportunity to participate in the development process. ANSI does not develop standards. However,

- It provides the means for determining the need for standards.
- It ensures that qualified organizations develop those standards.
- It coordinates standards approval.

ANSI established the X3 category for information technology. Some of the current technologies that fall under the ANSI X3 category are listed in Table 28.

Table 28. *ANSI X3 Categories for Current Technologies*

ANSI Category	Technology
X3T10.1	Serial Storage Architecture (SSA)
X3T11	Fiber Channel, HIPPI and IPI
X3T12	Fiber Distributed Data Interface (FDDI)
X3T13	Advanced Technology Attachment (ATA) and Advanced Technology Attachment Packet Interface (ATAPI)

ANSI follows these steps to set standards:

1. Study group assembles to develop project proposal (six months).
2. Work group develops draft of proposed standard (six months)
3. Technical committee reviews and (possibly) approves draft (one year).
4. Standard is submitted to ISO (International Standards Organization) for installation.

The entire process can take from two to ten years.

ANSI's endorsement of particular guidelines, though not binding, exerts a powerful standardizing influence in the computer industry.

... and Complex

The SCSI specification defines an input/output (I/O) interface that is variously described as:

- Nonproprietary
- Device-independent
- Flexible
- Low- and high-level
- Intelligent
- Eight-bit
- Parallel
- Peer-to-peer

SCSI offers a defined command set that improves data exchange and enables the use of several different kinds of peripheral devices with one or more host computers.

These terms are explored in the sections that follow.

Essential Terminology

Because SCSI jargon is both esoteric and critical to understanding the underlying concepts, we think it best to acquaint you with some of the fundamentals immediately. Other sections will also begin with introductory terminology. All terms are also included in the Glossary.

- **Bus**

  Think of a bus as a conveyance for electrical signals rather than people. Essentially the bus is the wires in the cable that provide the physical means for such conveyance.

- **Host**

  The computer—specifically, its central processing unit (CPU) and SCSI chip.

- **Initiator**

  A SCSI device, usually the computer—or more specifically its SCSI chip—capable of initiating an operation. In multiple-host systems initiators (hosts) may also be targets.

 A multiple-host system is a system that has more than one computer connected to the SCSI bus.

- **Target**

  A SCSI device, usually the peripheral, that carries out the initiator's request.

PC Industry History

A discussion of SCSI's origins almost begs the issue: SCSI is still evolving. What's happening today will no doubt later be considered part of its origin. Already there is SCSI-2, and SCSI-3 is under development. Assume all references to SCSI herein mean SCSI-1, the original specifications from 1986.

 For more information about SCSI-2, see "SCSI-2: A Transition From SCSI-1" on page 193. For more information about SCSI-3, see "SCSI-3" on page 209.

Once the non-mainframe computer industry got started, its sprawling development defied control. Technologies spawned technologies, which were brought to market in many forms by manufacturers who pursued specific goals and niche markets. Some believed their implementation was superior to all others or hoped to establish a de facto standard that would reap substantial long-term rewards, perhaps even market domination.

There are two types of standards: de facto and agency, such as ANSI/IEEE, standards. De facto standards are set by users over time, rather than by an agency. ANSI and IEEE are standards agencies.

The good news was that without imposed uniformity, creativity was not constrained:

- From a developer's perspective, it meant they could try anything.
- From a buyer's perspective, it meant everything was available.

The bad news? Many of these products wouldn't work with anybody else's.

This pervasive incompatibility among different vendors' devices eroded buyer confidence and effectively limited the growth of the industry. In time, a consensus formed about the need for an open, or nonproprietary, standard that addressed host-to-peripheral communications. Device communications, particularly given the critical nature of data storage, was just too important to be ignored.

SCSI History

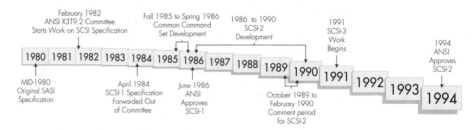

Figure 50. *SCSI time line*

A wide-ranging confluence of factors created SCSI, and not everybody agrees on all the details. Here is our version:

In the 1960s IBM Corporation developed a bus that later became the most common way for third-party vendors to connect peripherals to IBM mainframes, most often its Model 360. It was called the block multiplexer or OEM channel, and it became so popular that the federal government made it a processing standard (FIPS 60). It allows multiple peripherals to intercommunicate at the same time. Other computer manufacturers objected and took this decision to the courts, alleging that such an adoption gave IBM an unfair advantage.

FWB's Guide to Storage

OEM stands for original equipment manufacturer. It applies to a product that is manufactured by one enterprise then sold to another, where it is bundled and sold with the purchasing enterprise's own products.

The suit was unsuccessful, but the pressure it exerted may have later kept ANSI, which was looking to create an I/O bus standard, from adopting the OEM channel as it stood. ANSI, wanting to create a standard for a nonproprietary I/O bus, did consider the OEM channel before beginning work on the intelligent peripheral interface (IPI) in the early 1980s.

For more information on IPI, see Chapter 5, "Other Storage Interfaces."

About 1981, Shugart Associates, a disk drive maker, joined forces with NCR Corporation and came up with an interface based on the OEM channel architecture called SASI, for Shugart Associates System Interface.

The individuals responsible for SASI later went on to found Adaptec, Inc.

Unlike the OEM channel, SASI was intended as a low-cost, peer-to-peer interface. Shugart wanted a logical interface to data on drives, while NCR wanted extensions for large devices and differential cabling. Three manufacturers—DTC, Xebec and Western Digital—embraced SASI and built controllers for it. SASI eventually evolved into what is known today as SCSI.

A peer-to-peer interface involves two systems that communicate as equal partners, sharing the processing and control of the exchange.

In 1982, the ANSI committee founded the X3T9.2 standards accreditation group to create the SCSI standard. In 1983 the first SCSI chip from NCR appeared, the 5385, even before the SCSI-1 standard was finalized. A year later, the 5380 appeared with on-chip drivers, making inexpensive SCSI implementations possible.

Apple's SCSI Influence

Apple Computer Inc. hopped on the SCSI bandwagon before any other major company. They introduced a SCSI-ready Macintosh Plus in 1986. The Macintosh line has relied on SCSI ever since.

Apple has not relied exclusively on SCSI, however. In 1995 they implemented IDE drives in some of their newer machines, including PowerBooks. For more information, see "IDE" on page 236.

Apple chose the SCSI interface primarily for its speed, device independence, and expandability. Formerly—in the Macintosh 128 and 512, and in fact with most computers manufactured prior to 1986—hard disk drives were connected to an existing port designed for a slow device. This was usually a serial port, which was very slow and allowed connection of only one device. Connecting to the floppy drive port, although faster and allowing connection of two devices, was not much better. Because neither were designed for hard drives, an inconvenient boot floppy was necessary to start the drive.

 The serial port is a connector on a computer or peripheral device that can send and receive data one bit at a time. A floppy port can send a receive data in parallel but provides much slower performance than a SCSI port.

When Apple began shipping all Macintosh computers with a hard drive port that was standardized on SCSI—an interface that allowed the attachment of up to seven devices—a clear signal was sent to third-party vendors that here at last was something upon which they could standardize. This was a critical endorsement of the new interface.

Unlike many computers, the Macintosh "speaks" SCSI directly via a dedicated port, or connector. Because SCSI support is built-in, no adapter is required. This is true even of the low-end Macintoshes with one or no internal slots for peripherals. Every Macintosh can use basically the same SCSI peripherals.

PCs rarely have SCSI on the motherboard. Typically they require a host bus adapter card to provide SCSI support and connectors.

A Good Start...

To an ever increasing degree, SCSI works.

- It works for connecting different devices to operate together as part of a system, which is called interoperability or connectivity.
- It works for boosting I/O performance.
- It works for hardware economy.

Interoperability or connectivity

The SCSI specification enables diverse peripheral devices and one or more computer systems to work together. As many as seven SCSI devices can be connected to a computer in what is called a daisy chain.

Devices are distinguished by SCSI ID numbers. SCSI ID determines the priority a device will have when it seeks to gain control of the bus. For more information on daisy chains, see "Physical connections" on page 140.

SCSI is device-independent. It masks the internal operation of a peripheral from other peripherals and the computer, so the computer doesn't need to know much about them to communicate. SCSI does this by treating peripherals as logical units (rather than physical, or actual units) responding to a known language, also known as protocol. SCSI treats devices as storage abstractions. SCSI's ability to view its world in abstract terms is a powerful facilitator of its operations.

Each peripheral can comprise eight logical unit numbers (LUN—the numerical representation of the peripheral's address). Consequently, the capability to daisy chain seven peripherals to a host means that you are allowed a total of 56 logical units on a SCSI bus.

 LUNs allow for addressing subunits within a peripheral device. Using a CD-ROM jukebox as an example, the jukebox is identified by its SCSI ID, and the individual drive mechanisms within the jukebox are identified by LUNs.

In principle, SCSI is like the United Nations. It's a universal forum that can accommodate a diverse world of manufacturers. Through SCSI, manufacturers can offer products that are unique but still compatible with other vendors' hardware. Even implementations of emerging technologies can be connected easily to a computer system if they speak SCSI (and more and more of them do).

Still, device independence is not complete. Special software is required to fully exploit new or dissimilar device types. This special software is called a device driver, or driver. It enables the host computer (initiator) and a peripheral device (target) to communicate with each other. For example, a device driver would be needed if a system that previously included only the initiator and a hard disk drive expands with the addition of a scanner or CD-ROM drive.

 A device driver is software that tells a host how to connect to a peripheral. For more information, see "Device drivers" on page 181.

All devices on the SCSI bus are treated as equals in terms of their capability to communicate directly with other devices on the bus. Because of this, SCSI is considered a peer-to-peer interface.

Because SCSI defines standard physical and electrical connections for devices, connecting the parts of your system is easy.

SCSI also reduces software incompatibility. Drivers must utilize a SCSI Manager, or else much of SCSI's potential would be just be so much dead code. If drivers bypassed a SCSI Manager, they would have to be rewritten every time a machine shipped with a different SCSI chip or addressing modes.

For more information, see "SCSI Manager" on page 178, "Device drivers" on page 181, and "Call Chain" on page 183.

Boosting I/O performance

The SCSI bus operates in parallel, with each byte of information separated into its bits and sent simultaneously along eight parallel wires in the SCSI cable.

Bit is a contraction of "binary digit." A bit is always either a 0 (off) or a 1 (on). It is the basic unit of information used by a computer. There are eight bits of data per byte. Byte is a contraction of "binary digit eight."

Because the SCSI specification describes such wiring—as well as other electrical operations and physical connections—it is considered a low-level interface. Yet SCSI also presents programmers with a nonphysical abstraction (a logical perspective) that can be manipulated with software. Because the SCSI specification details this command structure, it is also considered a high-level interface.

SCSI uses complete logical commands: for example, when accessing data on a hard disk drive, SCSI lets the initiator request a particular data block without having knowledge of where that data block physically resides on the drive. The SCSI drive takes this abstract (or logical) request and translates it into the specific request required to locate the data block. This reduces the inherent delay when information changes direction on the bus as devices communicate along the eight-bit-wide data path. It also reduces the amount of information that is exchanged, because one command takes care of several operational aspects at once.

By contrast, the OEM channel:

1. First had to say "Go to the X place."
2. Then had to wait to be told X had been found.
3. Finally, it had to issue a command to act on what resided in X.

SCSI is more efficient and direct. It says:

1. Find the X quality wherever it is, and act upon it in such and such a way.

SCSI is more logical and complete.

A SCSI peripheral's controller (a SCSI chip) provides intelligence, allowing the peripheral to store and manipulate data. This frees the host CPU to perform other tasks. Typical drives have embedded microprocessors on the controller board, such as Intel's 80C188 or 80C196, to control these operations. Drives using servos usually have dedicated servo processors that control actuator movement, motor speed, and motor spin up.

The SCSI chip, too, can free up the CPU by reducing an operation's dependence on the CPU during I/O. These chips are made by such companies as Adaptec, Qlogic and Symbios Logic.

For more information, see "SCSI Integrated Circuits (Chips)" on page 125.

Because only one SCSI device at a time may use the bus to send its signals and await a response, most SCSI peripheral devices are capable of leaving the bus, completing a time-consuming operation, and then returning. This is known as disconnect capability. In the meantime, the host can work with other devices, or another host can use the bus. The result: multiple operations are performed simultaneously.

A computer or peripheral using the bus is said to have gained control of the bus, and that is the term we will use to describe that event. But it may help your understanding to bear in mind the bus-as-carrier analogy, and to think of data as riding the bus between stations that are devices.

See "Signal lines" on page 133, and "Bus Phases" on page 169, for more information.

Hardware economy

SCSI relaxes constraints on the physical limits of the bus. The cable that connects SCSI devices can now reach 25 meters (about 80 feet) if used in a differential configuration. Apple and most PC host adapters, however, use the single-ended electrical specification, which is more restricted—six meters in length, or up to about 19 feet.

Differential SCSI is a SCSI cabling scheme that uses the difference between two lines to indicate whether a logic "1" or a logic "0" is being encoded. The benefits include longer maximum cable lengths, greater protection from noise and consequently faster data transfer rates.

For more information, see "Physical connections" on page 140.

... But It Needs Work

A widely acknowledged problem with SCSI is that its early strength—flexibility—is now a problem. The specification lacks specificity.

Revision 17B of SCSI-1 defined classes and formats of commands, but except for one required command—Request Sense—SCSI devices were on their own. It was too easy for vendor-unique commands to proliferate, which they did. Consequently, few SCSI controllers could plug-and-play with any SCSI peripheral. This was especially true between 1984 and 1987, and particularly for devices other than hard drives. Without the benefit (constraint?) of a market "tradition," implementations of newer technologies proliferated.

See "SCSI Manager" on page 178 for more information on SCSI commands.

There is, however, a more comprehensive de facto standard for commands, called the Common Command Set (CCS 4B), which was included in SCSI-2.

SCSI-2 also describes many new commands. SCSI-3 describes even more.

Since 1988, virtually all hard drive manufacturers have incorporated CCS or a subset of it, resulting in a reduction or elimination of vendor-unique commands. SCSI-2 also described CCS-like commands for non-hard disk devices.

For more information, see "SCSI-2 commands" on page 195.

Who Uses SCSI?

SCSI is becoming increasingly associated with high-end PCs, workstations, and fast hard drives, as well as achieving virtual exclusivity as the interface for state-of-the-art storage technologies such as external magnetic and optical disc drives, digital audio tape drives, WORM drives and CD Recordable drives.

The "Small" in Small Computer Systems Interface has become a misnomer.

SCSI is also gaining in popularity as computer systems continue to evolve into increasingly complex configurations, connecting such diverse peripherals as:

- Hard drives
- Scanners
- Printers

- Tape drives
- Magneto Optical drives
- Removable cartridge drives
- CD-ROM drives
- Cameras
- Plotters

Even IBM, long a staunch hold-out, is beginning to offer SCSI on most of its latest computers.

SCSI Integrated Circuits (Chips)

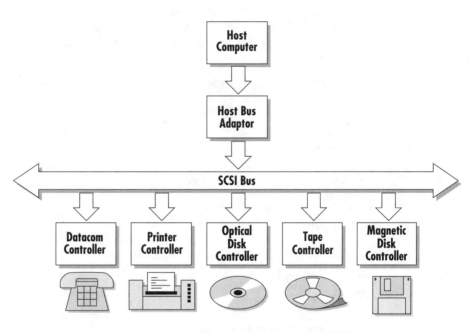

Figure 51. *Single host/multiple controllers*

Chip overview

The computer with SCSI or a SCSI host adapter uses an integrated circuit (IC) dedicated to handling SCSI operations. This IC is known as a SCSI interface controller. ICs are also called chips, because all ICs, SCSI or otherwise, reside in the computer on a silicon chip. The SCSI Manager controls the operation of this chip and provides it with an interface to the operating system software.

For more information, see "Call Chain" on page 183 and "SCSI Manager" on page 178.

The latest wave of SCSI chips on add-in cards dramatically reduces the amount of programming needed to perform a SCSI transaction by performing in hardware (the chip) many of the functions formerly handled by software. This frees the computer's CPU for other tasks.

The SCSI chip shipped in most current computers, however, does require some assistance, so the CPU is not entirely absolved from SCSI operations. Therefore, chip sophistication—how much of the SCSI operation the chip can handle by itself—affects overhead and performance.

 Some machines utilize a microprocessor dedicated to assisting the SCSI chip.

Among the chip's more critical responsibilities is managing the timing constraints defined in the SCSI specification, including the signal delays that are central to changing bus phases. This will be discussed in greater detail in the sections that follow.

 Communication across the SCSI bus is divided into stages known as phases. There are eight possible bus phases:

- Bus Free
- Arbitration
- Selection
- Reselection
- Command
- Data-In/Out
- Status
- Message-In/Out

For more information, see "Bus Phases" on page 169.

SCSI chip families

Symbios 53C8X/53C9X family

Symbios was formerly known as NCR. The original Macintosh line relied on Symbios's 5380 and 53C80 chips.

 The "C" in 53C80 is shorthand for CMOS, or Complementary Metal-Oxide Semiconductor. CMOS chips require less power to run.

The 5380, found in early Macs such as the Macintosh Plus, is fairly simple. It offers the lowest hardware cost to implement the SCSI specification, and controls the following interactions:

- Arbitrates for use of the bus
- Performs retries
- Selects a target
- Sends commands
- Transfers data

However, it needs the CPU to control many SCSI bus interactions, including:

- Instigating the SCSI bus phase transitions
- Reading the status
- Handling data transfers

All of the interactions that the 5380 controls take place in hardware. The 5380 also operates independently of the main CPU's clock speed (expressed in megahertz), which lets Apple use the chip in any Macintosh.

The Mac IIci as well as most other Macs use the 53C80; the Mac IIfx uses a customized 53C80 array. The IIfx integrates the 53C80 and a DMA controller on a single custom chip on the motherboard. The IIsi and the LC use the 85C80 chip, which offers on-board serial support in addition to SCSI, minimizing the number of chips needed to create the machine.

Later Macs such as the Quadra family utilized the 53C9X family of SCSI chips. The Quadra840AV/Centris 660AV used the 53C94. The Centris 610/650 and Quadra 605/700/800/900/950 used the 53C96. These chips combined faster 5 MB/s SCSI-2 performance with highly automated operation, and eliminated the need to tediously drive the chip through each SCSI phase.

Symbios Logic 53C7XX/53C8XX families

Symbios' 53C700 family includes an integrated DMA (direct memory access) controller, a separate IC to handle bus sequences, and a two-million-instruction-per-second RISC (Reduced Instruction Set Computing Chip) I/O processor core, which can read commands from external memory and control one or more complete I/O transactions without CPU intervention.

The 53C700 allows the SCSI bus to be closely coupled with the host CPU without having to add an intelligent host adapter. This minimizes overhead and avoids degrading the CPU's performance. The 53C700 family interfaces to Intel's 80X86 and Motorola's 68000 family with virtually no fuss, and can also be used on host adapter boards and with other ICs.

Most chips available today cannot move data faster than 5 MB/s, although many peripheral vendors claim their products support the 10 MB/s rates offered by Fast SCSI-2.

The Symbios 53C710, introduced in 1990, supports Fast SCSI-2's 10 MB/s synchronous transfer rates. The 537C20, a 1991 entrant, also meets the 10 MB/s data rates, and supports 16-bit 20 MB/s "Wide SCSI" transfers as well.

For more information on Fast/Wide SCSI, see "SCSI-2: A Transition From SCSI-1" on page 193.

The 53C8XX family takes the 7XX family one step further by adding a PCI interface to the chip and by increasing the scripting and performance features. The 53C810 is a fast SCSI-2 10 MB/s chip, the 53C825A is a Fast/Wide SCSI-2 20 MB/s chip, and the 53C875 is an Ultra SCSI 40 MB/s chip.

Qlogic ISP chip family

The Qlogic ISP family is a line of RISC-based SCSI chips designed for high performance. They combine a 7- to 18-MIPS RISC processor with a programmable SCSI back-end.

- The ISP1000 interfaces Fast/Wide SCSI-2 to the Sun S-Bus.
- The ISP1020 interfaces Fast/Wide SCSI-2 to the PCI bus.
- The ISP1040 interfaces the 40 MB/s Ultra SCSI to the PCI bus.
- The ISP1080 interfaces the 80 MB/s Ultra-2 SCSI to the PCI bus.
- The ISP2100 chip interfaces Fibre channel to the PCI bus.

MIPS stands for million instructions per second. It is a measure of a computer CPU's execution speed.

Apple custom SCSI chips

Apple designed a chip called the Curio which combined Ethernet, SCSI and Serial Communications. This chip was used in the initial PowerMac family (6100/7100/8100). It was also used in many PowerBooks. Following the Curio, Apple designed the MESH chip. It debuted in the first generation of Power Macintosh with PCI, the PowerMac 8500 and 9500. It is designed to provide Fast SCSI-2 10 MB/s performance with a minimal amount of overhead.

Modes

The SCSI chips function in one of three communications methods of operation, or modes:

- Normal

- Pseudo-DMA
- DMA

Normal

In Normal mode the Macintosh's CPU manages I/O communications. Using this program is a drain on the Macintosh's CPU, which slows I/O performance. This is also known as Polling method, in which the CPU checks that there has been a Request/Acknowledge handshake with every byte of information that is transferred.

 For more information, see "Data Transfer Options" on page 129.

Pseudo-DMA

In Pseudo-DMA (direct memory access) mode, the SCSI chip oversees data transfer, letting the CPU tend to other tasks. This is also known as the Blind Data Transfer method because the CPU checks in just once, before a block of data is transferred, and then turns things over to the SCSI chip. Blind transfers are much quicker than the polling method because larger chunks of information-blocks—as opposed to a byte—are transferred at a time.

 See "SCSI, Apple-Style" on page 173 for a discussion of problems with Blind transfers.

DMA

In DMA (direct memory access) mode, the SCSI chip is programmed to transfer data to and from the SCSI bus directly into main memory, eliminating the need for CPU intervention.

In practice, the modes operate in tandem, with data transfer starting out in Normal mode and then turning to Pseudo-DMA or DMA mode. During the data transfer, the processor checks the status register to ensure that transfer is occurring.

Data Transfer Options

Essential terminology

- **Handshake**

  To understand data transfer options, it's important first to understand the concept of the "handshake." As in human affairs, the SCSI handshake signifies completion of a deal. Only here, it's between the initiator and the target.

Whenever data is transferred between the initiator and a target, it is marked by a Request/Acknowledge handshake. Either the initiator or target makes a request, and that request is acknowledged by its recipient.

 For more information on handshakes, see the Request and Acknowledge entries in "Control signals" on page 134.

- **Data Transfer Modes**

  Data transfer occurs in either one of two modes, or protocols:

  – Asynchronous
  – Synchronous

  The mode used is determined by the SCSI chip and via messages between the initiator and target, usually after a bus reset.

- **Bus Reset**

  A bus reset is a method of clearing (and consequently stopping) all action on the SCSI bus and returning to a known, free state.

Asynchronous data transfer

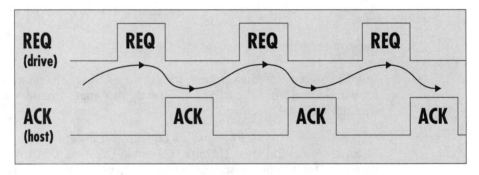

Figure 52. Asynchronous data transfer mode

Asynchronous is the most common method of data transfer, and was the mode used by many computers for all bus phases. PCs have used the synchronous mode from their inception. Asynchronous data transfer requires a Request/Acknowledge handshake for the movement of every information byte.

The SCSI bus in asynchronous mode offers a transfer rate of up to 5 MB/s. The SCSI specification doesn't define an upper limit for the asynchronous transfer rate. Instead, it defines minimum timing (about 250 nanoseconds) for the Request and Acknowledge control signals, which control information transfer in the asynchronous mode.

Fast SCSI uses a timing of about 100 ns, while Ultra SCSI uses a timing of about 50 ns.

Asynchronous data transfer is effectively limited, however, by cable impedance and other transmission-line problems, including whether the cable is operating at its optimal temperature and voltages. Asynchronous data transfers would slow down as the length of cabling was increased. A system with 6 meters of cabling could have a data transfer rate that may be degraded by 25 percent over a short one-meter setup. Cabling limits are addressed in the SCSI-2 specification.

 NOTE For more information, see "Signal lines" on page 133 and "SCSI-2: A Transition From SCSI-1" on page 193.

The asynchronous mode is the data transfer default. It is in effect at power-up, after a Bus Device Reset message, and after a hard reset condition.

 A Bus Device Reset is a message that is sent to reset the operation of a specific device. A hard reset is toggling a SCSI line to reset all devices on the SCSI bus.

Synchronous data transfer

Synchronous transfers allow a series of bytes to be exchanged before a Request/Acknowledge handshake is required. The number of Requests and Acknowledges will eventually match, but they are allowed to get ahead of one another. It may only be used for data transfer in the Data Phase, following a Selection Phase in which the SCSI ID for both the initiator and target are asserted. Not all SCSI devices support synchronous data transfer.

 NOTE For more information, see "Bus Phases" on page 169.

Synchronous mode can have a "burst" data transfer rate as fast as 5 MB/s—40 MB/s in SCSI-2. Sustained rates are much slower. This is quicker than some interfaces, but not as fast as others that employ different cabling schemes.

 NOTE See Chapter 5, "Other Storage Interfaces," for comparison.

Synchronous data transfer rates are not as limited by cabling as asynchronous data transfer rates are.

Negotiating synchronous transfer

The target and initiator must agree to use synchronous data transfer in a negotiation process that establishes certain parameters. These parameters include the transfer period (which determines transfer rate) and the Request/Acknowledge offset, which sets the maximum number of Request signals that may be sent before a corresponding Acknowledge signal is received. An agreement to use synchronous data transfer remains in effect until:

- A Bus Device Reset message is issued.
- A hard reset condition occurs.

OR

- One of the devices otherwise elects to modify the agreement.

 For more information, see "Bus Phases" on page 169.

Either the initiator or the target may recognize that negotiation for synchronous data transfer is required.

If the initiator recognizes the need, it asserts the Attention signal and sends the target a Synchronous Data Transfer Request message that indicates these parameters.

 For more information, see "Control signals" on page 134 and "Messages" on page 163.

The target chooses one of four options:

- It agrees.
- It stipulates a different transfer period and/or offset.
- It sets the offset to zero.

   A Request/Acknowledge offset of zero means the devices will use the asynchronous mode.

OR

- It sends a Message Reject message, which also results in the asynchronous mode.

If the target recognizes the need, it sends the initiator a Synchronous Data Transfer Request message that indicates these parameters.

One caveat needs to be considered when using devices with synchronous data transfer capability: following a reset or power-on, when a device first receives a command that requires data transfer, it will begin the negotiation for synchronous data transfer. The host must be able to do the following:

- Negotiate to reach either a synchronous or asynchronous data transfer agreement.

OR

- Handle the negotiation and reject it at some point, thus forcing the asynchronous transfer protocol.

OR

- Reject the request, thus forcing the asynchronous transfer protocol.

Signal lines

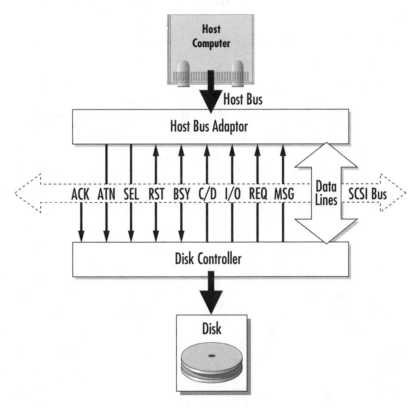

Figure 53. *Signal lines*

The SCSI bus is composed of up to 68 lines, depending on the electrical specification used, of which 18 are signal lines. Nine transmit data signals, and nine transmit control signals. The rest are connected to ground, except for number 25, which is left open. Data signal lines convey information in the form of data signals. Control signal lines convey control signals that determine communications and the bus phases.

Timing delays are critical. There is a required delay after each bus phase change before another signal will be sent. The initiator must wait before determining that it has gained control of the bus.

Data signals

Calling these signals "data" signals is somewhat imprecise. SCSI transfers not only data, but also command, status, message and SCSI ID information on these lines.

In SCSI parlance, "data" typically refers to the data class of information.

For information on corresponding bus phases, see "Bus Phases" on page 169.

Data signal lines are called DB (for Data Bus): DB7, DB6, DB5, DB4, DB3, DB2, DB1 and DB0. DB7 carries both the data and ID for the device with the highest priority, which is usually the computer; DB0 represents transmission of the least significant device. Each DB line may carry a different SCSI ID, and thus transmit data for a different device.

DB7, DB6, DB5, DB4, DB3, DB2, DB1, and DB0, however, add up to only eight lines. The ninth data-signal line is reserved for parity, which is a self-checking code that tracks the accuracy of binary digits (zeros and ones). If the protocol uses odd parity, as SCSI does, the total of the binary digits should always come out odd. If the total of the digits does not come out odd, error correction is automatically initiated.

Parity is a SCSI bus option in SCSI-1 but is required in SCSI-2. If used, parity must be supported by all SCSI devices on the bus. It is valid for all Information Transfer phases (Data, Command, Status, and Message) as well as the Selection and Reselection Phases.

For more information, see "Bus Phases" on page 169.

The Macintosh models previous to the Quadra 840av didn't use parity, while most PC SCSI host adapters did.

Control signals

Control signals direct communications and determine bus phases. There are nine control signals:

- Control/Data
- Input/Output
- Select

- Busy
- Message
- Request
- Acknowledge
- Attention
- Reset

The control signals are listed and defined in Table 29 on page 135. But first, it's important to understand some related terminology.

Essential terminology

- **Arbitration**

  How SCSI devices vie for control of the bus during an optional bus phase.

- **Assert**

  Usually assert means to send a control signal. However, for two control signals, Control/Data (C/D) and Input/Output (I/O), it means selecting one or the other.

- **Negate**

  Usually negate means to withdraw a control signal or indicate its absence.

- **Command Complete**

  The only message supported by all SCSI devices. Command Complete is sent by the target to the initiator to indicate:

  - It has executed the command (or a series of linked commands).
  - A valid status has been sent to the initiator.

  Command Complete is neutral. It is up to the status byte to indicate whether or not the command was completed successfully.

 For more information, see "Messages" on page 163.

The nine control signals

Table 29 lists and describes the nine control signals. The industry-standard nomenclature is in parenthesis.

Table 29. *The Nine Control Signals*

Signal	Description
Control/Data (C/D)	The target uses this signal to indicate whether control or data information is being transferred.
	If the signal is asserted (true or positive), command, status, or message information is being passed. A negated signal (false) means it's data.

Table 29. *The Nine Control Signals (Continued)*

Signal	Description
Input/Output (I/O)	The target uses this signal to indicate the transfer direction. Asserted (true) means it's going from initiator to target. Negated (false) means it's traveling from target to initiator.
Select (SEL)	The initiator asserts Select (and a SCSI Device ID on the DB line) to select a target that it wishes to perform a command. In systems that allow the target to disconnect while performing a command, the target also asserts Select to reconnect to the initiator. **NOTE:** A system that allows the target to disconnect while performing a command is called an arbitrating system. For more information, see "Bus Phases" on page 169.
Busy (BSY)	"Wired-or" or "Or-tied" signal that indicates the bus is in use. A "wired-or" or "or-tied" signal means it takes simultaneous signals from more than one device to be driven true or positive. The initiator and the competing targets assert Busy during the Arbitration Phase. During the Selection Phase, the selected target asserts Busy to acknowledge selection, while the targets that were not selected withdraw.
Message (MSG)	The target asserts Message to indicate that a message is being sent over DB lines.
Request (REQ)	The target asserts Request to initiate a data transfer. If the bus is in the Information-In Phase (the I/O signal is negated, so information is going from the target to the initiator), the initiator responds to requests by accepting data from the bus. If it's Information Out (I/O signal is asserted, so the flow is initiator to target), the initiator places data on the bus. The initiator then asserts Acknowledge.
Acknowledge (ACK)	The flip side of the Request/Acknowledge coin. The initiator asserts Acknowledge to let the target know it's complied with the request. The Request/Acknowledge handshake takes place after every information transfer. For more information on handshakes, see "Data Transfer Options" on page 129.
Attention (ATN)	The initiator asserts Attention to let the target know it has a message available. If the target supports optional messages, it can ask for the message by going into the Message-Out Phase.
Reset (RST)	"Wired-or" signal that clears the bus. RST creates a Bus Reset condition. For more information, see "Bus Conditions" on page 151. Reset may be used by any SCSI device on the bus. Usually, it is asserted only by the initiator, and typically only during power-up; however, the initiator may use it to reset a device that is not responding.

Control signals and bus phases

Table 30 illustrates which control signals are asserted on which device (initiator or target) during the various Bus Phases. The Data Bus column (DB) lists the devices that are asserting their IDs during each phase. The Reset control signal is not represented because it clears the bus rather than asserts itself during any of the Bus Phases.

NOTE For more information about Bus Phases, see "Bus Phases" on page 169.

Table 30. *Signals Asserted During Different Bus Phases*

Bus Phase	BSY	SEL	C/D, I/O, MSG, REQ	ACK/ATN	DB (7–0, P)
Bus Free	None	None	None	None	None
Arbitration	All	Winner	None	None	All Active
Select	INIT/TGT	INIT	None	INIT	INIT
Reselect	INIT/TGT	TGT	TGT	INIT	TGT
Command	TGT	None	TGT	INIT	INIT
Data-In	TGT	None	TGT	INIT	TGT
Data-Out	TGT	None	TGT	INIT	INIT
Status	TGT	None	TGT	INIT	TGT
MSG-In	TGT	None	TGT	INIT	TGT
MSG-out	TGT	None	TGT	INIT	INIT

INIT = Initiator
TGT = Target

SCSI ID

The SCSI device ID ("ID" is shorthand for identification) is a number that identifies the individual SCSI device, and so is sometimes referred to as a SCSI Device *address*. It has two purposes:

- First, it allows SCSI devices to find one another along the bus. An ID allows one device to distinguish itself and to call another device on the bus, identify itself and query the other device for its ID.

- Second, the SCSI ID allows the devices to be ranked, or prioritized, so that the bus can control which device gains access at a particular time. Those with higher IDs are admitted before those with lower IDs. This is important because only one pair of SCSI devices at a time—an initiator and a target—can be in active communication.

Each SCSI device must get its own unique SCSI ID number, which refers to the data signal line the SCSI device uses (Table 31).

Table 31. *Data Buses and Related SCSI IDs*

Data Bus	SCSI ID
DB0	SCSI ID = 0
DB1	SCSI ID = 1
DB2	SCSI ID = 2
DB3	SCSI ID = 3
DB4	SCSI ID = 4
DB5	SCSI ID = 5
DB6	SCSI ID = 6
DB7	SCSI ID = 7

You do not have to assign the ID numbers sequentially. For example, it's fine to have only three SCSI devices that are numbered ID6, ID3, and ID2. The IDs are not related to the physical order in which the devices are arranged along the bus. ID7 is usually reserved for the host computer.

If SCSI IDs conflict, neither device is likely to boot, and either could be damaged. SCSI IDs are usually changed through software or by accessing a switch or jumper on the back of the drive.

As noted in the Data Signal Lines section, the eight data signal lines (or Data Bus lines) are called DB7, DB6, DB5, DB4, DB3, DB2, DB1, and DB0. (The ninth line is reserved for parity.) DB7 carries the highest priority ID (important for arbitration) and is usually reserved for the computer; DB6 is next, and so on. If the computer has an internal hard disk, it is usually connected to DB0, and has 0 as its ID number.

The SCSI ID code is transmitted during the Selection and Reselection phases.

See "Pin assignments" on page 146 for more information on how this is implemented.

Apple SCSI peripherals are shipped with pre-assigned SCSI ID numbers. If you don't have more than one of the same type of Apple SCSI device on the bus, there should be no need to change ID numbers. On other companies' external peripherals, for both PCs and the Macintosh, IDs are usually set by changing a thumbwheel or pressing push buttons. Some of these devices may require a utility program for setting IDs.

 On the Macintosh, FWB's Hard Disk ToolKit can set the SCSI IDs of most such devices. FWB's Disk ToolKit for Windows should be available in late 1996.

SCSI cables

Cabling is often overlooked when putting together a system, and that is a mistake. Sloppy or poor-quality cabling is a common source of many problems. In fact, much of the work of SCSI-2 and SCSI-3 involves improving SCSI's external cabling schemes, such as placing all data signal and parity lines on the outside of round cables and putting control signal lines at the center, to minimize the effects of signal noise from the data lines. Some premium quality cables have used this scheme since the advent of SCSI-1.

For more information on upcoming cable implementations, see "SCSI-2 highlights" on page 203.

Internal SCSI cables are usually 50-pin flat ribbon cables. They usually run from the SCSI host adapter to each drive inside the computer.

For external SCSI cables, to ensure high quality, we recommend the use of double-shielded, twisted-pair, 28 AWG wiring. REQ and ACK should be together with GND in the middle. Control signals should be placed out side of the REQ/ACK layer. The data and parity signals should be on the outside layer.

For more information on REQ, ACK and GND, see "Essential terminology" on page 129.

Devices are connected to the computer on the SCSI bus by daisy-chaining cables: one SCSI device is plugged into the computer's SCSI port, and then a second device is plugged into the first device, and so on, up to a total of seven devices, not including the computer.

Cables typically have a characteristic impedance of 100 ohms. We recommend that you use cables with the same impedance, and ideally ones that come from the same company. Cables from different companies or with dissimilar impedances may create signal noise and other irregularities, and place an increased burden on proper termination. Cabling becomes more critical as faster data transfer rates are achieved.

Impedance refers to a measure of the total opposition to current flow in an alternating current (AC) circuit.

For more information on termination, see "Termination" on page 146.

Because most SCSI devices have two 50-pin ports, standard SCSI cables include at least one 50-pin connector.

Your system may include three types of SCSI cables:

- SCSI System cable
- Peripheral Interface cable
- Cable extender

SCSI System cable

The SCSI System cable attaches the first SCSI device on the bus to the computer.

Macintosh versions have a male 25-pin connector to connect to the computer, and a 50-pin connector to plug into the SCSI device. This cable is often referred to as 25-50 cable.

Figure 54. *25-50 Macintosh SCSI system cable*

PC versions have a male 50-pin high-density connector to connect to the SCSI host adapter, and a 50-pin connector to plug into the SCSI device.

Figure 55. *50-high density 50 PC SCSI system cable*

Peripheral Interface cable

The Peripheral Interface cable lets you daisy chain SCSI devices, one after the other, up to a total of seven, not including the computer.

This cable has two (male-male) 50-pin connectors. It is referred to as a 50-50 cable.

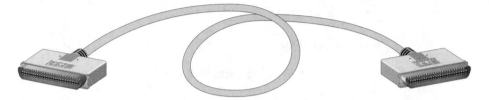

Figure 56. *50-50 peripheral interface cable*

The cables are used to daisy chain external devices (Figure 57).

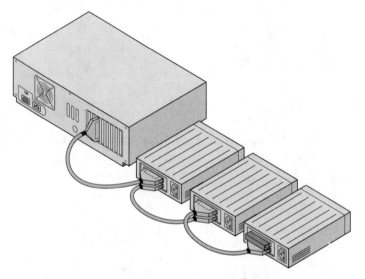

Figure 57. *Daisy chaining external devices*

Cable extender

The Cable extender functions as an extension cord. Cable extenders can be attached to one another (male-female), to a System cable, and to a Peripheral Interface Cable.

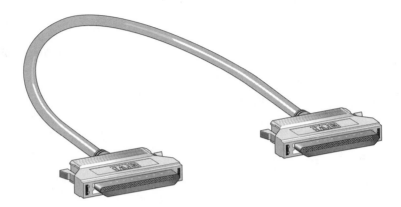

Figure 58. *Cable extender*

Systems that support SCSI-2 Fast and Wide have a male, 68-pin, high-density connector to connect to the SCSI host adapter, and a 68-pin connector to plug into the wide SCSI device. Some Wide host adapters include a 68-50 cable to attach narrow SCSI devices to a Wide SCSI bus.

Figure 59. *Internal fast/wide drive with a 68-pin connector*

There is also a small length of a cable with connectors, called a stub, that connects internally from the SCSI port to the SCSI device housed inside its box.

There are limits to the length of the SCSI bus, beyond which the signals begin to deteriorate. A realistic and safe guideline is 3 meters (about 10 feet).

NOTE See "SCSI-2 highlights" on page 203 for cabling limitations for fast and wide SCSI.

Electrical specifications

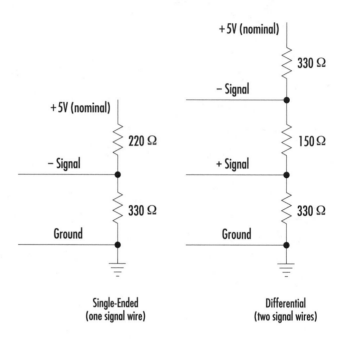

Figure 60. Termination circuits for single-ended and differential devices

One of two electrical specifications may be used for the cabling that connects SCSI devices:

- Single-ended
- Differential

These cabling schemes are not compatible and therefore cannot be mixed on the same bus.

Single-ended is much more common industry-wide, because it is less expensive and is adequate for systems that perform at a low level. However, it relies on tight termination tolerances. Going beyond its narrow margin of error can cause problems. The Macintosh line uses single-ended exclusively, as do most PCs. Third-party vendors provide differential support.

Single-ended

In a single-ended configuration, signals on a cable are differentiated according to the voltage of a single wire (up to as high as 5 volts) relative to a common ground (0 volts).

A signal line will be recognized as asserted (true) or negative (false) according to the strength of its signal and whether it is active high or active low:

- Active high signals are asserted when the signal strength is above a certain voltage, which is typically over 2.5 volts (plus or minus a five percent margin of error).
- Active low signals are those that are asserted when the voltage falls below a stated level, which is typically under 0.4 volts. Windows of error may occur if the bus misinterprets a signal that is close to the cutoff. Proper termination is crucial in controlling these glitches.

This specification is intended for cables up to six meters long (about 19 feet) and for connecting internal SCSI devices. Apple ignores this convention by using single-ended cable to connect everything, both internal and external devices. However, this is not actually a violation of the SCSI specifications.

Differential

A differential cable configuration determines signals by contrasting the voltage difference between two wires. It is mainly intended for connecting devices externally. Differential has the advantage of allowing cable lengths up to 25 meters (about 80 feet). It is also more robust and less subject than single-ended to signal noise and other termination problems.

However, differential cabling requires more powerful drivers, which in turn require an additional chip. The device itself and the SCSI port host adapter must be designed to use differential cabling, which would boost the device's price. For these reasons, systems that use a differential electrical specification are less popular than single-ended.

Connectors

The Macintosh line primarily uses a DB25-pin external SCSI connector. (The exception is the PowerBook, which uses a small, square 30-pin connector.) Twenty-five pins means the cable has 25 lines for transferring information.

For more information, see "Pin assignments" on page 146.

The Macintosh SE II and newer Macintosh models provide two SCSI connectors:

- The standard DB-25 external connector, located in the back of the Macintosh
- An internal, 50-pin, dual-row header connector for internal hard disks, located inside the Macintosh

PowerBooks use a 30-pin connector.

 Some Macintosh models have two SCSI chips for dual channel SCSI. These models include the Quadra 900/950, PowerMac 8100, and PowerMac 8500/9500. On the Quadra 900/950s, the second internal SCSI connector is hidden under the power supply. On the others, the internal SCSI connector is on a different channel than the external.

Early IBM PS/2 models used 60-pin high-density external SCSI cables. Most PC and Macintosh SCSI host adapters use high-density 50- or 68-pin cables. Most external SCSI devices have two 50-pin Centronics-style ports that accommodate the SCSI standard connector described above.

 Centronics is a printer manufacturer whose 50-pin connector has become an industry standard.

 See "SCSI-2 highlights" on page 203 for information on upcoming connector implementations.

Pin assignments

Termination

Figure 61. 68-pin SCSI terminator

Termination means closing off the ends of the circuit, to accomplish two things:

- To absorb the signals at each end and thus dampen reflections and signal resonance.
- To create enough difference between low and high signal levels for the devices on the bus to differentiate between the signals and thus communicate efficiently.

Devices chained together on a SCSI bus form an electronic signal path. Signals tend to rebound off the end of the SCSI path and cause interference. Interference can cause problems with your computer and/or one or more of your SCSI devices.

Termination on a SCSI bus:

- Preserves high transmission speeds
- Cleans up the signal along the length of the bus
- Provides a reasonable degree of immunity from electrical noise

Termination is required for the SCSI bus to work. A bad signal anywhere on the chain can cause all of the SCSI devices, in some cases the computer itself, to function improperly.

Types of Termination

Physically, terminators generally take three forms. Electrically, terminators are the same, varying only in where and how they are installed. Table 32 lists and describes types of termination.

Table 32. Types of Termination

Terminator	Description
On-Device Terminators	These are known as resistor packs (or sips or dips). You only remove them to add a second drive or to add a drive to a system where the motherboard is terminated. They reside on the SCSI device itself and are almost always removable. Always note the orientation of the resistor packs before attempting to remove them. They are polarized and must not be inserted backwards. Some newer drives have resistors permanently mounted on the drive. On these drives, there is a jumper to enable or disable termination.
External Terminator Blocks or Plugs	These are short plug-like devices and are inserted between an external hard drive's SCSI connector and the SCSI cable, or on the second connector if one exists. (See Figure 61.) Don't confuse these with the on-device terminators. On-device literally means on the drive mechanism—not on the external connector. Never use the external terminator when the drive inside a cabinet has terminators installed on it.
Main logic board terminators	These may look like a SIMM or a narrow plug. They are used only when there is no internal hard drive in the Macintosh. On the Macintosh, main logic board terminators are inserted into the 50-pin SCSI connector on the main logic board where the cable for an internal drive would normally connect. These main logic board terminators are keyed (a polarity notch) and must never be inserted backwards. The Quadra 800/900/950 have a terminator on the internal drive cable itself. This means that internal SCSI devices should not be terminated.

Table 32. *Types of Termination (Continued)*

Terminator	Description
Switched Termination	Some SCSI peripheral vendors also use switched termination. This means they have a type of switch that controls whether or not the device is terminated. A switched termination terminator is actually either an on-device terminator or an external terminator block or plug, but is controlled electronically via a switch.

How important is termination?

Terminating resistors, usually referred to as either terminators or resistors, tell the computer where the SCSI bus begins and ends. They also play a role in matching the impedance of the various cables on your system (especially important if devices are daisy-chained). The significance of termination increases as cable lengths and data transfer rates increase.

Proper termination is critical for ensuring that voltages, and thus signals, are accurately conveyed on the bus. Improper termination can cause the following problems:

- Erratic operation (such as power-up problems)
- Signal noise (reflected or unwanted signals or voltages)
- General bus failure

Symptoms of improper termination include the following:

- Hard disk drives that do not spin up immediately upon being powered-on
- Drives that spin up but do not mount (do not appear on the Desktop or do not display a drive letter)
- A system that won't boot-up
- A system that shows a sad icon (Macintosh only)
- System error
- A system that crashes when copying a lot of data
- A "hang" during data transfer or information access

Termination do's and don'ts

In most cases SCSI signals must be terminated at the physical start and end-points of the bus. There should be exactly two terminators:

- One for the first physical device on the bus
- One for the last physical device on the bus

Devices considered to be on the bus include all internal and external devices. Typically, the SCSI bus starts with the host computer.

Each additional terminator beyond the recommended two increases the signal intensity and, apart from wreaking havoc with the signals, can cause damage to sensitive components. Devices in the middle of the bus must have their terminators removed. We recommend that you return the device to the vendor for this procedure unless the terminator is external to the device.

It is not always easy to tell which type of termination a device requires. This can be determined by consulting the device's owner's manual, contacting the vendor or opening the chassis and poking around inside for terminators (we do not endorse the latter approach). If a device requires internal termination, we recommend that it be set by a qualified technician. If the device requires external termination, most users are qualified to attach an external terminator to one of the external SCSI ports usually found on the back of the device.

Terminators are available in both 50-pin versions for narrow SCSI and 68-pin versions for Wide SCSI.

Termination power

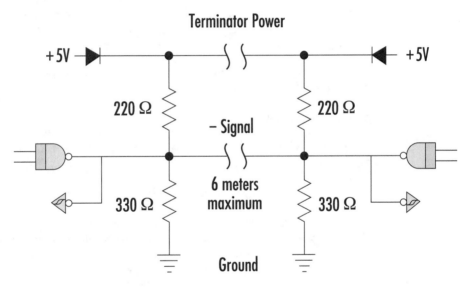

Figure 62. *Termination power circuit*

In order to be properly terminated, a device on the SCSI bus requires terminating resistors and terminator power for those resistors. Terminator power generally runs in the 4.25V to 5.25V range, with currents in the 900 to 1500mA range.

In general, the SCSI device is responsible for providing its own terminator power via a diode that prevents power from flowing back to the SCSI device. If a device does not provide this power, it may not work properly.

Some of the devices that supply termination power (TERMPWR) to the SCSI bus can cause problems if they are used on the internal bus of the Power Macintosh 8100/8150/9150. Any drives attached to this bus should be configured with TERMPWR disabled, regardless of whether they are terminated or not.

The SCSI specification requires terminator power to be provided by the SCSI connector, but the PowerBook family and the old Macintosh Plus depart from the ANSI guidelines here. The rest of the Macintosh line can provide terminator power to devices connected to its external SCSI port:

- If the Macintosh detects that an external SCSI device **does not** provide its own terminator power, then the Macintosh will provide it.
- If the Macintosh detects that an external device **does** provide its own terminator power, then the Macintosh won't provide it.

When the Macintosh does provide terminator power to externally connected devices, it draws that power from its own power supply. One possible disadvantage to this is that on a system with many attached devices, it could weaken the effectiveness of the power supply.

Most Macintosh and PC SCSI host adapters provide terminator power to both internal and external SCSI devices.

Termination examples

Table 33 provides examples of how to set termination for various system configurations.

Table 33. *Examples of Termination*

System Configuration	Termination
Internal hard disk drive	It must be internally terminated. It is the first physical device on the bus.
No internal hard drive	The internal SCSI port must be terminated.
One external device on the bus	The last drive must be terminated. It is assumed to be the last device.
Two SCSI devices daisy-chained to one SCSI port	The device furthest from the host (in terms of cable length) must be terminated.

Active Termination

As SCSI performance continued to improve, newer methods of termination were needed to handle data integrity problems that arose with the faster SCSI-2 buses. The main problem was double-clocking of REQ and ACK lines, caused by coupling of parallel signal wires, especially when they were not shielded.

Active termination attempts to address impedance mismatches by compensating for voltage. The SCSI-2 specification adds a voltage regulator to provide about 24mA of current into each asserted SCSI line over a considerable range of terminator power values. The original SCSI-1 specification provided only 20mA when terminator power was at optimal value.

Forced Perfect Termination (FPT)

FPT was developed by IBM. It uses a resistor/diode network to pull current up until the diode threshold is crossed. The diode then maintains the voltage at the desired level. These terminators brought current levels into the 30 to 40mA range. FPT is used on the REQ, ACK and SEL signals.

For more information on REQ, ACK and SEL signals, see "Essential terminology" on page 129.

Active Negation

Active Negation adds drive circuitry to SCSI bus drivers that drive the line high when it is negated. Driving the lines high ensures that REQ and ACK signals are clearly recognized. For maximum utility, all devices on the bus should use this technology. Terminators are still needed to absorb the reflections at each end of the bus.

Bus Conditions

A bus condition affects all attached devices and cannot be ignored. It is a critical operation mode and thus overrides other lines. There are two bus conditions:

- Attention
- Reset

Attention condition

The Attention condition results when the initiator signals the target that it has a message ready. The initiator asserts the Attention control signal during any phase except Bus Free or Arbitration. The target retrieves the message at its convenience using a Message-Out Phase. The initiator can only assert Attention if it supports optional messages.

For more information, see "Bus Phases" on page 169.

Reset condition

The Reset condition kicks every device off the bus. It is caused when a SCSI device asserts the Reset control signal. A Reset condition may occur at any time, forcing the bus into the Bus Free Phase. Targets may go through a complete power on self test (POST) sequence and clear out pending or current operations.

Further, SCSI devices support either one of two reset options:

- Hard
- Soft

As their names imply, Hard is more severe, and Soft is more forgiving.

Hard Reset

The Hard Reset option:

- Knocks out all commands in process
- Drops all SCSI device reservations (for disconnects and command queuing)
- Returns all operating modes to their default conditions

This condition is asserted on the Reset signal line and goes out to all devices.

Soft Reset

In contrast, the Soft Reset option will:

- Try to complete commands that were in process
- Hold on to all SCSI device reservations
- Maintain the SCSI device operating mode

The Soft Reset option has the advantage of allowing the initiator to reset the bus without affecting other initiators in a multiple-host system.

This condition is communicated via the Bus Device Reset message and is directed toward a specific device. In this way, it is distinguished from the other bus conditions.

Executing Commands

Command Descriptor Block

The Command Descriptor Block (CDB) is a six-, ten-, or twelve-byte data structure residing in the computer's memory that contains the command code and other information needed by a target to execute a command.

A target executes a command in three stages:

1. It gets and decodes command information from the CDB.
2. It transfers or receives data, if required.
3. It sends status information.

For more information, see "Bus Phases" on page 169.

Each command is sent from the computer to a device as a CDB. There are several groups of CDBs. Each member in a group has similar offsets (locations in the CDB where certain parameters can always be found). Group 0 and Group 1 are the most prevalent:

- Group 0 CDBs contain Group 0 commands and are six bytes long.
- Group 1 CDBs contain Group 1 commands and are ten bytes long.

Group 1 commands are used more frequently for larger capacity peripherals (more than one GB), which have greater addressing needs. Group 2 commands are also ten-byte commands.

Table 34 lists the information in a Group 0 Command Descriptor Block.

Table 34. *Group 0 Command Descriptor Block*

	Bit 7	Bit 6	Bit 5	Bit 4	Bit 3	Bit 2	Bit 1	Bit 0
Byte 00	0	0	0	Command Opcode				
Byte 01	Logical Unit Number (LUN)			Logical Address (NS6)				
Byte 02	Logical Address							
Byte 03	Logical Address (LS6)							
Byte 04	Transfer Length (Number of Blocks)							
Byte 05	Control Byte							

Table 35 lists the information in a Group 1 Command Descriptor Block.

Table 35. *Group 1 Command Descriptor Block*

	Bit 7	Bit 6	Bit 5	Bit 4	Bit 3	Bit 2	Bit 1	Bit 0
Byte 00	0	0	1	Command Opcode				
Byte 01	Logical Unit Number (LUN)			Reserved				
Byte 02	Logical Address (MSR)							
Byte 03	Logical Address							
Byte 04	Logical Address							
Byte 05	Logical Access (LS6)							
Byte 06	Reserved (CO)							
Byte 07	Transfer Length (Number of Blocks) (MSB)							
Byte 08	Transfer Length (Number of Blocks) (LSB)							
Byte 09	Control Byte							
	Reserved fields are always set to zeros.							

Table 36 lists the information in a Group 5 Command Descriptor Block.

Table 36. *Group 5 Command Descriptor Block*

	Bit 7	Bit 6	Bit 5	Bit 4	Bit 3	Bit 2	Bit 1	Bit 0
Byte 00	0	0	1	Command Opcode				
Byte 01	Logical Unit Number (LUN)			Reserved				
Byte 02	Logical Address (MSR)							
Byte 03	Logical Address							
Byte 04	Logical Address							
Byte 05	Logical Access (LS6)							

Table 36. *Group 5 Command Descriptor Block (Continued)*

	Bit 7	Bit 6	Bit 5	Bit 4	Bit 3	Bit 2	Bit 1	Bit 0
Byte 06	Transfer Length (Number of Blocks) (MSB)							
Byte 07	Transfer Length (Number of Blocks)							
Byte 08	Transfer Length (Number of Blocks)							
Byte 09	Transfer Length (Number of Blocks) (LSB)							
Byte 10	Reserved (C0)							
Byte 11	Control Byte							
	Reserved fields are always set to zeros.							

Some commands require more information than can be conveyed in even a ten-byte CDB. For these, the CDB includes a "count byte" that tells the SCSI hard drive how many bytes it should request from the computer in the data phase, after it gets the CDB. SCSI-2 provides for a Group 5, 12-byte CDB that sends more information.

Pointers

The target tracks the execution of command information, a byte at a time, by placing "pointers" within the CDB. There are two types of pointers to keep track of command, status, and data transfers:

- Current (or active)
- Saved

The target saves the pointer values so it can return to that byte if necessary. There is only one set of current pointers per initiator, but there may be multiple sets of saved pointers—a total of up to seven sets.

Although SCSI is otherwise optimized for I/O, this command overhead—having to build and process SCSI CDBs—slows throughput because it is performed on every SCSI transaction. Minimizing the number of CDBs will speed I/O.

For an example of CDBs in action, see "Bus Phases" on page 169.

Essential terminology

- **Sense Data**

  Sense Data informs on errors resulting from the previous command from the same initiator. It is saved until retrieved by that initiator or until another command is received from that initiator. There is an Extended Sense format, which provides more detailed information, and a Non-extended Sense format for devices that do not support Extended Sense.

- **Sense Key**

  The Sense Key bit is contained in the Sense Data. It is an error code indicating a particular classification of error.

Defined commands

The following are defined commands. SCSI-2 specification requires that the Common Command Set (CCS) be supported by SCSI-2 devices.

The opcodes (operation codes) are listed for each command:

- Group 0, or six-byte, commands have opcodes between 00_H and $1F_H$.
- Group 1, or ten-byte, commands have opcodes from 20_H to $3F_H$.
- Group 2, or ten-byte, commands have opcodes from 40_H to $5F_H$.

Commands marked with a plus sign (+) are accomplished without disk access. A command followed by (NON) is not part of the CCS.

Table 37. *General Device Commands and Opcodes*

Command	Opcode	Description
Test Unit Ready	00_H	Checks if the drive is prepared to accept commands requiring disk access. If it is, the completion status byte indicates Good and the sense key is set to No Sense. If it is not ready, the status byte will indicate Check Condition, with the sense key set to Not Ready.
Rezero Unit	01_H	Requests that the drive actuator be moved to the cylinder zero and head zero position.

Table 37. *General Device Commands and Opcodes (Continued)*

Command	Opcode	Description
Request Sense +	03$_H$	Requests that sense data be sent to the initiator. Sense data is detailed error information generated by the previous command from the same initiator. It is saved until it is retrieved by that initiator or until another command is received from that initiator. There is an Extended Sense format and a Non-extended Sense format for devices that do not support Extended Sense. The Sense Key field helps determine why the error occurred. Table 38 on page 159 lists and describes the Sense Key fields.
Format Unit	04$_H$	Assigns logical blocks to physical sectors, optimizing sequential access and avoiding areas known or found to be defective. Formatting options vary with different drives. Loss of data typically occurs when this command executes. We recommend backing up data first.
Reassign Blocks	07$_H$	Requests the drive to reassign defective logical block(s) to areas of the platter reserved for this purpose. The drive keeps and updates a known defect list. Defective logical blocks that have already been reassigned by the automatic reallocation feature of Mode Select will be reassigned again.
Read	08$_H$	Requests that the target transfer data to the initiator.
Write	0A$_H$	Requests that the data transferred to the target be written to the medium. It specifies the logical block address at which to begin, and the number of contiguous logical blocks of data to be transferred.
Seek	0B$_H$	Requests that the target position its head actuator at a specified logical block address.
Inquiry +	12$_H$	Requests that target identification information—manufacturer, model, and parameter specifications—be sent to the initiator. This includes the device's model number and various revision levels, as well as whether it contains removable media and supports the Common Command Set or SCSI-2.
Mode Select +	15$_H$	No disk access required if the Save Parameters bit is not set. Allows the initiator to specify the operating parameters of the drive, and optionally to save them for future commands. A Mode Select command overrides previous parameters. Executing Mode Select in a multi-initiator system creates a Unit Attention condition for all other initiators.

Table 37. *General Device Commands and Opcodes (Continued)*

Command	Opcode	Description
Reserve	16$_H$	Requests that a logical unit be reserved for an initiator or some other specified SCSI device.
		The initiator will have exclusive use of the drive until one of the following conditions exists: the same initiator issues another valid Reservation command superseding the last command; a Reset message from any initiator is received; or a hard reset occurs.
		No error will occur if an initiator attempts to reserve a logical unit it has already reserved. Drives already reserved will return a Reservation Conflict status; however, if disconnection is supported, the drive will queue the Reserve request and disconnect. If some other initiator issues a Release command, the reserved drive will ignore it.
Release	17$_H$	Requests that a drive's reservation be canceled.
		The Release message is only valid when issued by the initiator that reserved the drive. No error will occur if an initiator attempts to release a logical unit that is not reserved.
Copy	18$_H$	Provides the means to copy data from one logical unit to another or the same logical unit. The logical unit may reside on the same or different SCSI device. This command requires that the device support disconnect.
Mode Sense +	1A$_H$	No disk access is required if Save Parameters are not read. Enables the target to report its operating parameters to the initiator in either its current, saved, changeable, or default categories. This command complements Mode Select.
Start/Stop Unit	1B$_H$	Requests that the drive be spun up or spun down. Can cause removable media to be ejected.
Receive Diagnostic Result + (NON)	1C$_H$	Requests that the results of the self-test be sent to the initiator.
Send Diagnostic +	1D$_H$	Requests that the drive to perform diagnostic tests on itself. This is usually followed by a Receive Diagnostic Result command.
Prevent/Allow Media Removal +	1E$_H$	Enables or disables the ejection of removable media.
Read Capacity (NON)	25$_H$	Requests the target send information regarding the capacity and block size of the drive.
Read Extended (NON)	2A$_H$	Same as Read command, but can access more blocks.
Write Extended (NON)	2B$_H$	Same as Write command, but can access more blocks.
Seek Extended (NON)	2E$_H$	Same as Seek command, but can access more blocks.

Table 37. *General Device Commands and Opcodes (Continued)*

Command	Opcode	Description
Write and Verify	2F$_H$	Requests that the drive write the data it has received from the initiator, and to verify that it has been correctly written to the medium. Useful for optical drives.
Verify (NON)	2F$_H$	Requests the drive to verify that it has correctly written data on the medium.
Read Defect Data (NON)	37$_H$	Requests that the drive transfer data to the initiator regarding defects on the medium.
Write Buffer (NON)	3B$_H$	A diagnostic command for testing the target's memory and the SCSI bus integrity. It is used in conjunction with the Read Buffer command. Neither command affects data storage.
Read Buffer	3C$_H$	See Write Buffer command.
Read Long (NON)	3E$_H$	Requests that the drive transfer a sector of data, followed by error-correcting code (ECC) data, to the initiator. This command is intended for diagnostic purposes and is usually followed by the Write Long command.
Write Long (NON)	3F$_H$	Requests that the data usually transferred by the Read Long command be written to the specified logical block address. The number and order of bytes should match those in the Read Long command.

 The SCSI-2 specification also introduces new commands. See "SCSI-2 commands" on page 195 for more information.

Table 38. *Sense Keys*

Sense Key		Description
0$_H$	No Sense	No error occurred.
1$_H$	Recovered Error	Command successful but recover action was needed.
2$_H$	Not Ready	Device not ready to be accessed.
3$_H$	Medium Error	Non-recoverable error caused by media flaw.
4$_H$	Hardware Error	Non-recoverable error caused by hardware problem.
5$_H$	Illegal Request	The command or data contained illegal parameter(s).
6$_H$	Unit Attention	Bus reset or medium changed.

Table 38. *Sense Keys (Continued)*

Sense Key		Description
7_H	Data Protect	Write protect error.
8_H	Blank Check	Blank media encountered.
A_H	Copy Aborted	SCSI Copy operation canceled.
B_H	Aborted Command	Target aborted command.
C_H	Equal	Search Data Command successful.
D_H	Volume Overflow	End of media encountered with data left to be written.
E_H	Miscompare	Source data doesn't match data from disk.
F_H	Reserved	

The ASC (Byte 12) and ASCQ (Byte 13) fields within sense data provide more information on exactly what the error was. Table 39 lists common sense keys and ASC and ASCQ decoding.

Table 39. *Common Sense Keys with ASC and ASCQ Decoding*

Sense Key		ASC	ASCQ	Description
01	Recovered Error	18	8X	Recovered ECC.
01	Recovered Error	19	00	Defect List Error.
01	Recovered Error	1C	00	Defect List not found.
02	Not Ready	04	00	LUN not ready, unknown cause.
02	Not Ready	04	01	LUN not ready, becoming ready.
02	Not Ready	04	02	LUN not ready, formatting required.
02	Not Ready	04	04	LUN not ready, formatting.
02	Not Ready	31	01	Formatting failed.
02	Not Ready	40	80	RAM Failure.

Table 39. *Common Sense Keys with ASC and ASCQ Decoding (Continued)*

Sense Key		ASC	ASCQ	Description
02	Not Ready	40	83	RAM Failure.
02	Not Ready	40	84	RAM Failure.
03	Medium Error	11	00	Unrecovered Read Error.
03	Medium Error	11	03	Multiple Read Errors.
03	Medium Error	18	8X	Recovered ECC.
03	Medium Error	27	00	Write Protected.
04	Hardware Error	00	00	No Additional data.
04	Hardware Error	40	XX	Diagnostic Failure on component XX.
04	Hardware Error	41	00	Data Path Failure.
05	Illegal Request	1A	00	Parm List Length Error.
05	Illegal Request	20	00	Invalid Command Operation Code.
05	Illegal Request	21	00	LBA out of range.
05	Illegal Request	24	00	Invalid field in CDB.
05	Illegal Request	25	00	LUN not supported.
05	Illegal Request	26	00	Invalid field in Parm List.
05	Illegal Request	26	20	Parm Value invalid.
05	Illegal Request	2C	00	Command Sequence Error.
05	Illegal Request	3D	00	Invalid Bits in Identify Message.
06	Unit Attention	29	00	Power On, Reset, or Bus Device Reset.
06	Unit Attention	2F	00	Command Cleared by Another Initiator.

Table 39. *Common Sense Keys with ASC and ASCQ Decoding (Continued)*

Sense Key		ASC	ASCQ	Description
06	Unit Attention	2A	01	Mode Parameters Changed.
07	Write Protect	27	00	Write Protect Error.
0B	Aborted Command	00	00	No Additional Sense.
0B	Aborted Command	25	00	LUN not supported.
0B	Aborted Command	41	00	Data path Failure.
0B	Aborted Command	45	00	Select or Reselect Failure.
0B	Aborted Command	47	00	SCSI Parity Error.
0B	Aborted Command	48	00	Initiator Detected Error Message.
0B	Aborted Command	49	00	Invalid Message Error.
0B	Aborted Command	4E	00	Overlapped Command Attempted.
0E	Miscompare	00	00	No Additional Sense.

Mode Pages

Background

A device's behavior, or "mode," is determined by its operating parameters. These mode parameters are grouped into related pages that are numbered for easy reference. A mode page is the minimum unit that can be specified by the Mode Select or Mode Sense command.

NOTE

For more information, see "Commands" on page 156.

A page consists of multiple parameters that must be specified whenever a page is invoked:

- Changeable parameters may be set to any acceptable value.
- Nonchangeable parameters must be set to zero or left unchanged.

Although optional, mode pages are of interest to users who wish to customize the operation of their drive.

Essential terminology

- **Mode Parameter List**

  The Mode Parameter List is sent by the initiator to the drive during the Data Out Phase. This list contains the following:

  - Header
  - Zero or more Block Descriptors
  - Mode pages

- **Header**

  The Header specifies the following:

  - What type of storage medium, if any, is used in the drive

    A setting of zero for the medium type, which is the default, indicates that the medium is nonremovable.

  - The length in bytes of all Block Descriptors

- **Block Descriptor**

  The Block Descriptor specifies the logical block length for the drive including the following:

  - Density code, which is the density of the medium—usually used only for tape drives
  - Number of logical blocks on the medium in the density code
  - Block length, which is the length in bytes of each logical block described by the block descriptor

  The rest of the data consists of one or more mode pages. Consult the "SCSI Configure" section in FWB's *Hard Disk ToolKit User Guide* for details.

Messages

SCSI messages are communications between the initiator and target for the purpose of interface management. A message can be sent in both directions: message-out from initiator to target, or message-in from target to initiator.

There are three types of message formats:

- single-byte
- two-byte
- extended (three-byte or longer)

The messages in Table 40 are defined by the SCSI specification. With the exception of Command Complete, support for these messages in SCSI-1 is optional. The SCSI-2 specification mandates support for a few of them and provides additional content to the definitions of others.

For more information on changes introduced in SCSI-2, see "SCSI-2 highlights" on page 203.

Table 40. SCSI Messages

Message	Hex	In/Out	Description
Command Complete	00	In	Sent by the target to the initiator to indicate: • It has executed the command (or a series of linked commands) • A valid status has been sent to the initiator. Command Complete is neutral. It is up to the status byte to indicate whether or not the command was completed successfully. All SCSI devices must support the Command Complete message. A Command Complete or Disconnect message must precede a target's releasing the Busy signal. If the initiator detects that this has happened—as indicated by the resulting Bus Free Phase—it should consider that an error has occurred. For more information, see "Control signals" on page 134 and "Bus Phases" on page 169.
In = Target to Initiator Out = Initiator to Target			

Table 40. *SCSI Messages (Continued)*

Message	Hex	In/Out	Description
Extended Messages	01	I/O	Messages that require more than two bytes to send the necessary information. The messages supported by the disk drive are: • Modify Data Pointers (In) Requests adding signed argument to the value of the current data pointer. • Synchronous Data Transfer (I/O) Sent to establish synchronous data transfer and its parameters, including: – The transfer period, which determines transfer rate. – The Request/Acknowledge offset, which sets the maximum number of Request signals that may be sent before a corresponding Acknowledge signal is received. Zero means the devices are using the asynchronous mode. Other than zero indicates a synchronous transfer mode has been agreed upon. Macintoshes previous to the PCI versions do not support synchronous data transfers although virtually all Macintosh and PC SCSI host adapters support synchronous data transfers. • Wide Data Transfer (I/O) Establishes an agreement between two SCSI devices on the width of the data path to be used for Data Phase transfers between two devices. Initiated whenever it is appropriate to negotiate a new transfer width agreement, or whenever a previously agreed transfer width agreement may have become invalid. For example, after: – A Hard Reset condition – A Bus Device Reset message – A power cycle For more information, see "Data Transfer Options" on page 129.
Save Data Pointer	02	In	Sent from the target to tell the initiator to save the present active data pointer for that target. For more information, see "Executing Commands" on page 153.
Restore Pointers	03	In	Directs the initiator to restore saved pointers to the active state.
Disconnect	04	In	Sent by the target to the initiator in Arbitrating systems to indicate that it is going to release the Busy signal and thus disconnect, and that it will be necessary to reconnect later to complete the operation. A Disconnect or Command Complete message must precede a target's releasing the Busy signal. If the initiator detects that this has happened—as indicated by the resulting Bus Free Phase—it should consider that an error has occurred.

In = Target to Initiator
Out = Initiator to Target

Table 40. *SCSI Messages (Continued)*

Message	Hex	In/Out	Description
Initiator Detected Error	05	Out	Sent by the initiator if it detects an error. The initiator will retry the operation. The target will respond with a Check Condition status, which terminates the operation.
Abort	06	Out	Clears the operation. All pending data and status for the initiator issuing the Abort message are also cleared, and the initiator and target involved enter the Bus Free Phase. No status or ending message will be sent for the operation. In multi-initiator systems, the pending data and status for other initiators will be left intact.
Message Reject	07	Out	Sent by either the initiator or target to indicate that the last message was either deemed inappropriate or was for some other reason not implemented. For the initiator to send this message: • It asserts the Attention signal. • Then it sends its Acknowledge for the Request/Acknowledge handshake of the message that it is rejecting. For the target to send this message: • It goes to the Message In Phase and sends it. • Then it requests additional message bytes from the initiator. It does this so the initiator knows which message is being rejected. For more information, see "Bus Phases" on page 169.
No Operation	08	Out	The initiator's response to a target's request for a message, if the initiator has no message to send.
Message Parity Error	09	Out	What the initiator tells the target if one or more bytes in the last message received had a parity error. For the initiator to send this message: • It asserts the Attention signal. • Then it sends its Acknowledge for the Request/Acknowledge handshake of the message that it is rejecting. It does this so the target knows which message has the parity error.
Linked Command Complete	0A	In	Sent by the target to tell the initiator that a linked command has been executed and a status byte has been sent. The initiator sets its pointers to the initial state for the next linked command. For more information, see "Executing Commands" on page 153.
Linked Command Complete (With Flag)	0B	In	Sent by the target to tell the initiator that a linked command (with the flag bit set) has been executed and a status byte has been sent. The initiator sets its pointers to the initial state for the next linked command.

In = Target to Initiator
Out = Initiator to Target

Table 40. *SCSI Messages (Continued)*

Message	Hex	In/Out	Description
Abort Tag	0D	Out	When one or more initiators have multiple I/O processes to be queued by a target, each I/O process must have its own queue tag. In such circumstances, the Abort Tag message is active (usable). Otherwise, it is unavailable. • The initiator sends the Abort Tag message to the target and, following successful receipt, creates a Bus Free phase. • The target clears out the identified I/O process whether it has started or is waiting. • All other pending status, data and commands for other queued or executing processes are not affected.
Clear Queue	0E	Out	When one or more initiators have multiple I/O processes to be queued by a target, each I/O process must have its own queue tag. In such circumstances, the Clear Queue message is active (usable). Otherwise, it may or may not be usable. • The initiator sends the Clear Queue message to the target and, following successful receipt, creates a Bus Free phase. • All I/O processes from all initiators in the queue for the specified logical unit are cleared from the queue. • All similarly identified executing processes are stopped. • All pending status and data for that logical unit for all initiators are cleared. • No status or ending message is sent.
Terminate I/O Process	11	Out	Terminates current I/O processes without corrupting the medium (e.g., hard disk).
Simple Queue Tag	20	I/O	Specifies that the I/O process be placed in the disk drive's I/O process queue for execution. The order of execution can be arranged by the disk drive in accordance with an algorithm. This message is also sent by the target when it reconnects to the initiator.
Head of Queue Tag	21	Out	Specifies that the I/O process be placed first in the identified logical unit's queue for execution. In-progress I/O is not preempted. A subsequent I/O process received with this message goes to the head of the queue for execution in last-in, first-out (LIFO) order.
Ordered Queue Tag	22	Out	Specifies that the I/O process be placed in the disk drive's I/O process queue for execution in the order received, with respect to other commands with this message. NOTE: Processes with Head of Queue Tag messages jump ahead of processes with Ordered Queue Tag messages.

In = Target to Initiator
Out = Initiator to Target

Table 40. SCSI Messages (Continued)

Message	Hex	In/Out	Description
Ignore Wide Residue	23	Out	Used with wide (16-bit) data transfer. Indicates that the number of valid bytes sent during the last REQ/ACK handshake of a Data-In phase is less than the negotiated transfer width. The "ignore" field indicates the number of invalid data bytes transferred.
Identify	80 to FF	I/O	Sent by either the initiator or target to establish the physical path connection between the two. The Identify bits are set as follows: • Bit 7 is always set to one to distinguish Identify from other messages. • Bit 6 may be set only by the initiator, and indicates whether or not it supports disconnection and reconnection. It also indicates whether Save Data Pointer, Restore Pointer, and Disconnect messages are supported. • Bits 2 to 0 specify a logical unit number in a target, and must be set to zero. Identify is required in SCSI-2.
Bus Device Reset	D0	I/O	Issued by the initiator to clear all current commands and pending operations. It forces a Bus Free Phase for all devices on the SCSI bus, but does not affect Mode Select command parameters. This is message initiates a Soft Reset. For more information, see "Mode Pages" on page 162.

In = Target to Initiator
Out = Initiator to Target

Bus Phases

Communication across the SCSI bus is divided into stages known as phases. There are eight possible bus phases:

- Bus Free
- Arbitration
- Selection
- Reselection
- Command
- Data-In/Out
- Status
- Message-In/Out

 NOTE See Table 42 on page 171 for a description of each of the bus phases.

Phases are driven by both control signals and preceding phases. The SCSI bus incorporates numerous time delays to ensure all the signals are at the right voltage level before changing phases. However, there is a maximum time delay after which the target will "time-out" and release the bus if signals don't arrive in time. (The bus won't wait forever.)

Bus phase sequences are represented in the following illustrations. Figure 63 illustrates a bus phase sequence for a system that supports arbitration, where devices on the SCSI bus negotiate for bus access. Arbitration is essential to multiple-host systems and is required in SCSI-2.

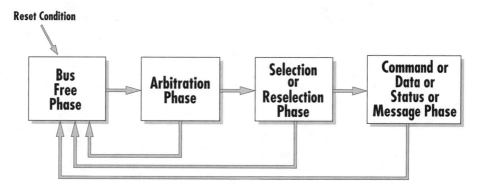

Figure 63. *Phase sequence with arbitration*

Figure 64 illustrates a bus phase sequence on a system that does not support arbitration.

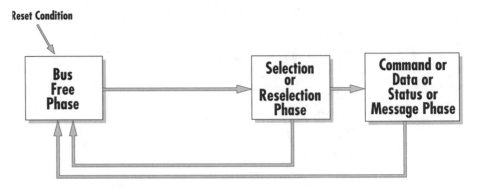

Figure 64. Phase sequence without arbitration

The first four bus phases, Bus Free, Arbitration, Selection, and Reselection, are controlled by the Select, Busy, and Input/Output control signals. The sequence of these phases is limited:

- The Arbitration Phase can only be entered from the Bus Free Phase.
- The Selection or Reselection Phases can only be entered from the Arbitration Phase.
- The Bus Free Phase, however, can be entered from any other phase.

 For more information on control signals, see "Control signals" on page 134.

The next four bus phases, Command, Data In/Out, Status, and Message In/Out, are called the Information Transfer phases. Unlike the first four phases, there are no restrictions on the sequence of occurrence in these phases. The Information Transfer phases are controlled by the Message, Control/Data, and Input/output control signals. Because the target drives these three signals, the target controls changing from one of theses phases to the next.

 The initiator's only way to disrupt the target's control over the Information Transfer phases is to create a bus condition. For more information, see "Bus Conditions" on page 151.

Table 41 illustrates which of the Information Transfer phases is active when the Message, Control/Data and Input/Output control signals are either asserted or negated.

Table 41. *Control Signals and Information Transfer Phases*

Control Signals				
MSG	**C/D**	**I/O**	**Phase**	**Direction**
0	0	0	Data-Out	Out
0	0	1	Data-In	In
0	1	0	Command	Out
0	1	1	Status	In
1	1	0	Message-Out	Out
1	1	1	Message-In	In

0 = Negated   In = Target to Initiator
1 = Asserted   Out = Initiator to Target

Table 42 lists the eight possible bus phases and describes their related activities.

Table 42. *The Eight Possible Bus Phases*

Bus Phase	Description
Bus Free	The bus is empty; no one is riding. This is SCSI's starting point at power-up, after a Reset, and where it returns when a command is completed. Both the Busy and Select signals must be negated for a defined period of time before this phase is entered.
Arbitration	This phase is where SCSI devices, including the computer, can vie for bus access. 1. Competing devices assert their SCSI ID number and the Busy signal on the appropriate DB line. 2. The computer waits a defined period before examining the bus. 3. The device with the highest priority SCSI ID "wins" the arbitration, gains control of the bus, and asserts the Select signal. Arbitration is necessary for multi-host systems, and is required in SCSI-2. Following Arbitration, the system goes to either the Selection or Reselection Phase. Non-Arbitrating systems skip Arbitration and go directly to Selection or Reselection.

Table 42. *The Eight Possible Bus Phases (Continued)*

Bus Phase	Description
Selection	In this phase an initiator selects a target device. Once selected, the target determines: • What information will be sent down the bus • When it will be sent • Whether the information is going to, or leaving, the host (Also see the Information Transfer Phases described below.) An initiator, usually the computer, selects a device by: 1. Asserting the device's ID number on the appropriate DB line. 2. Negating the Busy and I/O signals. The target: 1. Detects its asserted SCSI ID, and the negated Busy and I/O signals (I/O is negated to distinguish this phase from Reselection. A positive I/O indicates communication flow is from the target to the initiator.) 2. Asserts a Busy signal, causing the initiator to get off the bus. 3. Negates the Select signal.
Reselection	In Arbitrating systems, a target that has disconnected from the bus (in order to perform a time-consuming task) gets reconnected in this phase. A target device asserts the Reselection signal and its own ID number. It gets reconnected if the bus is free or its SCSI ID has a priority higher than another device that is asserting the Select signal.
Command	In this phase the target requests command information from the initiator. 1. The target device first asserts the Request signal. 2. The host, usually the Macintosh, goes to the Command Data Block (CDB) indicated by the Command Pointer, gets the information byte, sends it along the bus, and asserts the Acknowledge signal. 3. The target picks the command information off the bus and negates its Request signal. 4. When the host detects that Request has been negated, it gets off the bus and increments the Command Pointer in the CDB. This process is repeated until all bytes of information in the CDB requested by the target have been transferred. The target interprets the command code and locates the requested data block on the specified logical unit number. It then enters the Data-In Phase.
Data-In/Out	The Data-In Phase allows the target to ask for data to be sent from the target to the initiator. In the Data-Out Phase, the target asks to receive data from the initiator. Data is transferred in either the asynchronous or synchronous data transfer mode. In the Data-In Phase: 1. Target puts the first byte of data on the bus and asserts the Request signal. 2. Host takes the data byte, puts it in memory, and asserts the Acknowledge signal. 3. Target then negates the Request signal and puts the second byte on the bus. 4. Host increments the data pointer in the CDB. 5. Target then asserts Request and repeats the process until all bytes in the logical data block have been transferred to the host's memory.

Table 42. *The Eight Possible Bus Phases (Continued)*

Bus Phase	Description
Status	Here the target sends a byte of information to the initiator that indicates the success or failure of a command (or a series of linked commands).
	The Status Phase is critical for error detection and defect management. The status bytes and their meanings are listed below:
	<ul><li>00 Good</li><li>02 Check Condition</li><li>04 Condition Met</li><li>08 Busy</li><li>10 Intermediate</li></ul> <ul><li>14 Intermediate-Condition Met</li><li>18 Reservation Conflict</li><li>22 Command Terminated</li><li>28 Queue Full</li></ul>
	A single status byte always follows the Command Complete message. This status byte is an error code that describes any errors that may have occurred. A Check Condition status indicates that an error has occurred. The status byte is cleared if the command is completed successfully. If not successful (if an error occurred), the next command can request sense data to figure out what the problem was.
	1. The target enters the Status Phase by putting its Status information on the bus and asserting the Request signal. 2. The host accepts the status and puts it where the Status Pointer indicates. Then it increments the Status Pointer in the CDB and asserts the Acknowledge signal. 3. The target then negates the Request signal.
Message-In/Out	In the Message-In Phase, the target may request to send a message to the initiator.
	The Message-Out Phase is invoked by the target only in response to an Attention condition generated by the initiator. It can be generated at any time.
	For more information, see "Bus Conditions" on page 151.
	Since not all SCSI devices support messages, this is optional. If the Identify message is not sent before the Command Phase is entered, it is assumed that messages are not supported.
	A Command Complete message is always sent at the conclusion of every SCSI command operation. The target places the Command Complete message on the bus and asserts the Request signal. The host accepts it and asserts the Acknowledge signal. The target then negates the Request signal, gets off the bus, negates its Busy signal, and the phase returns to Bus Free.

SCSI, Apple-Style

Apple has included SCSI controllers in all Macintosh CPUs beginning with the Macintosh Plus in 1986. Despite this long history, some of Apple's SCSI implementations—as contained in the SCSI Manager and SCSI chip—have caused problems. The following subsections describe some of these.

Fast reset

After a SCSI bus reset, devices have only 250 milliseconds to get data on the bus. Certain devices cannot meet this requirement and are locked out of the bus following a reset, which causes problems with mounting volumes on these drives.

Unit attention condition

A SCSI device enters the Unit Attention Condition whenever it or the bus has been hit by one of the following:

- A hard reset
- A power-up reset
- A reset generated by a Bus Device Reset message

 For more information, on resets see "Bus Conditions" on page 151.

It may also occur in certain other situations that cause a shock to the device. This feature is mandatory in SCSI-2.

A device in Unit Attention Condition wants to let a host know that it has been traumatized and should be queried regarding its status. If the next command the target receives is either Inquiry or Request Sense, everything is fine; the device sends a status message reflecting Unit Attention Condition and then exits that condition. If the command is anything else, however, the target completely rejects it and sends a Check Condition status code; saying, in effect, "Check me out before doing anything else." The target tries this tack only once.

If the initiator ignores the Unit Attention Condition and the target's request—which it can do—it will reissue the command and this time the target will comply (so much for the target's "intelligence").

The Unit Attention Condition feature causes power-up problems when used with Macintosh Plus ROMs:

 ROM is permanently stored data in memory. It usually contains the permanent instructions for a computer's general housekeeping operations.

1. At power-up time, the ROM code tries to read bootstrap information from each SCSI device on the bus. It only tries once, going on to the next device if refused.

 Bootstrap information is a sequence of instructions whose execution causes additional instructions to be loaded and executed until a complete computer program is loaded into storage.

2. Because power-up causes the device to go into the Unit Attention Condition, the device refuses the command, asking instead that its condition be checked before responding to any command.

3. However, the Macintosh moves on to the next device.

4. The ROM code resets the bus if it can't read from even one SCSI device, and tries them all again.

5. Resetting the bus puts all SCSI peripherals into the Unit Attention Condition again.

6. The loop could go on forever, and the devices would not boot up.

This was fixed in the "Platinum" colored Macintosh Plus ROMs, so that only one SCSI Reset would be sent.

Unit attention also caused problems on early Macintoshes prior to the IIci when users tried to set a drive as the startup drive.

Some manufacturers have produced special Macintosh-specific versions of their drives that don't implement the Unit Attention Condition. Unit attention may also be disabled via jumpers or firmware changes, or by adjusting a mode parameter in Mode Page 0. Other companies resorted to cutting the RST line on the SCSI drive cable so it would never get a hard reset.

Parity checking

Parity checking caused problems with early Macintoshes prior to SCSI Manager 4.3. Parity typically had to be disabled on drives to enable compatibility.

 The Macintosh Centris 660AV and Quadra 840AV were the first machines sold with SCSI Manager 4.3.

Blind data transfers

In the Macintosh Plus, the 68000 microprocessor couldn't properly handle the SCSI Req/Ack handshaking protocol because it had no hardware line for relaying handshaking or interrupts. The 68000 did not know if a drive was responding during handshaking. Drivers had to either handshake every byte, a very slow process called polled I/O, or had to blindly hope that data was ready.

 For more information on handshakes, see "Data Transfer Options" on page 129.

Apple's answer was to include hardware support on the Macintosh SE and above for the hardware handshake line. Many Macintosh models still did not support SCSI Direct Memory Access (DMA), so if data did not show up consistently with no more than 16-microseconds between bytes, the SCSI bus would generate a bus-error and cause the Macintosh to crash or transfer invalid data.

Some devices, such as early Conner Peripheral's hard drives, had hiccups in data transfers when they were larger than the track buffer on the drive. Workarounds were developed that limited data transfers to smaller sizes or had the driver define synchronization points, using transfer information blocks (TIB) when calling the SCSI Manager.

ANSI irregularities

The Macintosh SCSI port also differs from the ANSI specification in two ways:

- The Macintosh line uses a DB-25 connector instead of the standard 50-pin connector. An Apple SCSI System 25/50 adapter cable is available to convert the DB-25 to the standard DB-50 50-pin connector.
- The termination and termination power are nonstandard.

Apple exceptions to the SCSI specification

The Mac Plus does not include internal termination because it has no internal SCSI connector. According to Apple, the devices closest to and farthest away from the Macintosh Plus should be terminated. But if there is only one peripheral attached to the Plus, only that device needs a terminator.

The Macintosh IIfx is in a class by itself. One of its features is a SCSI chip that provides faster data transfer rates than possible with earlier Macs. This necessitates the use of a combination of the following three termination parts.

- Apple SCSI Cable Terminator II. This is a black external terminator that ships with the Macintosh IIfx. It includes a "glitch-eating" capacitor, as does the filter. (See explanation below.) Only one is used on the SCSI bus.

AND either

- Internal SCSI Termination Block. This provides the internal termination for IIfx machines without internal hard drives, and is installed by Apple when shipped.

OR

- Internal SCSI Filter. This provides filtration of SCSI lines for Macintosh IIfx internal drives on systems that shipped prior to March 19, 1990. It was installed by Apple when shipped.

Macintosh IIfx termination configuration is simple. There is one terminator installed internally in the Macintosh itself, and another externally at the end of the SCSI chain.

The reason these parts are required is that the IIfx's SCSI chip thinks that glitches on the Request line are genuine signals. The internal SCSI filter is actually a capacitor that may be thought of as a glitch-eater. The glitches occur when a majority of data lines change their state simultaneously, which drains the terminator power line (TPWR line) and consequently causes a power spike on the Request line. The solution is to have the internal SCSI filter provide the TPWR line with a little extra current when needed.

 A notice in the Macintosh IIfx finished goods box instructs customers to return self-terminated SCSI devices to the service provider to have the termination disabled.

Newer Macintosh computers, starting with the Centris 660AV/Quadra 840AV and continuing through the Power Macintosh line, include automatic termination when no internal device is connected. When this occurs, special circuitry terminates the bus on the logic board near the external connector. Previous Quadras and Macintosh II series computers required a motherboard in-line terminator to be connected when a system had external drives but no internal ones.

The PowerBook 100 and 200 series have unusual termination requirements:

- When you attach an external drive to one of these PowerBooks, you must connect it to the PowerBook with a cable that has a built-in terminator, and plug an external terminator into the second SCSI port on the external drive.

- If you daisy-chain external devices to one of these PowerBooks, you must use a cable with a built-in terminator and terminate the last device on the chain.

- If you use one of these PowerBooks in SCSI disk mode—where it is used as an external drive attached to a host computer—there must be a terminator connecting the cable leading from the PowerBook to the cable leading from the host.

 See the documentation that came with you PowerBook for specifics on termination for these computers.

PowerBook SCSI

PowerBook laptops continue Apple's tradition of using SCSI. They did utilize a new proprietary, high-density, 30-pin cable (HDI-30) to save space. PowerBooks starting with the PowerBook150 and PowerBook5300 started to use IDE drives internally but continued to have SCSI ports externally.

 IDE stands for Integrated Drive Electronics. It is a control system for storage devices where most of the control is contained on the device itself.

Some PowerBook computers support SCSI disk mode, which allows the internal hard disk to be mounted and used as an external drive by another Macintosh. To operate a PowerBook computer in SCSI disk mode, the user connects a special HDI-30 SCSI Disk Adapter cable between the external SCSI connectors on the PowerBook computer and the desktop computer and then starts both computers. The adapter cable grounds pin-1 of the HDI-30 connector, causing the PowerBook computer's ROM code to bypass the normal startup procedure and enter SCSI disk mode.

 PowerBook SCSI disk mode makes even IDE drives appear as SCSI drives.

SCSI Manager

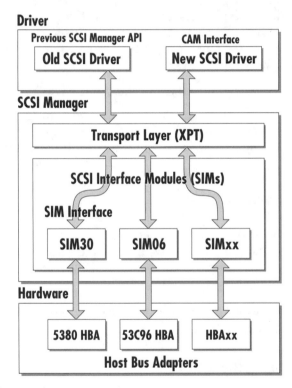

Figure 65. *SCSI Manager software hierarchy*

The SCSI Manager provides the interface between the SCSI software (operating system drivers or application programs) and hardware (chip). The SCSI Manager offers a well-defined set of calls that allows the software drivers or applications for different SCSI devices to use any Macintosh SCSI port smoothly, without worrying about the underlying hardware.

The original SCSI Manager code includes commands for all types of SCSI operations. Table 43 lists and describes the original code.

Table 43. *Original SCSI Manager Code*

Code	Description
SCSIGet	Arbitrates for control of the SCSI bus.
SCSISelect	Selects the target device.
SCSICmd	Sends the command in the Command Phase that tells the target what operation to perform. It indicates whether the command is six or ten bytes long (Group 0, 1, 2 and 5).
SCSIRead	Read data from device.
SCSIRBlind	Read data without handshaking every byte.
SCSIWrite	Write data to device.
SCSIWBlind	Write data without handshaking every byte.
SCSIComplete	Tells the Macintosh how long it should wait for the target to complete the command, and returns the status and message bytes.
SCSIReset	Resets the bus.
SCSIStat	Gets bus status information.
SCSIMsgIn	Receives a message from target.
SCSIMsgOut	Sends message to target.
SCSISelAtn	Selects a target device and sets ATN line active.

SCSI commands are more fully described in "Commands" on page 156.

SCSI Manager 4.3, introduced with the Quadra 840AV in 1993, increased the power of SCSI on the Macintosh by allowing it to support most of the SCSI-2 specification, including:

- Disconnect/reconnect
- Parity detection
- Synchronous transfers
- Multiple buses and LUNs
- Asynchronous operation

The new interface was much more modern. There was no need to drive all SCSI bus phases. It also enabled full support of third-party expansion cards and DMA, while maintaining backward compatibility with software. However, running old drivers under SCSI Manager 4.3 imposed a 20 percent performance penalty. SCSI Manager 4.3 also added more overhead on small data transfers, causing a slight slowdown compared to the earlier SCSI Manager.

SCSI Manager 4.3 is also supported on all Macintosh Quadras running System 7.5 or newer. (It is loaded from a System Extension.) It is present on all PowerMacs.

SCSI Manager 4.3 is based on ANSI X3.232 Common Access Method (CAM) but adds some Apple-specific improvements. CAM documents a layered architecture with a transport layer on top (XPT). The single XPT vector calls to one or more SCSI interface modules (SIM) layers. Each SIM controls a single host bus adapter (HBA).

Parameter blocks

A common SCSI Manager 4.3 data structure is the parameter block. A parameter block is the basic unit of data that is exchanged between a program and the SCSI Manager. Each client of the SCSI Manager allocates a SCSI parameter block and fills in the required fields before passing it to the SCSI Action function. A function-specific SCSI parameter block consists of two parts:

- The header (SCSIHdr), contained in all SCSI parameter blocks.
- The body, which contains information specific to the active function.

Figure 66 illustrates a typical SCSI parameter block header.

```
#define SCSIPBHdr \
struct SCSIHdr  *qLink;          //  (internal) Q link to next PB
short           qType;           //  (unused) Q type
ushort          scVer;           //  -> version of the PB
ushort          scPBLen;         //  -> length of the entire PB
FunctionType    scFunctionCode;  //  -> function selector
OSErr           scResult;        //  <- returned result
DeviceIdent     scDeviceIdent;   //  -> (bus + target + LUN)
CallbackProc    scCompFn;        //  -> callback on completion function
ulong           scFlags;         //  -> flags for operation
// end of SCSIPBHdr
```

Figure 66. *Typical parameter block construct*

Table 44 lists and describes SCSI Manager 4.3 calls. This information would be included in the body of the parameter block.

Calls are requests or instructions from the initiator or target.

Table 44. *SCSI Manager 4.3 Calls*

Call	Description
SCSIAction	Performs a SCSI action.
SCSI_ExecIO	Performs an I/O Command.
SCSI_AbortCommand	Aborts a command.
SCSI_ResetBus	Resets a SCSI bus.
SCSI_ResetDevice	Resets one device.
SCSI_TerminateIO	Terminates an incomplete I/O.
SCSI_GetVirtualIDInfo	Gets information on a specific device.
SCSI_ReleaseQ	Releases a frozen queue.
SCSI_BusInquiry	Gets information on a host bus adapter (HBA).
SCSIRegisterBus	Registers a new SCSI bus.
SCSIDeregisterBus	Deregisters a SCSI bus.
SIMinit	Initializes a SIM.
SIMAction	XPT uses this to call SIM.

SCSI Manager 4.3 is present in ROM on all machines newer than the Quadra 840AV. It is also supported on all Quadra models utilizing 53C9X series SCSI chips when running System 7.5 or newer. It was not included in any Power-Books before 1996.

 Apple's future System 8, also known as Copland, is rumored to be introducing another SCSI Manager model. It is expected to borrow heavily from DEC VMS and Windows NT's layered driver architecture.

Device drivers

A device driver on the Macintosh is the software program that translates operating system requests into the SCSI commands that direct the operations of a SCSI peripheral. It does this via the SCSI Manager and SCSI chip. Properly written software drivers communicate with a SCSI device via the SCSI Manager and SCSI chip and maintain the device at peak performance throughout its lifetime. Among the devices that SCSI drivers control are the following:

• Hard drives

- Removable drives
- Scanners
- Tape drives
- Printers
- Film recorders
- Digital cameras
- CD-ROM drives

Device drivers are required for all classes of devices. There are drivers for fixed and removable disk drives as well as special drivers used to implement drive spanning and data striping.

 Corrupt drivers cannot usually be detected by diagnostic utilities. If you are unable to get a particular device to work by itself, reinstalling the driver will often help.

Requests

Table 45 lists the five requests to which a driver responds.

Table 45. *Driver Requests*

Request	Description
Open	This is where the driver is first called and initializes itself, allocates memory, and generally gets ready for business. Open typically occurs in the boot-up or mounting process.
Close	At this request, the driver shuts down, deallocates memory, and usually turns off.
Prime	Following a Prime request, the driver will perform a task, typically a read or write.
Status	Seldom used in SCSI.
Control	This request queries the driver for "where" data is located, including Finder and icon data, and puts the driver in different operational modes.

Input

The driver is capable of receiving the following input after receiving a request:

- The number of bytes the access is offset from the start of the partition. This is the logical address that the driver will translate into a drive's block address.

- The driver can determine the following:
  - If it was called as the result of a Read or Write command.
  - Whether the command was made asynchronously or synchronously.
- How many bytes of data are requested.
- The address of the I/O buffer.

If the driver was called for an asynchronous request, it will also accept the address of a completion routine that will be called when the request has been processed.

Output

Device drivers can return the following information to the computer's operating system:

- The number of bytes actually transferred.
- An error code (zero, if no error occurred).

Call Chain

Now that you've waded through the command structures, understand the functioning of the SCSI chip and device controllers, and have an appreciation for device drivers, the SCSI Manager, and hard drive technology, we can fit them all together. This is a "behind the scenes" look at how information is routed in a computer system that uses SCSI.

Host computers and devices that communicate in a structured manner do so in a complicated sequence of continuous calls known as the call chain.

Calls are requests or instructions from the initiator or target. The call chain represents the many layers through which calls pass and the levels at which they are translated—in effect, readied for the next level.

The sequence is "modular"; that is, each step is distinct and self-contained. This is the result of purposeful intent by good engineers. If an aspect of the call chain is improved, only the layer affected needs to be changed.

Our example is the common call chain involved in writing data to a hard disk.

1. First, the application in which you are working makes a write call to the Macintosh's File Manager.

 The File Manager is a software library typically located in ROM that manages I/O flow to and from files.

---

2. The File Manager translates the write call into another protocol and sends it to the Macintosh's Device Manager, a lower-level software library that typically also resides in ROM.

3. The Device Manager:

   a. Translates the call into a parameter block the Device Driver will recognize.

   b. Calls the appropriate driver for the volume to be accessed.

4. The Device Driver, residing in RAM, sends the write call, which it translates into a sequence of calls, to the SCSI Manager:

   - To gain control of the SCSI bus
   - To select a particular device for I/O
   - To send a command
   - To write the appropriate data
   - To complete the operation

5. The SCSI Manager takes these calls and turns them into a form that the SCSI chip can use to send commands across the bus.

6. The SCSI chip sends electrical signals across the bus that correspond to the above calls.

7. These signals are received by the SCSI chip on the SCSI peripheral. This chip provides the device's intelligence. It is controlled by a CPU on the device, which is part of the peripheral's controller board.

8. The controller CPU coordinates the specific operations of the original call and oversees its completion by writing data to the platter.

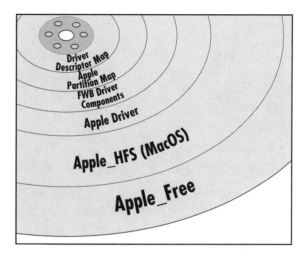

Figure 67. *Partition map*

Having described what drivers are, what the call chain is, and how drives function, we can now describe how the Macintosh places data on the disk.

Data is physically laid out on the disk according to specifications set forth by *Inside Macintosh V* and *Inside Macintosh: Devices*. Block zero contains the driver descriptor map (DDM). The DDM is the first data read from the disk and contains the following:

- The number of blocks on the device
- The block size
- The number of drivers
- The location and size of the first driver

The boot code in the ROM of the Macintosh reads in the driver descriptor map, then loads the driver into memory and executes it.

The partition map is contained on a series of blocks, beginning with block one. Each partition map entry occupies one block and contains information on the following:

- Name of the partition
- Processor type
- Type of partition
- Partition status

- Partition size
- More

The partition map can vary in size from a few to hundreds of blocks. Partitions can be created for:

- HFS
- A/UX
- ProDOS
- Drivers
- Partition maps
- Scratch space
- Custom partitions (as with RAID configurations)

After the partition map comes each partition in sequence. Every block on the disk must belong to a partition. Even free space on the disk is stored within a partition.

Inside the Mac HFS partition

The Macintosh HFS partition contains structures to help the Macintosh operating system boot the computer and locate information on files and folders. This data structure is set up when initializing the partition for the Macintosh within the hard disk setup utility program. The following data structures are written to disk:

- Boot blocks
- Volume information block (VIB)
- Volume bitmap
- Extents tree
- Catalog tree
- File data area

The boot blocks on each HFS partition occupy blocks zero and one. They are filled in with data when a System Folder is copied into the partition. The boot blocks contain the following:

- Information that allows the system to start up from the System Folder
- Information on the maximum number of open files
- The name of the debugger
- The names of system files

The volume information block is a master directory block that contains important information on the volume including:

- Its name and type
- The number of files and folders on the volume
- The allocation block size
- Pointers to the location of files

There is a backup copy of this near the end of the disk.

The volume bit map is a directory structure that keeps track of allocation blocks that are in use and that are free. It is used to determine where to put data that needs space and where to free up space when a file is deleted.

The extents tree and catalog tree are data structures that track the location and statistics for all files and folders on the disk. Each file has a record that indicates:

- Its name
- ID
- Type
- Creator
- Size
- Creation and modification date
- Other file information

The file data area is the space on disk where data is stored in allocation block-sized chunks.

Macintosh volume limits

Systems prior to 7.5 were limited in size to 2 GB per volume. System 7.5 increased this to 4 GB per volume, while the PowerMacintosh with PCI raised the limit to 2 terabytes (TB). As a volume gets larger, its smallest unit of allocation grows because there are only 65535 block units that can be allocated to a given volume. A 1 GB volume has an allocation block size of 16 KB. This means that a file with one character of data in it will consume 16 KB of disk space. A 2 TB volume has a minimum allocation block size of a whopping 32 MB!

 A terabyte is equal to 10^{12}, and is written out as 1,000,000,000,000.

Multiple partitions can be created on larger disks to minimize allocation block size. Minimizing allocation block size allows more real data to be stored on a given drive. Partitions can be used to organized like data and to create storage areas for data that could be password-protected and/or encrypted.

You can use disk utility software, such as FWB's Hard Disk ToolKit, to create partitions on your storage media.

Macintosh SCSI performance

Macintosh SCSI performance has improved significantly from the first implementation on the Macintosh Plus. Apple has remained conservative and been slow to adopt new technologies that improve data transfer rates (Table 46).

Table 46. *Progress of Data Transfer Rates in the Macintosh*

Macintosh	Maximum SCSI Transfer Rate
Plus	0.3 MB/s
SE	0.7 MB/s
Macintosh II family	2.8 - 4.5 MB/s
Quadra family	3.8 - 4.5 MB/s
Power Macintosh family	3.8 - 4.5 MB/s
Power Macintosh with PCI family	4.5 - 10 MB/s

The original SCSI implementations in the Plus and SE were limited to under one megabyte a second by the SCSI hardware and software implementation. The later Macintosh II, Quadra and Power Macintosh families increased SCSI performance but were still limited to performing slower asynchronous data transfers. The first members of the PowerMacintosh with PCI family finally introduced synchronous data transfers on their internal SCSI buses, increasing data rates to 10 MB/s.

Third parties, including FWB, produce SCSI accelerator add-in cards that break the SCSI bottleneck inherent in the Macintosh architecture. The data transfer rates on these cards are often two to four times faster than the standard data transfer rates. At a time when the Macintosh was transferring 10 MB/s, third parties were handling 40 MB/s.

PC SCSI Implementation

SCSI host adapters were initially difficult to install on PCs. Many contained lots of jumper settings. Any single setting could conflict with another card and cause problems. SCSI was also actually slower for many single-tasking applications because it introduced a lot of overhead over the very efficient IDE interface.

 A jumper is a pair of pins on a circuit board. A jumper block is a small plastic-covered metal connector used to connect jumpers. Jumpers and jumper blocks are used to set device parameters, such as the SCSI ID.

SCSI has also been slow to take off on the PC because of many conflicting standards and software driver dependencies. In the early days of the PC, there were as many as three separate incompatible standards being promoted:

- Microsoft originally promoted a Layered Architecture for Device Drivers (LADDR) with the advent of OS/2.
- Adaptec presented Advanced SCSI Programming Interface (ASPI) in 1988.
- Future Domain promoted ANSI's Common Access Method (CAM).
- IBM OS/2 promoted Adapter Device Driver (ADD).
- Novell promoted Host Adapter Module (HAM).

If you had three SCSI host adapters from different vendors, you could need to load three separate sets of drivers even though all were talking SCSI. You would also need a driver for each additional operating system.

By the mid-90's things had calmed down. ASPI became the dominant standard on the PC with virtually everyone supporting it—including Microsoft, in Windows95. Standardizing on ASPI allowed host adapter manufacturers to simply produce an ASPI layer. Application and driver developers could write ASPI-compliant software that would run on any ASPI-compatible adapter. ASPI became the SCSI programming interface of choice on DOS, Windows, OS/2 and Novell Netware.

ASPI for Win32 calls

Table 47 lists and describes the calls ASPI for Win32 makes to access SCSI devices.

 Calls are requests or instructions from the initiator or target.

Table 47. *ASPI for Win32 Calls*

Call	Description
GetASPI32SupportInfo	Gets information on host adapters installed.

Table 47. *ASPI for Win32 Calls (Continued)*

Call	Description
SendASPI32Command	Sends a command. The command codes include:

SC_HA_INQUIRY	Host adapter inquiry
SC_GET_DEV_TYPE	Gets information on a SCSI device
SC_EXEC_SCSI_CMD	Executes SCSI I/O Command
SC_ABORT_SRB	Aborts SCSI I/O Command
SC_RESET_DEV	Resets SCSI Device
SC_GET_DISK_INFO	Gets SCSI Disk Information
SC_RESCAN_SCSI_BUS	Rescans SCSI Bus

ASPI for Win32 is fully re-entrant, permitting overlapped asynchronous I/O.

DOS

Most PC SCSI host adapters include a SCSI BIOS boot ROM on board. This BIOS is used to initialize the SCSI chip on startup and to support the transparent operation of the adapter under DOS through the standard INT13 BIOS interface. Because the host adapter has its own BIOS, the drives on a SCSI card need not be set up with the computer's Setup utility. The SCSI drive would appear like a normal drive to DOS. One could use standard DOS utilities such as FDISK and FORMAT to partition and high-level format the drive. Application software would run transparently. SCSI drives could also co-exist with IDE drives, although the system would attempt to startup from IDE drives first.

The INT13 BIOS interface is the standard method of accessing a PC hard disk.

DOS versions prior to 5 supported only two drives. Versions later than 5 support up to seven physical drives. DOS supports up to 24 partitions (Drive letter C: through Z:). DOS 3.X supports up to 32 MB per partition. Versions after that expanded on this limit.

Windows®

The original Windows 3.0 communicated with SCSI drives through the standard INT13 BIOS mechanism. Bus mastering SCSI Controllers needed to support the Virtual DMA Services (VDS) standard to ensure compatibility with memory extensions such as Expanded Memory Specification (EMS). The real mode INT13 interface ensured compatibility but at the expense of performance. On every I/O, the computer needed to switch from 386 enhanced mode to real mode as many as six times to perform the I/O. This made I/O slow.

With the advent of Windows 3.1 and Windows for Workgroups 3.11, Microsoft created a 32-bit fastdisk interface that SCSI drivers could be hooked into. Each of these fastdisk drivers was hardware-dependent. The operating system came with a built-in fastdisk driver for IDE drives smaller than 528 MB. These drivers allowed the computer to remain in enhanced mode, significantly improving performance. This was also known as 32-bit disk access. Windows for Workgroups added 32-bit file access or VFAT.386 and VCACHE.386. These drivers install 32-bit operating system components for caching and for the disk file system. The old DOS Smartdrive was now needed only to cache floppy and CD-ROM drives.

Vendors also had to produce proprietary Windows ASPI (WinASPI.DLL) implementation to support third-party storage software under Windows.

Windows 95 and NT

These newer operating systems were designed from the ground up to accommodate SCSI. Microsoft and Intel even put together a Plug-and-Play specification to make adding SCSI host adapters easier. Windows 95 and NT feature layered driver architectures. SCSI host adapter vendors simply need to supply a small Miniport driver to support the new operating systems.

 "NT" stands for new technology.

The Miniport driver is essentially a hardware-specific translation layer that abstracts the I/O architecture of the host adapter. It initializes and configures the adapter, starts I/O, verifies the adapter state, and resets the SCSI bus. Hard drive, removable and CD-ROM drivers are built into the operating system. ASPI support is also available in both operating systems, with NT having a 32-bit version—ASPI32—built-in. SCSI host adapters still need BIOS Boot ROMs to facilitate booting the operating systems.

Windows NT has support for multiple requests per unit, so it can exploit tagged command queuing. It also has built in support for RAID. The workstation version includes RAID 0 and 1, while the server version adds support for RAID 5.

PC Plug-and-Play

The Plug-and-Play specification was created by Intel, Microsoft and Compaq to make it easier to add adapter boards into PCs. It was primarily designed to make the allocation of interrupt, DMA and I/O port addresses automatic when using ISA-based cards. (Previously you had to manually adjust jumpers.) It also mandated the need for self-resetting terminator power fuses and for a special SCSI icon on the back of the adapter. To be implemented, the Plug-and-Play standard required additions to the computer BIOS.

This specification was also extended to SCSI by including a new standard called SCAM (SCSI Configured Auto Magically). SCAM is a protocol that allows a host adapter to set the SCSI ID number of devices on the SCSI bus, preventing ID conflicts, and to set termination automatically. The protocol uses a SCAM master that isolates devices by toggling SCSI lines. It is compatible with legacy devices whose IDs are not changeable. Two levels of SCAM compliance have been defined. The more advanced level allows multiple initiators and hot plugging. SCAM acceptance has been slow, with few SCAM compliant peripherals available in 1995.

 SCAM acceptance has been hindered by the fact that PCs can't have SCSI IDs moved around. This would cause problems with the assigning of drive letters.

PC SCSI performance

PC SCSI performance has improved significantly from the first implementations on the ISA bus. Improvements in bus technology combined with newer SCSI chips have driven performance to new levels. Each computer model below was coupled with the fastest SCSI host adapter at the time.

Table 48. *Overview of Improved Transfer Rates in PCs*

Computer and Bus	Maximum SCSI Transfer Rate
IBM AT 80286/8 - ISA	2.5 MB/s
PC Compatible 80386/33 - ISA	3.0 MB/s
IBM PS/2 Model 80 80386/16 - MCA	7.0 MB/s
PC Compatible 80486/33 - EISA	7.5 MB/s
PC Compatible 80486/66 - VL	20 MB/s
PC Compatible P5-133 - PCI	40 MB/s

PC SCSI data transfer performance has mainly been limited by computer expansion bus limitations. Virtually all PC SCSI implementations have handled synchronous data transfers and disconnect/reconnect since inception. Manufacturers of PC SCSI host adapters were quick to add support for Fast/Wide SCSI-2 and Fast-20 SCSI.

To help you sort out the SCSI variations, we offer this list:

- **Fast SCSI-2 means transfer rates at 10 MB/s on an 8-bit narrow bus.**
- **Fast/Wide SCSI-2 means transfer rates at 20 MB/s on a 16-bit wide bus.**
- **Ultra SCSI (same as Fast 20) means transfer rates at 20 MB/s on an 8-bit narrow bus.**
- **Ultra Wide SCSI means transfer rates at 40 MB/s on a 16-bit wide bus.**

SCSI-2: A Transition From SCSI-1

The SCSI-2 specification has been developed by ANSI Task Group X3T9.2 on Lower-Level Interfaces, with:

- John B. Lohmeyer, Chair
- I. Dal Allan, Vice-Chair
- Lawrence J. Lamers, Secretary

The SCSI-2 specification was approved by ANSI's Technical Committee X3T9 on I/O interfaces, with:

- Del Shoemaker, Chair
- Robert L. Fink, Vice-Chair

ANSI began work on SCSI-2 in 1986, even before SCSI-1 Revision 17B had been formally adopted. There was no technical rationale for doing so—the specification for SCSI-2 was far from complete—but at some point work must be committed to print.

SCSI-2 Revision 10c was approved in August of 1990 as an American National Standard. However, several errors and ambiguities were discovered during the review period, and it was returned to committee for correction and clarification. The result was Revision 10L, which was introduced in September 1993. It became a published ANSI standard before the end of 1994 as X3.131-1994. It became an ISO standard in 1996.

ANSI has designed SCSI-2 to be backward compatible with SCSI-1. Devices using the new standard will work with those that use the old standard. All command, status and message information will continue to be transferred in the eight-bit asynchronous mode.

How can you tell if your device is SCSI-1 or SCSI-2? Use the Inquiry command to show not only whether the device is SCSI-1 or SCSI-2, but which features are implemented. A drive could be SCSI-2 but offer none of SCSI-2's new features that significantly boost performance. The Program's Info function in FWB's HDT SCSI Configure will tell you about the "SCSI-2ness" of a drive.

SCSI-2 overview

SCSI-2 builds on the SCSI-1 specification in the following ways:

- Defines extensions to the SCSI-1 specification
- Provides more complete standardization of SCSI-1 command sets
- Describes the necessary mechanical, electrical, and functional qualities that will allow for interoperability of devices meeting the new standard

To meet these demands, SCSI-2 devices require more intelligence and firmware than their SCSI-1 counterparts.

SCSI-2 furthers the goal of SCSI-1 to promote device-independence within a class of devices. It provides for the implementation of vendor-unique fields and codes, and sets aside fields and codes for future standardization.

Another key objective of SCSI-2 is placing device-independent intelligence on the SCSI device itself. This requires a command set that will allow an operating system to get the necessary initialization information from the SCSI-2 device. Parameters that are not required by the operating system for operation, initialization, or system tuning will be managed exclusively by the SCSI-2 device.

The structure of the published SCSI-2 specification, although much larger than SCSI-1, makes it more understandable to the layman as well as the engineer. Rather than following a numeric sequence that caters to those who wish to memorize the message and opcode tables, alphabetization and organization are the new order of the day.

The specification is organized along device class lines, with descriptions of each model's characteristics. SCSI-1 defined the following types of devices:

- Random access
- Sequential access
- Printer
- Processor
- Worm
- Read-only random access

SCSI-2 added the following types of devices:

- CD-ROM
- Scanner

- Magneto Optical
- Medium Changers
- Communication devices

Separate sections of the specification that address particular devices, many of which received new command sets, include the following devices:

- CD ROM (which replace Read-Only)
- Scanners
- Optical memory (which provide for WORM, ROM, and erasable media)

SCSI-2 removes support for the following SCSI-1 features and options:

- Single initiator option
- Non-arbitrating systems option
- SCSI-1 alternative 1 shielded connector
- Non-extended sense data option
- Reservation queuing option
- Read-only device command set

SCSI-2 commands

All existing SCSI-1 command sets were enhanced in SCSI-2:

- Device models were added.
- Extended sense and Inquiry data were expanded.
- Pages for Mode Select and Mode Sense were detailed for all device types.
- The Change Definition, Log Select, Log Sense and Read and Write Buffer commands were added for all device types.
- The Copy command definition was expanded.
- The direct-access command set added cache management and greater control over defect management.
- The sequential-access device command set received several mode pages, some designed to support partitioned media.
- The Write-Once command set added several new commands.

SCSI command sets were added for the following devices:

- CD-ROM
- Scanner
- Medium Changer
- Communications

SCSI-2 also caused the following:

- Addition of device models
- Expansion of extended request sense
- Expansion of inquiry data

Additionally, the Copy command was expanded to support inexact block size and image copies.

Commands are listed below with their opcodes. Only those commands not already included in the CCS are indicated below.

Mandatory (M) commands

No new mandatory commands beyond the CCS have been included in SCSI-2.

Optional (O) commands

Table 49. *Optional Commands and Opcodes Introduced in SCSI-2*

Command	Opcode	Description
Change Definition	40$_H$	Modifies the operating definition of the selected logical unit or target with respect to commands from the initiator. It is used to implement switching between SCSI-1 and SCSI-2 mode and to tell which mode is currently active.
Compare	39$_H$	Provides the means to compare data from one logical unit to another or to the same logical unit. It does this in a manner similar to the Copy command, except that with Compare, the source data is compared with the destination data on a byte-by-byte basis.
Copy and Verify	3A$_H$	The same as the Copy command, except that a verification of the data written to the destination logical unit occurs after the copy is completed.
Lock Unlock Cache	36$_H$	Requests that the target either disallow or allow logical blocks (within the range specified) to be removed from the cache memory by the target's cache replacement algorithm. Locked logical blocks may be written to the media when modified, but a copy of the modified logical block remains in the cache. This is good for locking data or applications into the cache.
Log Select	4C$_H$	Lets the initiator manage statistical information that the SCSI device maintains about itself or its logical units. The log can be reset. Targets that implement Log Select must also support Log Sense.
Log Sense	4D$_H$	Lets the initiator retrieve statistical information that the SCSI device maintains about itself or its logical units, typically cache information or error logs. It is complementary to the Log Select command.
Pre-Fetch	34$_H$	Requests that the target transfer the specified logical blocks to the cache memory on the drive, and determines when the status will be sent. No data is transferred to the initiator.
Prevent/Allow Medium Removal	1E$_H$	Requests that the target either prevent or allow the removal of the medium in the logical unit.
Read Defect Data	37$_H$	Requests that the target transfer data regarding defects in the medium to the initiator. Data on both factory and grown defects can be requested. If the target cannot comply, it will send the Check Condition status.
Receive Diagnostics	1C$_H$	Requests that analysis data be sent to the initiator after completion of a Send Diagnostics command. For more information, see "Commands" on page 156.

Table 49. *Optional Commands and Opcodes Introduced in SCSI-2*

Command	Opcode	Description
Search Data	30_H	Looks through one or more logical blocks for equality or inequality to a data pattern. There are Search Data Equal, Search Data High, and Search Data Low commands.
	31_H	
	32_H	
Set Limits	33_H	Defines the range within which subsequent linked commands may operate.
Synchronize Cache	35_H	Ensures that logical blocks in the cache memory, within the specified range, have their most recent data value recorded in the medium. This command will update the medium if necessary.
Write and Verify	$2E_H$	Asks the target to: 1. Take the data transferred from the initiator. 2. Write it to the medium. 3. Verify that it is correctly written
Write Same	41_H	Requests that the target write the single block of data transferred by the initiator to the medium multiple times.

Opcodes reserved for vendor-unique commands (V)

Figure 68 lists the opcodes that are reserved for the unique commands developed and used by vendors.

02_H	$0D_H$	13_H	22_H	29_H
05_H	$0E_H$	14_H	23_H	$2C_H$
06_H	$0F_H$	19_H	24_H	$2D_H$
09_H	10_H	20_H	26_H	$C0_H$
$0C_H$	11_H	21_H	27_H	FF_H

Figure 68. *Opcodes reserved for vendor-unique commands*

Special CD-ROM commands

In the SCSI-2 specification, CD-ROM devices utilize special commands to perform operations. Commands marked with an "O" are optional; commands marked with an "M" are mandatory.

Table 50. *Commands and Opcodes for CD-ROM Devices*

Command	O/M	Opcode	Description
Audio Scan	O	BA_H	Performs fast forward/fast reverse audio scanning.
Pause/Resume	O	$4B_H$	Pauses audio/resumes playing audio.
Play Audio (10)	O	45_H	Plays audio.
Play Audio (12)	O	$A5_H$	Plays audio on larger discs.
Play Audio MSF	O	47_H	Plays audio in minutes, seconds format.
Play Track Relative (10)	O	49_H	Plays a track relative to the current position.
Play Track Relative (12)	O	$A9_H$	Plays a track relative to the current position on larger discs.
Play CD-ROM XA (12)	O	BD_H	Plays an XA formatted track. **NOTE:** XA stands for extended architecture.
Read CD	M	BE_H	Reads data from CD.
Read CD MSF	M	$B9_H$	Reads data from CD in MSF format.
Read Header	M	44_H	Reads header data from CD.
Read Sub-Channel	M	42_H	Reads CD Sub-Channel data.
Read TOC	M	43_H	Returns list of recorded tracks.
Send CD-ROM XA ADPCM DATA	O	BC_H	Plays XA formatted audio. **NOTE:** XA stands for extended architecture.
Set CD-ROM Speed	O	$B8_H$	Sets the spin rate of the CD-ROM.
Stop Play/Scan	M	$4E_H$	Stops audio playing.

Special tape device commands

In the SCSI-2 specification, tape devices utilize special commands to perform operations. Commands marked with an "O" are optional; commands marked with an "M" are mandatory.

Table 51. *Commands and Opcodes for Tape Devices*

Command	O/M	Opcode	Description
Erase	M	19_H	Erases the tape.
Locate	O	$2B_H$	Seeks to a block on the tape.
Load/Unload	O	$1B_H$	Loads the tape into the drive or unloads it.
Read Block Limits	M	05_H	Returns possible block lengths.
Read Position	O	34_H	Returns the current position of the head.
Rewind	M	01_H	Performs fast reverse rewinding of the tape.
Space	M	11_H	Performs fast forward/fast reverse tape seeking.
Write Filemarks	M	11_H	Writes a tape marker point to the current position.

Special communications device commands

In the SCSI-2 specification, communication devices utilize a special command to perform erase operations. The Erase command is mandatory.

Table 52. *Commands and Opcodes for Communication Devices*

Command	O/M	Opcode	Description
Erase	M	19_H	Erases the tape.

SCSI-2 Mode Pages

The SCSI-2 specification defines additional mode pages. In addition to specifically defined mode pages, there are reserved and vendor-specific mode pages. The defined pages are listed and described in Table 53.

Table 53. SCSI-2 Defined Mode Pages

Mode Page	Opcode	Description
Caching Parameters	08$_H$	Defines the parameters affecting use of the cache, including: • Sending the Good status • The length of the pre-fetch logical blocks • Whether the target can take Read data from the medium but not the cache • Disable or enable write cache
Control Mode	0A$_H$	Controls several SCSI-2 features that are applicable to all device types, such as: • Tagged queuing • Extended contingent allegiance • Asynchronous event notification • Error logging
Disconnect Reconnect	02$_H$	Lets the initiator tune the performance of the SCSI bus, including: • Maximum time the target can assert Busy without a Request/Acknowledge handshake • Maximum time the target will wait after releasing the bus before attempting to reselect.
Flexible Disk	05$_H$	Controls and reports flexible drive parameters, including: • Number of read/write heads used • Number of sectors per revolution per head • Number of data bytes per sector that an initiator can read or write
Format Device	03$_H$	Specifies the medium format, including the number of: • Tracks • Alternate tracks • Alternate sectors per zone • Alternate tracks per logical unit • Sectors per track • Data bytes per physical sector
Medium Types Supported	0B$_H$	Contains a list of the medium types implemented by the target for logical units.
Notch and Partition	0C$_H$	Applies to direct-access devices that implement a variable number of blocks per cylinder, and indicates such things as the maximum number of notches allowed by the logical unit and their boundaries.
Read-Write Error Recovery	01$_H$	Specifies the numerous error recovery parameters the target uses during any command that performs a read or write operation to the media.

Table 53. *SCSI-2 Defined Mode Pages (Continued)*

Mode Page	Opcode	Description
Rigid Disk Geometry	04$_H$	Specifies parameters for direct-access devices that use a rigid disk drive, including: • The number of heads used for data storage • Where the landing zone is located • Rotational position locking
Verify Error Recovery	07$_H$	Specifies the error recovery parameters the target uses during the Verify, Write and Verify, and Copy and Verify commands, including: • The number of times the target will attempt its recovery algorithm • The largest burst data error for which data error correction may be attempted
Peripheral Device	09$_H$	Passes vendor-specific information between an initiator and a peripheral interface "below" the target (that is, between the target and the peripheral device), including SCSI, ESDI, IPI.

SCSI-2 CD-ROM Mode Pages

The SCSI-2 specification defines additional mode pages for use by CD-ROM devices. In addition to specifically defined mode pages, there are reserved and vendor-specific mode pages. The defined pages are listed below along with their codes.

Table 54. *SCSI-2 Defined CD-ROM Mode Pages*

Mode Page	Opcode	Description
CD-ROM	0D$_H$	Defines the parameters affecting use of CD-ROMs.
CD-ROM Audio Control	0E$_H$	Defines the parameters affecting the playing of audio on CD-ROM discs.

SCSI-2 Tape Mode Pages

The SCSI-2 specification defines additional mode pages for use by tape devices. In addition to specifically defined mode pages, there are reserved and vendor-specific mode pages. The defined pages are listed below along with their codes.

Table 55. *SCSI-2 Defined Tape Mode Pages*

Mode Page	Opcode	Description
Device Configuration	10$_H$	Allows programs to read and customize the mode that the tape drive is operating in.

Table 55. *SCSI-2 Defined Tape Mode Pages (Continued)*

Mode Page	Opcode	Description
Medium Partition	11ₕ–14ₕ	Allows programs to read how the tape is partitioned.

SCSI-2 highlights

The following excerpts have been selected from the 600-plus page SCSI-2 specification, which establishes future guidelines and helps broaden the commonality that devices must support. SCSI-2 was submitted to ANSI as X3.131-1993.

Required features

The SCSI-2 specification mandates that SCSI-2 devices support the following:

These requirements are discussed in greater detail below.

- Common Command Set (CCS)
- Initiator provision of termination power (100 ohms)
- Parity Checking
- Bus Arbitration
- Rotational Position Locking (RPL)
- Contingent Allegiance
- Extended Sense Keys and Sense Codes

The Common Command Set

The Common Command Set (CCS), considered a de facto standard among SCSI hard drive manufacturers, has become a central feature of SCSI-2. Since 1988, virtually all hard drive manufacturers have incorporated CCS or a subset of it. ANSI CCS 4B (as CCS is formally known today) will represent the minimum level of commonality all SCSI-2 devices must support.

SCSI-1's goal of manufacturer compatibility was thwarted by an industry proliferation of undocumented vendor-unique features. Differences in hardware required custom programs and unique microcode. This self-defeating diversity provided the impetus for creation of the CCS, which defines the following:

- Data structures for Mode Select and Mode Sense commands
- Defect management of the Format command
- Error recovery procedures
- Numerous other command functions

CCS was the beginning of SCSI-2, but it is only for disk drives. The first efforts of the SCSI-2 technical committee focused on using the SCSI interface with tapes and optical discs, as well as other devices.

However, the SCSI-2 specification has gone far beyond applying CCS to various types of devices.

Termination power

SCSI-2 requires that initiators provide termination power, and defines an active terminator that lowers termination to 100 ohms.

SCSI-1 specified 132-ohm termination for the single-ended electrical specification. Unfortunately, that was mismatched with cable impedance, which is typically below 100 ohms. The result is that the terminator allowed for greater current than the cable could handle. The signal noise thus caused errors at faster data transfer rates, or when many devices were attached.

Parity checking

SCSI-2 mandates inclusion of parity checking.

Required messages

A basic set of messages is defined and required, even though most devices already support them.

Table 56. *SCSI-2 Required Messages*

Hex Code	Message Name
00	Command Complete
05	Initiator Detected Error
06	Abort
07	Message Reject
08	No Operation
09	Message Parity Error
0C	Bus Device Reset
80	Identify

For a list of SCSI messages and descriptions, see "Messages" on page 163.

Bus arbitration

Bus Arbitration is now required, and the arbitration delay has been lengthened from 2.2 to 2.4 ms.

Rotational Position Locking (RPL)

This features causes synchronization of drive spindles, so the spinning of multiple disks can be coordinated. This is critical for faster transfer rates in disk arrays.

NOTE For more information on disk arrays, see "What Is RAID?" on page 61.

Contingent Allegiance

SCSI-1 did not deal with deferred errors in systems with buffers. However, deferred errors will occur if anything goes wrong after the target has accepted the data into the buffer and sent the Good status, when the target writes the buffer contents to the media. Targets in the Contingent Allegiance state reject commands until the error status is cleared.

Sense keys and sense codes

Sense keys and sense codes have been formalized and extended. Specifics on the type of error being reported help engineers (or their programs) analyze errors or failures in the field or on the fly.

Optional features

The SCSI specification still allows for optional features, as well the flexibility of vendor-unique implementations. If supported, optional features must be implemented in uniform accordance with the SCSI-2 specification.

Tagged command queuing

Tagged command queuing will enhance SCSI's I/O capabilities. Rather than ask the initiator for a new command each time it finishes an operation, a "popular" peripheral can have the initiator queue, or line up, commands, so they're ready to go when the device is free.

Up to 256 commands may be queued, and the initiator can specify the order in which the target is to execute them. This ability to prioritize queued commands allows the target to operate more efficiently. For example, a hard disk drive can read from one data block to the next according to how closely they are situated, rather than hopping around from block to block according to the order in which the commands were received. Devices with this feature are compatible with devices that do not support command queuing.

Command queuing is among the more difficult SCSI-2 benefits to implement. It may cause the vendor to run into firmware problems if attention is not paid to the types of commands being queued prior to their being sorted. For example, if a Write and a Read command were queued, and the Read command was executed first because doing so was most efficient for the target, it is possible that the Write command was sent to modify the same data block that is now being read. In this case, the Read command would read "old" data. Queuing is really only helpful when used on multitasking operating systems.

Optional messages have been added to support command queuing capabilities. Also, the operating system must support multitasking, or multiple commands would never be issued.

Command linking

Command linking allows two or more SCSI commands to be linked together. If a linked flag is set in the CDB, the completion of one command triggers the execution of the following command, saving arbitration time.

Improvements in terminator design and driver technology

Improvements in terminator design and driver technology may be required to support fast SCSI on a single-ended cable (this is now one of SCSI-3's goals).

Fast SCSI

Fast SCSI uses the standard 50-pin connector to double the maximum data transfer rate to 10 MB/s in fast synchronous mode. (Up to 10 mega-transfers per second.) It does this by cutting synchronous transfer timings in half. However, this works only with modern SCSI chips, which were not used in the Macintosh for many years, but are available through third-party add-ons.

Wide SCSI

Wide SCSI is an option that increases the SCSI data path from eight to 16 or even 32 bits. (Commands, status, messages and arbitration are still transferred as eight bits for compatibility with SCSI-1.) It does this by using a second 68-conductor "B" cable that has 24 extra data lines. The standard 50-pin cable remains, still handling eight bits. This two-cable requirement (50- and 68-pin) may be impractical for many systems because the additional cable requires space for a second connector —space that may not exist.

SCSI-3 describes a 68-pin "P" cable that will support arbitration and data transfers at 16 bits. Most vendors have adopted this scheme. This 68-pin cable makes it difficult to daisy-chain standard 50-pin narrow SCSI devices to the 68-pin wide devices. It is possible to do this, with the wide devices connected first and the narrow ones later, but terminating the upper 8-bits and sending the lower 8-bits through is very difficult. Usually the best strategy is to connect all wide devices to the host adapter's internal or external port and connect narrow ones to the other port. Most host adapters allow for partial termination of the terminators on the card.

Both Fast and Wide SCSI can exist on the same bus. Combined, rates of 40 MB/s are possible. However, implementing Fast and/or Wide SCSI capabilities may require silicon changes in the SCSI protocol chip. Because much information will continue to be transferred in the eight-bit asynchronous mode, fast and wide capabilities may not significantly impact the I/O rates of your system unless you use fast drives and CPUs.

Optional messages

Optional messages have been added to support wide-transfer capabilities.

Smaller, high-density connectors

Smaller, high-density connectors (DB-50) are stipulated to fit in tighter spaces and make room for an increased number of pins.

12-byte Command Descriptor Block

A 12-byte Command Descriptor Block (CDB) has been defined, allowing for more complex commands and access to a larger range of data. This format is supported by the following commands:

- Read
- Search Data Equal
- Search Data High
- Search Data Low
- Set Limits
- Write
- Write and Verify
- Verify

Asynchronous Event Notification

Asynchronous event notification (AEN) is a protocol that can be used to inform processor devices that an asynchronous event has occurred. Instead of the initiator polling, the target would notify the initiator.

Optional extended contingent allegiance

Extended contingent allegiance is now optional. It is a sleep mode in which devices won't respond to other requests for access, and command queuing is suspended.

The SCSI-2 Common Access Method (CAM)

In October 1988 a group of 40 peripheral suppliers led by Adaptec, Inc. formed the Common Access Method (CAM) Committee to establish a common software interface for attaching SCSI peripherals. Such an interface would be independent of the host bus adapter (HBA) hardware implementation. ANSI completed final action on CAM in early 1996. It was adopted as ANSI X3.232:1996, SCSI-2 Common Access Method Transport and SCSI Interface Module.

CAM reduces the number of drivers needed by an HBA and its peripherals on various operating systems. Its modular design allows the use of only those software drivers that belong with the SCSI peripherals. CAM also addresses the use of a protocol chip on the motherboard and the ATA (Advanced Technology Bus Attachment) interface as a method of attaching SCSI peripherals.

Macintoshes do not require SCSI adapters, but instead offer the SCSI Manager and SCSI chips on the motherboard. However, because the SCSI Manager solution is vendor-specific, SCSI devices intended for use with the Macintosh must have Macintosh-tuned device driver software. CAM's major goal is to provide one interface across all hardware platforms, Macintosh included, to ease software development for every new system.

CAM did not become very important for PCs, where the profusion of manufacturers' HBAs and software drivers has caused significant software-compatibility problems. ASPI became the dominant standard.

The CAM committee's proposals consider the SCSI-2 CAM Transport (or XPT) and SCSI Interface Module (SIM).

 The XPT is a layer of software that programs and peripheral drivers use to initiate the execution of CAM functions. SIMs are modules that execute the SCSI commands.

Macintoshes were not impacted immediately by CAM development. They benefited indirectly as CAM accelerated SCSI's marketplace acceptance and helped with third-party SCSI accelerator add-ons that had no such standard (such as NuBus SCSI cards). Apple later adopted CAM as part of their SCSI Manager 4.3 interface.

Details of CAM operation

With CAM, requests for SCSI I/O from the peripheral driver are made through the XPT interface. The XPT receives the request as a CAM Control Block (CCB), which is a data structure containing the action required. The XPT function routes CCBs to a lower level SIM.

The XPT allocates CCB resources—such as getting and releasing CCBs—independent of the operating system. It also ensures the CCBs are properly formatted and the fields needed to accomplish a request are primed.

To prevent each driver from having to scan the SCSI bus for devices at initialization, the XPT detects all installed SCSI devices and constructs an internal table, which is accessed by drivers and programs.

The XPT function may be a separate element or incorporated with the SIM into a single module. Either way, a logical separation between the two is maintained to distinguish among SIMs that may be loaded.

The SIM function processes SCSI requests and manages the hardware-independent interface to the HBA.

SIM services do the following:

- Monitor I/O behavior and perform error recovery if needed
- Manage data transfer hardware, such as DMA circuitry
- Queue multiple operations for single or multiple LUNs, "freezing" the queuing of requests as necessary to perform queue recovery
- Post results back to the initiating device driver
- Manage the selection, disconnection, reconnection, and data pointers of the SCSI HBA protocol

The CAM committee is also polishing up specifications for the ATA interface, which specifies how a peripheral controller can emulate the original IBM AT hard disk drive interface. This is important because a lot of software requires that the hardware look precisely like an IBM machine in order to run. ATA and EATA (Extended ATA) defines for vendors how to create interfaces for SCSI (and other) peripherals that the operating system will "accept" as normal.

SCSI-3

The ANSI committee responsible for SCSI-2 realized that the only way it was going to complete SCSI-2 was to begin planning SCSI-3.

SCSI-3's main target is extending SCSI-2's functionality so that it is suitable for much higher performance rates, while maintaining backward compatibility with present SCSI.

The SCSI-3 specification has numerous goals, including better cabling schemes for Fast and Wide SCSI. In fact, some of these cabling schemes may be standardized before the SCSI-3 specification is released.

The SCSI-3 specification consists of many files, each covering a specific area. This allows different teams to concentrate on different areas. It also allows the different parts of the specification to be approved as they are finalized. Table 57 lists the files and topics covered in SCSI-3.

Table 57. *SCSI-3 Files and Topics*

File	Topic	Description
F20	SCSI-3 Fast-20 Parallel Interface (20 MB/s on 8-bit bus or 40 MB/s on 16-bit)	Also part of the specification and a proposed X3T10/855D standard is Fast-20 or Ultra-SCSI. This basically doubles the data rate and allows 40 MB/s transfers over a 16-bit wide SCSI bus or 20 MB/s over an 8-bit wide SCSI bus. This performance boost is achieved by faster synchronous negotiation speeds. It is intended to bridge the gap before serial SCSI takes off. The first drives for this standard started to appear in 1995. The main limiting factor was that cabling was now half the length of the previous generation. Cabling needed to be 90 ohms and only active termination could be used. Other cable tolerances were also more stringent. Single-ended buses could be three meters in length when using four maximum capacitance devices, or 1.5 meters when using five to eight devices. Differential buses could now be 25 meters in length.
FCP	SCSI-3 Fibre Channel Protocol (for Fibre Channel)	This part of SCSI-3 describes the Fibre Channel Protocol used in Fibre Channel implementations of serial SCSI. Fibre Channel allows for data transfer rates of up to 100 MB/s over small wires that can be up to 30 meters in length between devices. FCP defines a Fibre Channel mapping layer (FC-4) that uses the services defined by ANSI X3.230.199x (Fibre Channel - Physical and Signaling Interface [FC-PH]) to send SCSI commands and data between serial SCSI devices. This protocol involves sending and receiving this information using standard Fibre Channel frame and sequence formats. FCP functions with Fibre Channel point to point, fabrics, and arbitrated loops. It supports both the optical and electrical connections of Fibre Channel.

For more information see Chapter 4, "All About Serial SCSI." |

Table 57. *SCSI-3 Files and Topics (Continued)*

File	Topic	Description
GPP	SCSI-3 Generic Packetized Protocol Technical Report	SCSI-3 GPP describes packetizing SCSI, which allows it to be transported by cabling other than traditional parallel cable. This stretches the SCSI cable well beyond its current limits while adding support for very high-speed transfers. Serial implementations also use information packets for data transmission, a radical departure from the present SCSI architecture. It basically translates SCSI protocols into network protocols, where data is encapsulated in packets. The cable could then be: • Fiber-optic • Copper coaxial • Twisted pair • Wireless
MMC	SCSI-3 Multi-Media Commands (CD-ROM command set)	SCSI-3 MMC is an important new part of SCSI-3 that describes commands for multimedia devices (i.e., CD-ROM and CD-R). This document describes the various CD-ROM and CD audio disk formats. Some new and updated commands include: • Read CD Recorded Capacity (25_H) - Returns actual recorded capacity of CD. • Play Audio Track/Index (48_H) - Plays an audio track on the CD from an index point. • Seek ($2B_H$) - Seeks the head to a place on the CD. SCSI-3 MMC accommodates CD drives as fast as 16x drives. (2.8 MB/s) This specification also describes CD-R commands to do writing and incremental packet writing, and some actual examples of how to write discs.
SAM	SCSI-3 Architecture Model (what it means to be SCSI-3)	SCSI-3 Architecture Model describes the entire SCSI-3 specification and its functional partitioning into separate documents. It specifies a model for I/O system and device behavior that applies to all SCSI interconnects, protocols, access methods, and devices. This document contains lots of definitions and diagrams outlining basic terminology and nomenclature used throughout SCSI-3 documents. This document discusses basic SCSI events such as: • Request/responses • Resets • Request sense • Contingent allegiance • Task management

Table 57. *SCSI-3 Files and Topics (Continued)*

File	Topic	Description
SBC	SCSI-3 Block Commands (for direct-access devices e.g., disks)	SCSI-3 SBC is an important new part of SCSI-3 that describes commands for direct access block logical unit class devices (i.e., hard drives, worm, optical, and removables). Caching is documented more thoroughly than in the SCSI-2 specification. This part of SCSI-3 includes commands to support medium changer devices such as the Read Elements Status and Move Medium commands. Optical drives have the following additional commands: • Medium Scan (38_H) - to scan for contiguous written or blank blocks. • Read Generation (29_H) - to return the maximum generation address of a block. • Read Updated Block ($2D_H$) - to read a specific generation and block number. • Update Block ($3D_H$) - requests that the drive replace data on the medium with new data.
SBP	SCSI-3 Serial Bus Protocol (for IEEE P1394)	This part of SCSI-3 describes the serial bus protocol used in 1394 implementations of serial SCSI. It defines a new fixed length packet that supports the various SCSI-3 standards to deliver command, data and status over the 1394 bus. The SCSI-3 SBP command data structure (CDS) allows data and command to be linked together. SCSI-3 SBP also supports 1394's isochronous data transfers. For more information, see Chapter 4, "All About Serial SCSI."
SCC	SCSI-3 Controller Commands (for RAID controllers)	SCSI-3 SCC is an important new part of SCSI-3 that describes commands for controller devices (i.e., RAID controllers). It describes commands that are used to control RAID controllers. RAID controllers need to be commanded to set up arrays, configure arrays, rebuild arrays, and monitor arrays and their components. New commands include: • Maintenance ($A3/A4_H$) - Performs logical operations on the RAID such as reporting on individual components. • Report Redundancy Group (BA/BB_H) - Returns and sets information on how drives are grouped as RAID units. • Spare (BC/BD_H) - Returns and sets information on drives used as spares. • Volume Set (BE/BF_H) - Controls the generation of check data within an underlying redundancy group. SCSI-3 SCC also describes in detail mappings of logical units to volumes.

Table 57. *SCSI-3 Files and Topics (Continued)*

File	Topic	Description
SGC	SCSI-3 Graphics Commands (for scanners and printers)	The SCSI-3 SGC standard describes command and behavior of graphical SCSI peripherals. Graphical peripherals are capable of transferring a visual representation of data to and from the computer. The main graphical device that is covered is the scanner. SCSI Commands specific to scanners include: • Get Data Buffer Status (34_H) - Gets information about the data buffer in the scanner. • Get Window (25_H) - Gets information about previously defined scan window. • Object Position (31_H) - Provides positioning functions. Allows scanner element to be moved. • Read (28_H) - Transfers scanned data, mask, or gamma information to the computer. • Scan ($1B_H$) - Requests the scanner to begin the scan operation. • Send ($2A_H$) - Sends data from the computer to the device. • Set Window (24_H) - Sets up a image area window to be scanned. Mode pages supported include: • Page 03 - Measurements Units Page - Specifies the units of measurement used for calculating the displacement of window and for positioning an object.
SIP	SCSI-3 Interlocked Protocol (for parallel copper SCSI e.g., SPI)	This is an important new part of SCSI-3 that describes SCSI link protocols used for the standard SCSI parallel interface. It describes updates to SCSI protocols that are designed to allow coexistence with SCSI-2 devices on a SCSI-3 bus. SCSI-3 SIP covers content and sequencing of SCSI bus phases. Messages are the main item discussed. A new Target Transfer Disable message allows arrays to increase their performance.

Table 57. *SCSI-3 Files and Topics (Continued)*

File	Topic	Description
SMC	SCSI-3 Medium Changer Commands (for separate medium changer devices)	SCSI-3 SMC is an important new part of SCSI-3 that describes commands specific to medium changer devices (i.e., jukeboxes and autoloaders). Commands used to access medium changers include: • Exchange Medium (A6$_H$) - Switches one element in one address with another element in another address. • Initialize Element Status (07$_H$) - Causes the medium changer to check all of its slots for media elements. • Move Medium (A5$_H$) - Moves a unit of media from one slot to another. • Position to Element (2B$_H$) - Positions the media changer mechanism over a specified element. • Read Element Status (B8$_H$) - Causes the devices to report the status of internal media elements to the user. • Request Volume Element Address (B5$_H$) - Transfers the results of the Send Volume Tag command. • Send Volume Tag (B6$_H$) - Transfers a volume tag template to a medium changer element. Mode pages specific to medium changers include: • 1F - Device Capabilities • 1D - Element Address Assignment • 1E - Transport Geometry Parameters
SPC	SCSI-3 Primary Commands (common commands for all SCSI-3 devices)	This document describes common SCSI commands that could apply to all SCSI-3 devices. It describes the commands that must be implemented by all SCSI devices: • Inquiry • Request Sense • Send Diagnostic • Test Unit Ready SPC updates commands, such as Change Definition and Inquiry, to support new SCSI-3 device types. It covers basic medium changer commands such as: • Move Medium • Report LUNs Additional mode pages described in SPC include: • 09 - Peripheral Device Page • 1A - Power Condition Page • 1C - Informational Exceptions Control (Failure Logging) In the industry, this is also known as SMART or PFA. SMART is an acronym for Self-Monitoring, Analysis and Reporting Technology. PFA is an acronym for Predictive Failure Analysis. Both of these controls protect user data from predictable degradation in drive performance by analyzing information, such as number of recoverable errors, number of retries or slowing performance, and predicting when the drive is likely to die.

Table 57. SCSI-3 Files and Topics (Continued)

File	Topic	Description
SPI	SCSI-3 Parallel Interface (parallel copper hardware interface for SCSI-3)	SCSI-3 SPI describes the physical SCSI interconnection for standard parallel fast and wide SCSI. SCSI-3 SPI includes features such as the following: • 16-bit transfers on a single 68-pin connector • SCSI phase descriptions • Having up to 32 SCSI IDs per bus, which necessitates a "fairness" scheme to allow devices with low IDs to get on the bus • 32-bit data path on a second 68-pin cable (see "Wide SCSI" on page 206.) • More than eight devices per bus • Longer cables It also covers hot-plugging drives and SCSI configured auto-magically (SCAM).
SPI-2	SCSI-4 (?) SCSI Parallel Interconnect 2	The SPI-2 standard began to appear in 1995, before even SCSI-3 SPI was approved. This standard attempted to describe a physical layer that provides the following additional functionality over regular SCSI-3 parallel SCSI: • Minimal compatibility problems with old hardware and software • Cost parity between single-ended and differential SCSI devices • Compatibility between single-ended and differential SCSI • Fast 40/Ultra-2 data transfers up to 40 MB/s narrow and 80 MB/s wide. • Fast 80/Ultra-3 data transfers up to 80 MB/s narrow and 160 MB/s wide • Enabling of low voltage chips (3.3V) • Allow SCSI device detection and setting of bus type (single-ended/differential) • Enable the use of new smaller cabling scheme • Enable hot-plugging of devices into backplanes • Enable moving devices through the use of Bus Extenders or Bridges SPI-2 described: • Physical medium • Clock rates • Hardware drivers • Connectors • Cabling A major feature is Low voltage differential SCSI (LVD SCSI). LVD SCSI allows differential to be implemented without the need for expensive high voltage drivers. It's based on a networking standard. At speeds faster than Fast-20, single-ended termination is unusable and only differential is allowed. It is believed that cable lengths up to 12.5 meters can be allowed. LVD drives will automatically switch to normal single-ended mode for backward compatibility on older SCSI buses. SPI-2 will probably incorporate all of the original SPI specification.
SSA	SCSI-3 Serial Storage Architecture	SCSI-3 SSA corollary to the SCSI-3 specification describes the Serial Storage Architecture used in implementations of serial SCSI. For more information see Chapter 4, "All About Serial SCSI."

Table 57. SCSI-3 Files and Topics (Continued)

File	Topic	Description
SSC	SCSI-3 Stream Commands (for tapes and printers)	SSC describes an important new part of SCSI-3 that describes commands related to streaming devices (i.e., Tape, DAT, and printers). This part of SCSI-3 covers: • Sequential access devices • Printer devices • Processor devices • Communications devices These devices handle data in a sequential fashion and cannot randomly access data. Positioning is limited to either moving forwards or backwards on the medium. A new command introduced is: • Report Density Support - This command tells the caller what type of media the drive supports. Other commands from SCSI-2 are simply extended to support new devices or clarified for documentation.

Most projects are in X3T10 (formerly X3T9.2). FC-PH is in X3T11; SSA and SSP are in X3T10.1; 1394 is in IEEE.

SCSI-3 SPI was approved as a standard in 1995 as X3T10/855D Rev 15a.

There is no concrete agenda for publishing the SCSI-3 specification, although 1996 seems realistic. Parts of the SCSI-3 specification began appearing as early as 1991, and parts of it became approved starting in 1995.

For information on many other resources for facts about SCSI, see "Appendix A: Additional Information Sources," on page 311.

4

All About Serial SCSI

Overview

A revolution is occurring in the world of peripheral interconnections, bringing with it higher levels of performance, availability, fault tolerance and connectivity.

It's coming with four primary serial I/O interfaces:

- USB
- 1394 (FireWire)
- Fiber Channel
- SSA

These interfaces are discussed in greater depth starting on page 219.

Universal Serial Bus (USB) and FireWire are low to medium speed buses intended for desktop PC implementations. Fiber Channel and SSA are targeted at higher-end workstation and server markets and offer greatly enhanced I/O channel throughputs, previously seen only in large mainframe computers.

These innovative, high-performance serial interfaces are designed to connect a wide variety of devices to personal computers, workstations, servers, storage subsystems and networks.

Devices included the following:

- Disk drives
- Optical drives
- Tape drives
- CD-ROMs
- Host adapters
- RAID controllers
- Printers
- Video cameras
- VCRs

Traditionally, computer systems are tied together with parallel backplane buses (such as SCSI and ATA). Although this has served well in the past, designers are considering serial alternatives for four primary reasons:

- Physical Constraints
- Cost
- Performance
- Reliability

Physical constraints

Systems are getting smaller, and the space available for connectors is rapidly decreasing. Connector technology is having trouble keeping pace with the changes.

Cabling problems account for 50 percent of disk drive-related customer service calls.

Cost

Semiconductor technology is still on a fairly fast evolutionary path, while connector and inter-connect technology is relatively mature. For a fixed level of performance, the cost of an interconnect drops much faster if its implementation is semiconductor intensive instead of connector intensive.

Performance

Parallel data is reaching its limits in subsystem topologies. It is increasingly difficult to run large amounts of data over any distance with speeds approaching 40 MB/s. Servers, networks and video applications, to name a few, are demanding I/O in excess of 40 MB/s. This is very difficult to do with parallel interfaces.

Reliability

The primary point of failure in an interconnect is usually its physical connection. The fewer the signals, the simpler (and more reliable) the connector.

Now that lines are being drawn in the sand and more and more companies are starting to seriously consider using serial interfaces, what are the facts behind each of these technologies?

Current Serial Peripheral Interfaces range from low speed utility buses to very high performance network architectures. The following is a brief overview of four of these interfaces. This overview provides general information on performance and typical applications with an emphasis towards mass storage and

RAID technologies. Each of the interfaces discussed is detailed in a standards document that contains more in-depth technical information.

 For information on how to obtain copies of these standards documents, see "Appendix A: Additional Information Sources" on page 311.

USB

Universal Serial Bus (USB) is a specification jointly agreed upon by a working group consisting of:

- Compaq
- DEC
- Intel
- Microsoft
- NEC
- Northern Telecom

USB is a 12 Mb/s interface supporting up to 63 peripheral devices. USB is intended to support low-speed peripherals such as keyboards and pointing devices, and is not suitable for mass storage or video applications. USB supports automatic configuration ("plug-and-play") and hot-plugging.

 While USB doesn't implement Serial SCSI, it competes with 1394.

1394 (FireWire)

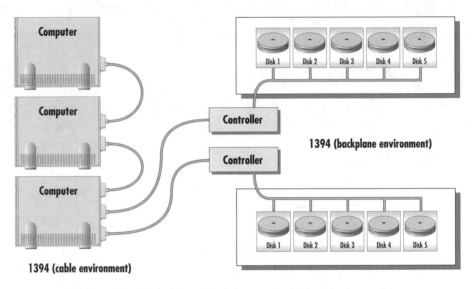

Figure 69. *1394 (FireWire) theoretical physical topology*

1394, also known to some as FireWire, is a low-level, low-cost serial interface that is designed for multiple consumer applications. FireWire is a joint Apple and Texas Instruments (TI) implementation of the IEEE 1394-1995 SerialBus standard. 1394 was approved as an IEEE standard in December 1995. It is a high-speed (100 to 400 Mb/s) serial bus supporting up to 64 peripheral devices. It is intended to replace the Apple Desktop Bus (ADB).

FireWire brings with it the following features:

- The ability to layer SCSI protocols onto the interface
  This allows for SCSI devices to be easily adapted.
- Support for automatic configuration ("plug-and-play") and hot-plugging
- Fully isochronous
  This means that a fixed slice of bandwidth can be dedicated to a particular peripheral, such as video. This support of isochronous service is a complement to such LAN architectures as ISDN, ATM and FDDI-2.

I/O Interconnects can be viewed in two ways:

- As a type of extended memory space
- As an I/O "channel" interface

When viewed as memory space or registers, the target devices are accessed by processor type commands, such as "read" or "write." A channel interface uses a higher-level protocol where commands to "read logical block" or "print page" would be used. FireWire uses the "memory space" interconnect model.

The serial bus is broken into two parts:

- The first part is the "backplane environment," which adapts to the host parallel bus.
- The second part is the "cable environment" and is specified in the 1394 document as supporting up to 16 physical connections (cable hops) between any two devices. Each hop can be up to 4.5 meters in length, yielding a total cable distance of 72 meters.

 1394 also specifies a low-voltage, GameBoy-like, differential type cable. No termination is required. It appears that 1394 will be used mainly in consumer audio/video products, set-top (cable) boxes, scanners and printers.

The first peripherals with 1394 interfaces were released in 1995 and included Digital Video camcorders from JVC, Sony and Panasonic. Vendors supporting 1394 include Apple, TI, IBM, Sony and Microsoft.

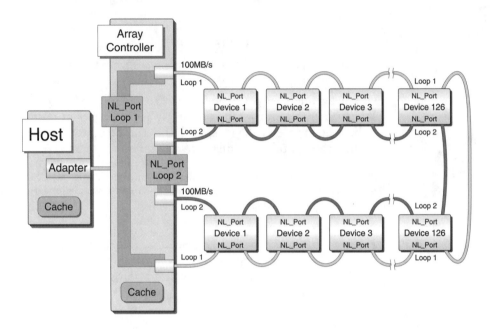

Figure 70. *Fiber channel arbitrated loop*

Background

Fiber Channel Arbitrated Loop (FC-AL) was developed as a byproduct of the Fiber Channel-like protocol that has been around for a couple of years (used in ESCON, IBM's peripheral interface) and an extension of the IPI interface. It is an architecture mainly geared toward connecting large scale host computers to storage subsystems and network hubs.

The Fiber Channel standard was initially developed by the Fiber Channel Specification Initiative (FCSI) in February 1993. FCSI was a consortium that included Hewlett-Packard, Sun Microsystems and IBM. The Fiber Channel Association (FCA) formed in August 1993, and in 1995 inherited the development and maintenance of the Fiber Channel standard from FCSI.

The Fiber Channel interface is a loop architecture, as opposed to a bus-like standard, such as SCSI or IPI. The Fiber Channel loop (Figure 70) can have any combination of hosts and disks up to a maximum of 126 devices.

Although the figure above suggests that the drives are connected by a cable running from device to device, the preferred approach is to attach disk drives directly to a backplane. This does the following:

- Eliminates cable congestion
- Makes hot plugging practical
- Simplifies mechanical designs

In fact, because the Fiber Channel drives use a shortened version of the SCA 40-pin connector used on parallel SCSI drives, they can easily be designed to fit into existing SCA drive cabinets.

 "SCA" stands for single connector attachment. It is a high-density connector that carries every type of signal passed along a SCSI bus, including SCSI ID, LED and spindle synchronization information. It is particularly suitable for hot-swapping—removing and inserting removable drives while the system is powered on—due to its timed pins. Timed pins allow for removing power first and ground last when a drive is disconnected, and attaching ground first and power last when a drive is plugged in.

The loop structure enables the rapid exchange of data from device to device. A PBC (Port Bypass Circuit), located on the backplane, is the logic that enables devices to be removed or inserted without disrupting the operation of the loop. In addition, the PBC logic can take drives off-line or bring them back on-line by sending a command to any device to remove it from loop operation or reinstall it onto the loop. Contrast the simplicity of the loop architecture used by Fiber Channel (Figure 70) to the parallel SCSI implementation (Figure 71).

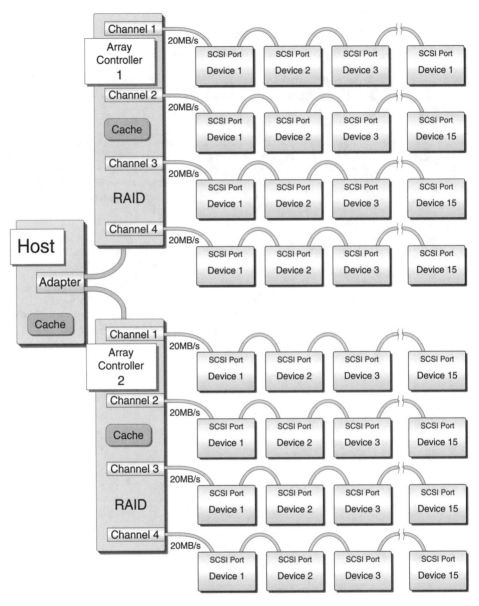

Figure 71. *SCSI parallel implementation*

Features of Fiber Channel Arbitrated Loop are listed in Table 58.

Table 58. *Features of a Fiber Channel Arbitrated Loop*

Feature	Value
Maximum Number of Devices	126
Maximum Data Rate	100 MB/s (1.062 GHz using an 8B/10B code) 200 MB/s (dual loop)
Maximum Cable Distance	30 meters between each device using coaxial cable (longer, with other cabling options such as optical, which can go 10 kilometers between devices)
Cable types	Twinaxial, Coaxial, Optical, Backplane
Fault tolerance	Dual Porting, Hot Plugging Drive Switches
Jumpers	None

Why use Fiber Channel?

SCSI has become the interface of choice for medium- and large-sized computing systems. At the same time, the computer industry's experience with SCSI has brought to light the need for improvements in the following:

- Cable distance
- Data rates
- Command overhead
- Array feature support
- Connectability

Cable distance limitations

SCSI comes in several different versions, but the majority of products shipping today are of the single-ended variety. (That is primarily because single-ended SCSI costs less and is widely available.) If a SCSI bus is limited to connecting devices found within a single cabinet, and the interface cable length does not exceed three meters, it is usually not a problem to use single-ended SCSI. The potential for SCSI signal problems increases, however, if the bus must link several cabinets, converting from an unshielded ribbon cable in one cabinet to an external shielded one, and then back again to a ribbon cable within the second cabinet. Differential SCSI solves this cabling issue, but usually requires that a system have both single-ended and differential ports because most non-disk peripherals use only single-ended SCSI.

Single-ended SCSI devices cannot be attached to a differential bus. Differential SCSI devices cannot be attached to a single-ended bus.

Higher data rates

Magnetic hard disk areal density is increasing at about 60 percent per year. Bit density (measured in bits per inch) is one of the two components of areal density. It increases at about 30 percent per year, and the data rate automatically increases proportionately. Disk rotation speeds have doubled over the last five years from 3,600 to 7,200 RPM, and they continue to climb. They also contribute to higher data rates. In the next few years, drives will be introduced that can sustain transfers in excess of 20 MB/s, thanks solely to improvements in bit density and rotational speed. Already there are disk drives on the market that can transfer data at rates over 10 MB/s. An interface limited to 20 MB/s can support only one drive at that data rate, making it technically impractical for future applications of faster drives.

SCSI protocols run on Fiber Channel, making it a cabling solution that can be quickly implemented on drivers and hard drives.

Fiber Channel also has benefits that go beyond current disk drive interface solutions. When compared to conventional interface technologies, Fiber Channel provides the following:

- Significantly higher bandwidth
- Superior drive array features
- Improved network storage capabilities

Bandwidth

A Fiber Channel loop supports data rates up to 100 MB/s. Slower versions are specified at 25 to 50 MB/s, but these aren't popular. Multiple loops of drives can achieve even more. Among the applications growing in popularity that demand this kind of data rate are video storage and retrieval, supercomputer modeling, and image processing. Moreover, as file servers replace mainframe computers, they will require ever-higher transaction rates to provide comparable levels of service. Using the FC-4 protocol, drives are attached through the Direct Disk Attach Profile protocol (DDA).

Since most UNIX and Windows servers lack the sophisticated I/O channel and controller structures of mainframe computers, they have not been able to match the large number of high-performance disk drives that enterprise systems can support. Fiber Channel loops attached to such high-performance buses as S-Bus or PCI—both of which run 70 MB/s or faster—offer I/O configurations that can sustain mainframe-like I/O rates. Performance estimates suggest that if a system requests the relatively short I/O transfers typical of business transaction processing (8 KB or less), more than 60 drives can be supported without saturating the loop and bogging down performance.

Comparing the single host adapter to the many channels and controllers mainframes employ to attach the same number of drives illustrates the remarkable economics of Fiber Channel-attached disk storage. With up to 9 GB per disk available, 63 drives on a loop would make over 570 GB available to a user on a single FC-AL host port. It will be possible for any workstation or system that has a single FC port or backplane slot to become a file server. No longer will file servers be characterized by large rack-mounted systems. With FC, they can be as small and unobtrusive as any office system.

Remote on-line storage

Since the Fiber Channel interface is part of (and fully compatible with) the Fiber Channel standard, optical cabling can be used in any part of a subsystem except the backplane. This makes it possible to have a disk subsystem quite a distance from the computer system it is attached to. Using single-mode fiber optics, on-line disk storage could be as far as six miles away.

Fiber Channel with optical transmission

A typical computer system could have disks within the system unit attached via the FC loop. The loop can be extended by using an electronic-to-optical adapter and lengths of fiber-optic cable. On the same loop running the internal disks, remote disks would appear to the system to be directly attached, in the same manner as the local disks. These could be used in any fashion, including mirroring of the local disks.

It makes a very attractive means for having a remote on-line copy of critical data, which could be used to continue operations should anything happen to the original computer system.

 For sources of information on Fiber Channel, see "Appendix A: Additional Information Sources."

Serial Storage Architecture (SSA)

SSA is based on a proven storage subsystem (the 1933) developed by IBM's European subsidiary in Havant, England. In 1993, IBM opened this system architecture and virtually gave the design on this technology to any company that asked for it. In 1995, the 1933 division bought itself out from IBM and is now called Xyratex.

IBM still has control over the development and manufacturing of future SSA silicon.

SSA is a powerful high-speed serial interface designed to connect high-capacity data storage devices, subsystems, servers and workstations. Designed with the future in mind, SSA facilitates migration from current SCSI equipment and will accommodate implementation of future configurations, including the use of fiber-optic connections. Only four signal wires are required, compared to 68 for the closest SCSI equivalent. SSA interfaces require no address switches and no discrete terminators.

SSA architecture operates at two protocol levels. The lower level, SSA-PH (for SSA Physical), defines the electrical characteristics, coding scheme and method of information transmission. The upper level maps SCSI commands into a form suitable for serial transmission. As a result, devices now using SCSI-2 can be upgraded to SSA with minimal code changes.

SSA offers superior performance over the interfaces commonly used today. Each SSA link is full-duplex and frame multiplexed simultaneously, resulting in data rates in the 20 MB/s range in each direction, with total throughput of 80 MB/s at each node (peripheral). As many as 127 devices can be connected per loop, with "hot plugging" supported. There can be up to 20 meters between nodes (680 meters with optical cabling).

The combination of low power, fewer components and fault isolation makes SSA highly reliable. Each node performs extensive error checking, and if errors occur, SSA provides transparent frame recovery. When SSA devices are configured in a loop (Figure 72), alternate paths to each device ensure that there is no single point of failure.

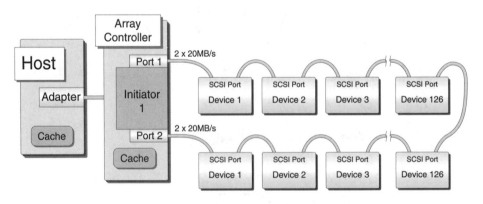

Figure 72. SSA single-domain implementation

Besides enjoying SSA's performance benefits, users will also appreciate SSA's compact four-wire cables and connectors, which have an overall diameter of less than 6 mm. SSA cables provide a welcome contrast to the cumbersome maze of 50- and 68-wire cables that mark a typical SCSI installation. The reduction in cabling yields a substantial cost improvement to customers. It provides higher levels of performance, fault tolerance, data availability and connectivity than is possible with today's parallel interfaces, such as SCSI, and is ideally suited for video applications, data servers and "mission critical" data.

 SCSI protocols operate on top of SSA link protocols, allowing drivers and peripherals to be easily adapted.

Among the functions provided with SSA is a unique capability called "spatial re-use," which allows data to be transferred concurrently at high speeds between many pairs of serially connected peripherals, without the need to route the data through the processor. This leads to more effective use of the system's resources in environments where users may be moving data from a CD-ROM to memory, from a disk drive to a tape backup unit, and from memory to a printer, all at the same time from the same processor.

SSA offers excellent performance. Its fundamental building block is a single port capable of carrying on two 20 MB/s conversations at once—one inbound and one outbound. An SSA node consists of two ports, allowing four conversations to be carried on simultaneously, for a total interface bandwidth of 80 MB/s.

 Future versions of SSA will support 40 MB/s links resulting in 160 MB/s total throughput.

Multiple domain configurations (Figure 73) further increase reliability and performance.

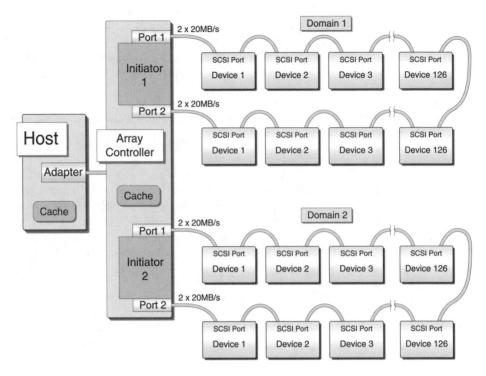

Figure 73. *SSA dual-domain implementation*

SSA's dual-port, full-duplex architecture allows peripherals to be connected in loop configurations designed to contain no single point of failure. SSA's serial interface loop significantly improves connectivity, while its auto-configuration capability allows the true potential for hot-plugging, plug-and-play and dynamic reconfiguring. Low cost is achieved through the use of compact cables and connectors and by embedding all circuitry into a single CMOS chip. SSA is fully compatible with the Fiber Channel Interface (FCI), which allows interconnection of processors separated by large distances.

SSA is supported by an increasing number of silicon, adapter, storage and system manufacturers, including members of the SSA Industry Association (SSA IA).

 The SSA IA was formed in 1995 to promote the acceptance of the SSA standard within the industry. Its membership includes more than 25 manufacturers of systems and peripheral products.

5

Other Storage Interfaces

Even though SCSI dominates its niche, it is not the only player in the interface game. Other technologies preceded SCSI and in some marketplaces have displaced it, primarily because of cost, compatibility and performance considerations. Chapter 5 describes the various other interfaces that dominate the PC-compatible marketplace.

ST-506/ST-412

In 1983, Al Shugart's Seagate Technologies introduced the ST-506 as a 5.25-inch, 5 MB hard drive on the IBM XT. Seagate's interface became the most popular for low-capacity MFM (modified frequency modulation) drives. Seagate later introduced the ST-412, which provided 12 MB of capacity.

Rumor has it that Seagate's name came about from Shugart's desire to have his company name begin with S, have a G in the middle, and T toward the end. His own name was already in use and consequently unavailable to him.

These early Seagate models provided a low-level serial interface. They were inexpensive to implement, not very extendable, and slow, with a one-bit-at-a-time 500 to 1000 KB/s transfer rate. The initial ST-506 drive had a 625 KB/s (5 Mb/s) internal transfer rate. Utilizing a 1:1 interleave on the controller, the peak data transfer rate was about 500 KB/s. The controller needed to have a track buffer to handle a 1:1 interleave. It was used only on hard drives and was known as a dumb interface because the drives had to be told how to access data by an external controller card. Two cables were used:

- A 34-pin drive control cable
- A 20-pin data cable

The control cable contained signals to select the drive, seek the head, and select a cylinder, head and sector of the drive.

NOTE

See Table 60 and Table 61 below for lists of ST-506 data signals.

The data cable transmitted data in a differential format. The controller card was programmed through the use of "Command Descriptor Blocks."

A Command Descriptor Block is typically a six-, ten- or twelve-byte data structure residing in the computer's memory. It contains the command code and other information needed by a target to execute a command.

See Table 59 below for a list of ST-506 commands and opcodes.

ST-506 commands

Table 59 lists the commands and opcodes in the ST-506 standard. Notice that many of these commands mirror ones later found in the SCSI standard.

For a look at SCSI commands and opcodes, see "Commands" on page 156.

Table 59. *ST-506 Commands and Opcodes*

Command	Opcode	Description
Test Drive Ready	00_H	Test to see if drive is ready.
Recalibrate	01_H	Recalibrate the head.
Request Sense	03_H	Return status information on drive.
Format Drive	04_H	Format entire drive.
Read Verify	05_H	Read data and verify its ECC (error correction code).
Format Track	06_H	Format a single track.
Format Bad Track	07_H	Format a single track and set bad block flag.
Read	08_H	Read data from disk.
Write	$0A_H$	Write data to disk.
Initialize Drive Char	$0C_H$	Set up drive characteristics.
Read ECC Burst	$0D_H$	Read ECC data.
Read Sector Buffer	$0E_H$	Read from RAM on drive.
Write Sector Buffer	$0F_H$	Write to RAM on drive.
Assign Alt Track	11_H	Reallocate bad sectors.
Controller RAM Test	$E0_H$	Test controller's RAM.
Drive Diagnostics	$E3_H$	Test the controller and drive.
Controller Diag	$E4_H$	Test the controller.

Table 59. *ST-506 Commands and Opcodes (Continued)*

Command	Opcode	Description
Read Long	E5$_H$	Read data along with ECC.
Write Long	E6$_H$	Write data along with ECC.
Return Drive Parms	FB$_H$	Get drive configuration information.
Set Step Rate	FC$_H$	Set how fast drive can step.

ST-506 data signals

Table 60 lists the data signals present on the 34-pin ST-506 connector. All signals are TTL compatible.

 TTL stands for transistor–transistor logic; it's a type of chip.

In the ST-506 interface's differential cabling scheme, signals are deemed on or off according to the following voltages:

- On is greater than 2.0 volts.
- Off is from 0 to 0.7 volts.

Table 60. *34-Pin ST-506 Data Signals*

Data Signal	Description
Direction	Which direction head is moving
Drive Select0-3	Specifies which of the 4 drives to access
Head Select0-2	Specifies which of the 8 heads to access
Index	Signals when index mark has passed
Ready	Signals when the drive is ready to be accessed
Seek Complete	Signals when the head has completed a move
Step	Triggers the drive to seek
Track0	Signals when head is moving to beginning
Write Gate	Determines if operation is read or write
Write Fault	Shows if an error occurred

Table 61 lists the signals present on the 20-pin ST-506 connector. All signals are standard TTL compatible.

In the ST-506 interface's differential cabling scheme, signals are deemed on or off according to the following voltages:

- On is greater than 2.0 volts.
- Off is from 0 to 0.7 volts.

Table 61. 20-Pin ST-506 Data Signals

Data Signal	Description
Drive Selected	Set if the drive is at the desired address.
Write Data	Data to be written.
Read Data	Data to be read.

Because the drive must be accessed with such low-level protocol, it is very difficult to create drives with variable zoned densities.

For more information on variable zone densities, see "Variable zone recording" on page 26.

Seagate wanted ST-506 to become a standard so that the computer industry could pattern its products on a single interface, assuring users of compatibility. Seagate placed the ST-506 interface in the public domain and provided specifications to anyone interested. The specifications eventually became the IEEE 412 standard.

ST-506 drives were configured for operation through the Setup program present in the ROM of the PC. The Setup program configured the CMOS configuration memory with the number and type of drives in the system. The types of drives supported were typically limited to a number of fixed choices. ST-506 controllers typically had a formatter program embedded in ROM, accessible only through DEBUG.

CMOS is an acronym for Complimentary (symmetry) Metal-Oxide Semiconductor. It is a microprocessor (memory chip) that permits many components to be packed together in a very small area.

With the introduction of faster, more powerful chips, manufacturers turned to RLL (run-length limited) encoding to meet enhanced I/O capabilities and storage requirements.

RLL (run-length limited) is an encoding scheme invented at IBM that employs a set of rules to determine the pulse pattern for each bit, based on the value of the preceding bits. RLL allows

50 percent more information than MFM (modified frequency modulation) to be recorded on a track. This is accomplished by recording more fluxes for every byte and packing them more tightly onto the surface of the hard disk. It is also referred to as 2,7 RLL because the recording scheme involves bit patterns with no more than seven and no less than two successive zeros.

ST-506 did not mandate one type of encoding, so these drives could be encoded with RLL by switching controllers. RLL encoding crammed more data onto the disk and improved data transfer rates by up to 50 percent, necessitating a faster interface. MFM drives had 17 sectors per track, whereas RLL drives had 26 sectors per track. A 1:1 interleaved RLL drive with 26 sectors per track had a transfer rate of about 800 KB/s.

NOTE For more information, see "Encoding processes" on page 27.

Later in 1984, with the advent of the IBM AT personal computer, ST-506 drives were interfaced in a similar way to the IBM XT, except that all I/O port addresses were moved and a secondary port was set up for another controller. The controller was made by Western Digital and was known as the WD1003-WA2. This controller and the need for backward compatibility has impacted the drive industry ever since. In the PC world, compatibility with standards is extremely important.

There are two types of standards: de facto and agency. De facto standards are set by an industry over time. Agency standards have been submitted to, and reviewed and approved by, a standards agency. ANSI and IEEE are standards agencies.

ESDI

Enhanced Small-Device Interface (ESDI) is an improved ST-506 interface that was developed in the mid-1980s and was championed by Maxtor. ESDI doubled ST-506's data transfer rate and allowed for selective reformatting of tracks. Otherwise, mechanically and electronically it was virtually identical to ST-506. It was device-specific and only used for hard disk drives, mostly those with very large capacity. It offered a maximum capacity of about 1 GB. These drives typically used RLL encoding to boost capacity. Two cables were used to interface drives:

- A 20-pin data cable
- A 34-pin control cable

ESDI was slightly less expensive to implement than SCSI, but typically allowed only two devices to be connected. It could continuously transfer data at up to 24 Mb/s. ESDI didn't require device drivers, which gave it an I/O boost. ESDI drives typically used a 5.25-inch form factor. They were appropriate mainly in servers used for networking PCs.

ESDI's main improvements were due to separate data-separator chips that were responsible for:

- Encoding data and clocks prior to recording on the disk
- Decoding data and clocks after reading them off the disk

Seeks to different tracks required only a single step command, in contrast to ST-506. One drawback was that the controller speed had to be synchronized with the speed of the hard drive. Getting a new drive meant getting a new controller. It also required a separate controller board. Up to seven drives per controller could be connected, although only two ports were provided.

Attempts were made to add tape and optical support, but no devices ever appeared. The standard eventually became the ANSI X3.170-1990 specification.

Some early optical drives used an ESDI interface between the drive and the drive's controller. This provided a SCSI connection to the host.

IDE

IDE stands for Intelligent Drive Electronics or Integrated Drive Electronics. IDE incorporates controller hardware onto the disk drive, which results in significant parts reduction and cost savings. IDE combines the physical and electrical protocols of ST-506 with the speed of ESDI. IDE drives can be "directly" plugged into a computer's expansion bus, providing the following benefits:

- A slot is saved.
- The need for a host adapter is eliminated.
- It's extremely easy to use.
- It's cheaper than SCSI.

The connections are identical to the PC AT bus, minus some of its 98 lines. Lines made obsolete by IDE include DMA, REQ and ACK, IRQs except 14, and memory strobe lines. It was offered in 8- and 16-bit parallel interface types.

Eight-bit drives, such as the MiniScribe 8450XT, are referred to as XT Interface Drives. Sixteen-bit are referred to as Standard AT Interface Drives. They are not interchangeable.

IBM even created its own version of IDE that allowed connection to its proprietary MicroChannel Architecture (MCA) bus present in early IBM PS/2 personal computers. This was now a parallel interface, offering a significant performance boost from the serial architecture of ST-506 and ESDI.

In a serial architecture data is transmitted one bit at a time. In a parallel architecture each byte (eight bits) is sent simultaneously using separate lines. Parallel architecture allows for much faster I/O than serial.

IDE is often used interchangeably with the terms AT or ATA, although ATA specifically references an implementation of IDE designed for the AT bus (either ISA or EISA bus). IDE denotes a drive that has a controller on board, hence a SCSI drive could be technically called an IDE drive.

AT stands for Advanced Technology. ATA stands for Advanced Technology Attachment. ATA-2 is an ANSI standard, while IDE is a de facto standard.

Origins of IDE

In the mid-1980s the initial champions of this technology included Compaq, Conner Peripherals, Imprimis and Western Digital. Compaq wanted to reduce the cost of the computer by eliminating host adapters. It also wanted to create laptops that didn't require that valuable slot real estate be taken up by host adapters. These and several other hard disk manufacturers produced a Common Access Method (CAM) specification that was submitted to ANSI in 1990 and became the X3.221-1994 standard. CAM defined a common method of accessing the hard disk on a personal computer. IDE became one of the most popular implementations of CAM.

Always gaining in popularity, IDE muscled out ST-506 because it offered more performance and capacity and, like ESDI, it did not require software drivers but used a standard WD1003, chip-based, translation mode instead.

IDE is typically implemented using a standard, 40-pin, 80 to 120 ohm impedance, unshielded, unterminated, flat ribbon cable. It costs significantly less to implement than SCSI:

- Single chip VLSI implementation of IDE is available for less than five dollars, compared to SCSI at fifty dollars.
- An IDE host adapter (nicknamed "paddle card") can cost five dollars where a SCSI host adapter can cost one hundred dollars.
- An IDE drive can be as much as fifty dollars cheaper than a SCSI drive.

VLSI stands for very-large-scale integration. It's a chip with 20- to 900-thousand logic gates per chip. Transistors form logic gates that control the flow of electrons through chips.

The cost differences result from a combination of cheaper parts, larger markets and economies of scale. IDE became so prevalent that in 1995 new 2.5-inch laptop drives completely switched over to IDE and ceased to be available in SCSI, forcing Apple to switch as well.

IDE and SCSI drives share a lot of electronics in common, so you will often find the same hard drive model offered with either interface. As a rule, the drive industry produces more IDE models in the lower capacity range and more SCSI models in the higher capacity range.

Original IDE did have some severe limitations:

- Drive capacity was limited to 528 MB (up from 40 MB of ST-506).
- Burst transfer rate was limited to a range of 4.0 to 8.33 MB/s (sustained data transfer rate was in the 1 to 2 MB/s range).
- Connectivity was limited to only two drives.
- Compatibility was limited to only hard drives.

IDE details

Masters and slaves

With IDE, one drive is a master and the other a slave, even though they don't control each other.

 A master ensures data transfer to one or more slave stations. There can be only one master on a data bus at a given time. A slave is the target selected by the master station to receive data.

A jumper setting on the drive sets the drive into either mode. The master drive performs signal decoding for the slave. Many drives support multiple master/slave modes. These modes include:

- ISA original
- Conner
- ATA/CAM

The ATA/CAM mode is not backward-compatible with ISA or Conner. The ISA original method has a couple of drawbacks:

- It's not able to tell when the slave drive is ready.
- It doesn't have an activity indicator if two drives are connected.

Conner added a method of determining when the slave drive was ready for the host. The ATA/CAM method is similar to Conner's method, but the polarity of one pin is reversed.

Handling bad sectors

Defective sectors on the disk were typically marked as such at the factory and not utilized. If a defect was encountered later, the drive would usually automatically map out the bad sector and utilize a spare sector. Some IDE drives could also have tracks reformatted to spare out bad sectors.

IDE data signals

Table 62 lists the signals present on the 40-pin IDE connector. All signals are TTL compatible.

In the IDE interface's differential cabling scheme, signals are deemed on or off according to the following voltages:

- On is greater than 2.0 volts.
- Off is from 0 to 0.7 volts.

Table 62. *40-Pin IDE Data Signals*

Data Signal	Description
RESET	Resets the drive during host power-up.
DD0-DD15	Carries 16-bits of data.
GND	Grounds the signal.
DIOW	Host I/O Write Strobe.
DIOR	Host I/O Read Strobe.
IOCHRDY	I/O Channel Ready used to throttle transfers.
DMACK	Host DMA Acknowledge.
DMARQ	Host DMA Request handshake.
INTRQ	Host Interrupt line when drive is selected.
DA0-2	Address line to select registers in task file.
CS0-1	Host Chip Select to select registers.
DASP	Host Slave Active to drive LED (ISA Mode).
	Drive active slave present (ATA/CAM Mode).
KEY	Key to allow cable to mate one way.
SPINSYNC or CBLSEL	Spindle synchronization or Cable Select.
IOCS16	Host I/O 16-bit enabled.

Table 62. *40-Pin IDE Data Signals (Continued)*

Data Signal	Description
PDIAG	Host Passed Diagnostic to detect Slave.

IDE registers

Table 63 lists the registers that are used for accessing IDE drives. They are all part of the Task File Register through which all communications with the CPU take place. This register is at memory location 1F0 on PCs. These registers are identical to the AT Fixed Disk Register Set.

 Registers are a temporary hardware storage area that assists with the speedy transfer of arithmetic/logical operations within the CPU.

Table 63. *IDE Registers for Accessing Drives*

Register	Memory Location	Details
Data Register	1F0	All data passes through this register.
Error Register	1F1	Contains status from last command.
Features Register	1F1	Formerly Write Precomp Register.
Sector Count	1F2	Number of sectors of data to read or write.
Sector Number	1F3	Starting sector number for I/O.
Cylinder Low	1F4	Low 8-bits of cylinder number (CHS mode).
		Middle 8-bits of block address (LBA mode).
Cylinder High	1F5	High 8-bits of cylinder number (CHS mode).
		High 8-bits of block address (LBA mode).
SDH Register	1F6	Drive and head number.
Status	1F7	Drive/Controller status.
Alternate Status	3F6	Same as Status except on Interrupt Acks.
Digital Out Reg	3F6	Drive Reset and Interrupt set.
Drive Adr Reg	3F7	Loopback of drive select and head select addresses.
Command Reg	1F7	Command to execute.

IDE commands

Table 64 lists commands that IDE drives perform. They are similar in nature to SCSI commands but are much more basic in their functionality.

Table 64. IDE Commands and Opcodes

Command	Opcode	Description
Recalibrate	10_H	Move read/write head to cylinder 0.
Read Sector(s)	$2x_H$	Read data from the drive, with or without retry and ECC bytes.
Write Sector(s)	$3x_H$	Write data to the drive, with or without retry and ECC bytes.
Read Verify Sectors	$4x_H$	Verifies the sectors are error free.
Format Track	50_H	Format a track on the drive to spare out any bad sectors. Few drives have a full format command.
Seek	70_H	Seek to the selected track.
Execute Drive Diagnostic	90_H	Perform internal diagnostic tests on the drive.
Initialize Drive Parameters	91_H	Setup head switch and cylinder increment points for multi sector ops.
Vendor Specific	$9A_H$	These are specific to Conner: <table><tr><td>Get Drive Feature</td><td>00</td><td>Reads what features are enabled on the drive.</td></tr><tr><td>Read Drv Switches</td><td>02</td><td>Returns what drive switches are set to.</td></tr><tr><td>Power Lock</td><td>08</td><td>Prevent drive from spinning down.</td></tr><tr><td>Power Unlock</td><td>09</td><td>Allow it to respond to Power Command.</td></tr></table>
Read Multiple	$C4_H$	Read multiple sectors with one command.
Write Multiple	$C5_H$	Write multiple sectors with one command.
Set Multiple Mode	$C6_H$	Enables the drive to perform multi-sector reads and writes. (Multiple of 2)
Read DMA	$C8_H$	Read data and enable controller to do Type B DMA Mode transfer
Write DMA	CA_H, CB_H	Write data and enable controller to do Type B DMA Mode transfer
Read Sector Buffer	$E4_H$	Read contents of drive's buffer
Power	$E5_H$	Set a drive to sleep, idle, or standby mode.

Table 64. *IDE Commands and Opcodes (Continued)*

Command	Opcode	Description
Write Sector Buffer	$E8_H$	Write data to the drive's buffer
Identify Drive	EC_H	Displays information on the drive including size of drive, features of drive, make, model, revision, transfer types and speeds.
Set Features	EF_H	Enable features on the drive. Read or write cache, ECC, retries, and transfer mode.
Translate	$F1_H$	Translate head, cylinder, and sector to physical location.
Physical Seek	$F2_H$	Seek to a given cylinder and head.
Retry Count	$F4_H$	Returns number of retries attempted after a Read, Read Verify, or Read Multiple command.

IDE data transfers

Transfers were handled via PIO (programmed I/O), where the processor handled the data transfers. These transfers were "blind" transfers because there was no handshaking to synchronize the transfer. Drives used the I/O Channel Ready (IORDY) signal to determine when I/Os were ready. The original PIO transfer rates are listed in Table 65.

Table 65. *IDE Data Transfer Rates*

Mode	Burst Speed
PIO Mode 0	3.33 MB/s (600 ns per word)
PIO Mode 1	5.22 MB/s (383 ns per word)
PIO Mode 2	8.33 MB/s (240 ns per word)
Singleword DMA Mode 0	2.08 MB/s (960 ns per word)
Singleword DMA Mode 1	4.17 MB/s (480 ns per word)
Singleword DMA Mode 2	8.33 MB/s (240 ns per word)
Multiword DMA Mode 0	4.17 MB/s (480 ns per word)

The typical PIO data transfer on a PC occurs in the following sequence:

1. Drive asserts IRQ14 (interrupt request) to indicate it is ready.
2. Data is transferred in 512-byte sectors.
3. Host drives IOR (I/O read) or IOW (I/O write) lines according to selected transfer mode.
4. If drive can't support or receive data fast enough it de-asserts IOCHRDY to throttle transfer.

 An IRQ is an interrupt request line. They are the lines that carry hardware interrupt signals to the processor on a PC.

The typical DMA data transfer occurs in the following sequence:

1. Host sets up DMA controller.
2. Read or Write DMA command issued.
3. Drive asserts DMARQ when it's ready to transfer data.
4. DMA controller responds with DMACK when bus control is granted.
5. Host drives IOR or IOW lines according to selected transfer mode.
6. Transfer finishes with DMARQ or DMACK dropped.
7. If drive can't support or receive data fast enough, it de-asserts DMARQ to throttle transfer.

IDE limitations

The most severe limitations were imposed as a consequence of the requirement for backward-compatibility with BIOS software that used the INT13 BIOS call that came with the original Western Digital WD1003 controller. This backward-compatibility allowed for IDE's transparency in not requiring new drivers for DOS and Windows 3.1. Other operating systems were not affected. The INT13 call only allowed for 1024 cylinders, 255 heads and 63 sectors to be accessed.

 8.4 GB IDE limited access to 65536 cylinders, 16 heads and 255 sectors per track.

The IDE task file registers limited the number of heads to 16, so the total capacity that could be accessed was $1024 \times 16 \times 63$, which equals 1,032,192 sectors, 528,482,302 bytes, or 528 million bytes.

 It is referred to as the 528 MB limit although it is really 516 MB in true mathematical terms.

Table 66 illustrates the data transfer limitations on a PC imposed by the combined limitations of BIOS and IDE.

Table 66. *IDE Data Transfer Limitations on a PC*

	Cylinder	Head	Sector
BIOS Limits	1024 (10 bits)	255 (8 bits)	63 (8 bits)
IDE Task File Limit	65535 (16 bits)	16 (4 bits)	255 (8 bits)
Least Common Denominator	1024	16	63

Many vendors such as AMI, Award and Phoenix bypassed this capacity limit by extending the allowable cylinder number by two or four bits. Other disk utility software also allowed this limit to be circumvented.

The ability to daisy-chain two drives from different vendors often did not work because of loopholes in the specification. IDE still did not possess the capability to multitask multiple commands like SCSI. With IDE, once a command was issued, the operating system had to wait until the command was complete before going on to another command. Power management was included in the original specification.

 Power management is an energy-saving feature. It is the ability of a system to recognize when it has been inactive for a (usually) user-specified amount of time, and consequently to spin down.

PC IDE implementation

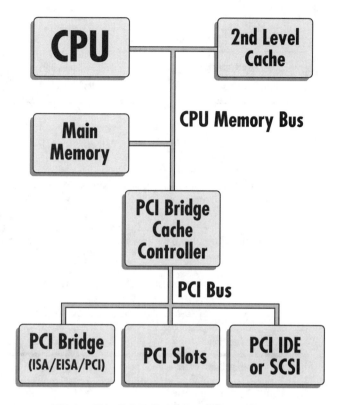

Figure 74. *PC PCI IDE implementation*

IDE drives are configured for operation in the computer's Setup utility. A modern BIOS automatically finds the capacity and configuration of an IDE drive. There is no longer a fixed amount of drive table entries in the BIOS as there was with ST-506 drives.

DOS applications use interrupts to communicate with devices. With IDE, applications access the hard drive using the call chain illustrated in Figure 75.

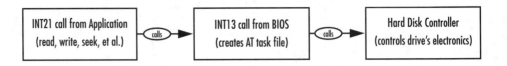

Figure 75. *IDE application call chain*

 An interrupt (INT) is a momentary suspension of processing caused by a deliberate instruction to interrupt the microprocessor.

Applications can use INT25 or INT26 to access the drive directly through the device manager.

Table 67 lists the function call codes available through INT13.

Table 67. *Call Codes Available Through INT13*

Call Code	Function	Call Code	Function
00_H	Reset Diskette(s) and/or head.	$0D_H$	Alternate Hard Drive Reset.
01_H	Read Hard Drive Status.	$0E_H$	Read Test Buffer.
02_H	Read Sectors.	$0F_H$	Write Test Buffer.
03_H	Write Sectors.	10_H	Test for Drive Ready.
04_H	Verify Sectors.	11_H	Recalibrate Drive.
05_H	Format Cylinder.	12_H	XT Controller RAM Diagnostic.
06_H	Format Bad Track on XT drive.	13_H	XT Controller Drive Diagnostic.
07_H	Format XT-type drive at cylinder.	14_H	Controller Internal Diagnostic.
08_H	Read Drive Parameters.	15_H	Get Hard Drive AT Type.
09_H	Initialize Drive Parameters.	16_H	Change of AT Disk Status.
$0A_H$	Read Long Sectors.	17_H	Set AT Disk Type.
$0B_H$	Write Long Sectors.	19_H	Park Drive Heads.
$0C_H$	Seek to Cylinder.	$1A_H$	Format ESDI Drive.

The INT13 call is limited to a 10-bit address of data.

DOS lays out data on the disk in a specific format. This format is laid down when a drive is high-level formatted with the DOS FDISK and FORMAT commands. FDISK is used for hard disk partitioning. It contains the specifications for partition size and assignments of the boot partition and the drive letter—this will always be "C," unless there are multiple hard disks. FORMAT lays out the DOS structure on the disk and establishes how and where files can be stored. Figure 76 illustrates a typical DOS disk layout after FDISK and FORMAT have been run.

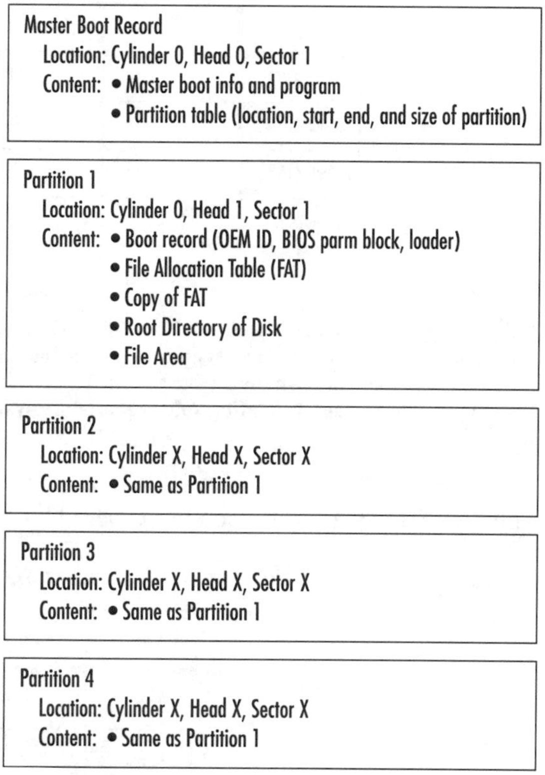

```
┌─────────────────────────────────────────────────────────────────┐
│ Master Boot Record                                                │
│    Location: Cylinder 0, Head 0, Sector 1                         │
│    Content: • Master boot info and program                        │
│             • Partition table (location, start, end, and size of  │
│               partition)                                          │
└─────────────────────────────────────────────────────────────────┘
┌─────────────────────────────────────────────────────────────────┐
│ Partition 1                                                       │
│    Location: Cylinder 0, Head 1, Sector 1                         │
│    Content: • Boot record (OEM ID, BIOS parm block, loader)       │
│             • File Allocation Table (FAT)                         │
│             • Copy of FAT                                          │
│             • Root Directory of Disk                              │
│             • File Area                                           │
└─────────────────────────────────────────────────────────────────┘
┌─────────────────────────────────────────────────────────────────┐
│ Partition 2                                                       │
│    Location: Cylinder X, Head X, Sector X                         │
│    Content: • Same as Partition 1                                 │
└─────────────────────────────────────────────────────────────────┘
┌─────────────────────────────────────────────────────────────────┐
│ Partition 3                                                       │
│    Location: Cylinder X, Head X, Sector X                         │
│    Content: • Same as Partition 1                                 │
└─────────────────────────────────────────────────────────────────┘
┌─────────────────────────────────────────────────────────────────┐
│ Partition 4                                                       │
│    Location: Cylinder X, Head X, Sector X                         │
│    Content: • Same as Partition 1                                 │
└─────────────────────────────────────────────────────────────────┘
```

Figure 76. DOS disk layout (3.0 and newer)

A primary partition is the first active partition on the disk. Boot files are always stored on a primary partition. On any disk, there can be only four primary partitions. Older DOS versions could support primary partitions of up to 32 MB.

Extended partitions are separate logical partitions that can be up to 8 GB in capacity. There can be many extended partitions because they include their own partition tables.

Partition tables store information on the location, starting point, ending point and size of each partition on a hard disk.

Table 68 lists the size limitations for partitions on various PC operating systems and the file systems each OS uses.

Table 68. Operating System Drive Capacity Access Limitations

	Drive Size	Partition Size	File System
DOS 6.X	8 GB	2 GB	FAT
Windows 3.X	8 GB	2 GB	FAT
Windows 95	137 GB	2 GB	VFAT
Windows NT	2 EX	2 EX	NTFS

"EX" stands for exabyte, which is 10^{18} or 1,000,000,000,000,000,000 bytes. FAT stands for file allocation table. Its purpose is to keep track of the locations of blocks in which the operating system has written data to a disk. (The "V" in VFAT stands for virtual.) NTFS stands for New Technology File System. It is Microsoft's proprietary system for tracking location of data on a hard disk.

The FAT File System is also encumbered by cluster size limitations (Table 69).

Table 69. FAT Cluster Size Limitations

Disk Size	Cluster Size
128–255 MB	4 KB
256–511 MB	8 KB
512–1023 MB	16 KB
1024–2048 MB	32 KB

Cluster size is the smallest unit of allocatable space. A file on a 1 GB drive that contains only one character nevertheless uses up 32 KB of space, because 32 KB is the smallest cluster or allocation unit allowed on a 1 GB drive. On

Windows NT, the NTFS file system utilizes a 4 KB cluster size for all volume sizes.

Macintosh IDE implementation

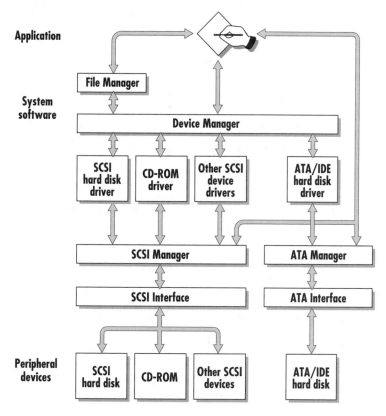

Figure 77. *Mac OS IDE implementation*

Several Macintosh computers have an IDE internal storage interface. Apple began using IDE in 1994, starting with the Quadra 630 and PowerBook 150. Apple's version of IDE is very similar to that used by the PC industry.

The block diagram in Figure 77 shows how IDE was interfaced to the Macintosh operating system. The ATA Manager ROM-based software provides an application programming interface between IDE drivers and the IDE interface hardware. IDE drivers provide partition, data and error handling services to the Macintosh operating system. These drivers make operating on IDE drives transparent to applications that communicate through the normal File Manager interface. Power management is supported.

Pin assignments on the IDE hard disk connector are similar to the IDE standard. Table 70 lists the IDE hard disk connector pin assignments.

Table 70. *IDE Hard Disk Connector Pin Assignments*

Pin Number	Signal Name	Pin Number	Signal Name	Pin Number	Signal Name
1	/RESET	15	DD1	28	Reserved
2	GROUND	16	DD14	29	Reserved
3	DD7	17	DD0	30	GROUND
4	DD8	18	DD15	31	INTRQ
5	DD6	19	GROUND	32	/IOCS16
6	DD9	20	KEY	33	DA1
7	DD5	21	Reserved	34	Reserved
8	DD10	22	GROUND	35	DA0
9	DD4	23	DIOW	36	DA2
10	DD11	24	GROUND	37	/CS0
11	DD3	25	DIOR	38	/CS1
12	DD12	26	GROUND	39	Reserved
13	DD2	27	IORDY	40	GROUND
14	DD13				

To match the big-endian format of Motorola's MC68030-compatible bus, the bytes are swapped:

- The lower byte of the IDE data bus, DD(0–7), is connected to the high byte of the upper word of the I/O bus, IOD(24–31).
- The higher byte of the IDE data bus, DD(8–15), is connected to the low byte of the upper word of the I/O bus, IOD(16–23).

 The term "word" is used here to denote the number of bits that constitute a common unit of information in a particular computer system. In this instance a word is 16 bits.

Calls to the ATA Manager are made with the ATA parameter block structure. This structure is very similar to that used by the SCSI Manager. The elements of a typical ATA Manager parameter block header are listed in Table 71.

Table 71. *ATA Manager Parameter Block Header Structure*

Category	Description
Ptr ataLink;	Reserved
short ataQType;	Type byte
uchar ataPBVers;	-->Parameter block version number
uchar hdrReserved;	Reserved
Ptr hdrReserved2;	Reserved
ProcPtr ataCompletion;	Completion routine
short ataResult;	<--Returned result
uchar MgrFCode;	-->Manager function code
uchar ataIOSpeed;	-->I/O timing class
ushort ataFlags;	-->Control options
short hdrReserved3;	Reserved
long deviceID;	-->Device ID
ulong TimeOut;	-->Transaction timeout value
Ptr ataPtr1;	Client storage Ptr 1
Ptr ataPtr2;	Client storage Ptr 2
ushort ataState;	Reserved, init to 0
short hdrReserved4;	Reserved
long hdrReserved5;	Reserved

Functions that the ATA Manager supports are listed in Table 72.

Table 72. *Functions Supported by the ATA Manager*

Function name	Code	Description
ATA_NOP	$00	No operation
ATA_ExecIO	$01	Execute ATA I/O
ATA_BusInquiry	$03	Bus inquiry

Table 72. *Functions Supported by the ATA Manager (Continued)*

Function name	Code	Description
ATA_QRelease	$04	I/O queue release
ATA_Abort	$10	Terminate command
ATA_ResetBus	$11	Reset IDE bus
ATA_RegAccess	$12	ATA device register access
ATA_Identify	$13	Get the drive identification data
ATA_DrvrRegister	$85	Register the drive reference number
ATA_FindRefNum	$86	Look up driver reference number
ATA_DrvrDeregister	$87	Deregister the driver reference number
ATA_MgrInquiry	$90	ATA Manager inquiry
ATA_MgrInit	$91	Initialize ATA Manager
ATA_MgrShutDown	$92	Shut down ATA Manager

Special considerations

Initial limitations of IDE in the Quadra 630, PowerBook 150 and Performa 5200/6200/6300 were that these machines could physically support only one IDE drive. There was no provision for a secondary IDE channel. The Power-Book 150 also always loaded an IDE driver from its ROM. This made it impossible to load a disk-based driver. Additionally, there was no support for ATAPI and no provision for the advanced transfer rate capabilities offered by DMA mode transfers. Only PIO Modes 0 to 3 were supported. LBA addressing, part of the ATA-2 specification, was supported. Drives larger than 528 MB could be utilized.

For more details, consult Apple's Developer Note on the Quadra 630 Computer, available on many Developer CD-ROMs from Apple.

Enhanced IDE

In 1994, Rich Rutledge of Western Digital proposed the Enhanced IDE specification. It was designed to supplant IDE and to eliminate its most glaring limitations. It was also popularized as Fast ATA by Seagate and Quantum, but without some of the extensions, like large capacity and ATAPI support. Fast ATA was designed to minimize the need to enhance system BIOS. Enhanced IDE was known as ATA-2 by other vendors. It became the AT Attachment

Interface with Extensions. A committee known as the Small Form Factor Committee oversaw this effort and produced a document known as X3.279-199x, which was submitted to ANSI.

Enhanced IDE allowed support of four IDE devices when two IDE channels were present. The primary channel was designed for high-speed hard disks, whereas the low-speed secondary channel was designed for non-hard disk devices. On PCs, the primary channel was located on interrupt request 14 (IRQ14), allowing it to continue to be universally supported à la ST-506. The secondary channel was located on IRQ15. Enhanced IDE also maintained IDE's ease of use and low cost.

Enhanced IDE allowed support of non-hard disk devices such as CD-ROM and tape. New interfacing modes broke the 528 MB barrier and allowed Enhanced IDE to support drives up to 8.4 GB in capacity. Logical block addressing (LBA) allowed for the increase in capacity potential.

LBA support caused the BIOS to create an Enhanced Drive Parameter Table (EDPT) during initialization. The EDPT was proposed by BIOS maker Phoenix Technologies. It contains two sets of drive parameter information. The first set is called CHS, for cylinder, head, sector. It provides a straight translation of BIOS cylinder, head and sector information, without reducing the number of heads supported from 255 to 16.

"From 255 to 16" represents the difference between the addressable capacity limits of BIOS (255-head capability) and IDE (16-head capability). Because IDE was limited to 16 heads, the far greater capability of the BIOS could not be tapped. The mechanism was limited to its lowest common denominator, 16.

The second set translates the cylinder, head, sector information into a 28-bit logical block address à la SCSI. This LBA addressing requires drive firmware support. An operating system does not need to be modified to support the larger volume capacity, but a system BIOS does need modification to support this feature.

The logical block address is derived from the formula illustrated in Figure 78.

$$\text{LBA} = [(\text{Cylinder} \times \text{Max. Head No.} + \text{Selected Head}) \times \frac{\text{Sectors}}{\text{Track}}] + (\text{Sector} - 1)$$

Figure 78. *The Formula for the Logical Block Address*

Faster transfer rate timings allowed data transfer rates to reach 11.1 MB/s (180 ns per word) with Mode 3 PIO transfers and 13.3 MB/s (150 ns per word) with multiword, DMA mode 1 data transfers. PIO transfers are where the processor handles the data transfer. DMA transfers are handled by the drive itself. Multiword DMA mode 1 transfers were typically implemented on high-performance local bus implementations. Enhanced IDE supports several DMA transfer rates. Type B DMA operates at 4 MB/s, while Type F DMA operates at either 6.67 MB/s or 8.33 MB/s. Type F is typically used on PCI machines. PCI also enables scatter/gather transfers, allowing for better virtual memory performance.

 Scatter/gather refers to reading logically contiguous blocks of data from a disk and storing them at discontiguous host computer memory addresses (scatter) and writing data from discontiguous host computer memory addresses to consecutive logical block addresses on a disk (gather).

Multiple block transfers were also now possible, allowing for a 20 to 30 percent increase in transfer rate over standard ATA performance (sustained rates in the 2 to 4 MB/s range). It was also implemented using a standard 40-pin ribbon cable to maintain backward compatibility. Cables had to be shorter than 18 inches and slew-rate control was required to control rise/fall times of signals. This level of performance helped satisfy the disk needs of the Intel Pentium class of machines.

With transfer rates so high, Enhanced IDE almost requires a very fast connection to the rest of the computer. It is almost always found interfacing to the rest of the machine via a 32-bit VESA or PCI local bus connection instead of the slower ISA bus. Older PC machines could utilize Enhanced IDE drives, but typically need their BIOS updated to handle some of the new features of the faster standard.

With these changes, IDE became the industry standard for mass storage interfaces in personal computers. It now offered performance on par with Fast SCSI-2. Users also demanded storage peripheral support beyond hard drives. An entire machine's I/O needs could now be handled by the IDE interface. Even Apple Computer switched to IDE drives in some of its products in 1994 with the advent of the Quadra 630 and PowerBook 150. IDE was fast and efficient for single-user computers. Best of all, it was cheap. Intel embedded Enhanced IDE in its PCI chipsets starting with its Triton chipset in 1995, virtually ensuring total acceptance in the PC industry.

The new standard also helped establish the PCMCIA-ATA standard, allowing flash memory cards and 1.8-inch disk drive PCMCIA drives to be accessed through normal ATA protocols. The latest version of this is known as the PC Card bus, a 32-bit, 33-MHz bus that marries PCI protocols to PCMCIA 3.0 electrical specifications.

This new standard also added new commands, most of which are optional. These are listed in Table 73.

Table 73. *Enhanced IDE Commands and Opcodes*

Command	Opcode	Description
NOP	00$_H$	No operation.
Download Microcode	92$_H$	Update firmware on drive.
Acknowledge Media Change	DB$_H$	For acknowledging media has changed.
Post Boot	DC$_H$	For removable media.
Pre Boot	DD$_H$	For removable media.
Door Lock	DE$_H$	For locking media in.
Door Unlock	DF$_H$	For unlocking media.
Write Same	E9$_H$	Write same data again and again.
Media Eject	ED$_H$	For ejecting media.

Enhanced IDE still did not possess the capability to multitask multiple commands like SCSI, so it was not very effective with high-end multitasking operating system environments such as Novell Netware, Windows NT, or UNIX. It could not handle large numbers of simultaneous I/O transactions from multiple users or threads. There were no features similar to SCSI's disconnect/reconnect, tagged command queuing or zero latency transfers. Enhanced IDE still could not connect a large number of devices, nor could it handle external devices.

Fast ATA-2

A slightly improved version of Enhanced IDE or Fast ATA-2 was championed by Seagate and Quantum. Fast ATA-2 supports data transfer rates of 16.6 MB/s via Mode 4 PIO or Mode 2 DMA.

ATAPI

Part of Enhanced IDE is the ATAPI specification (Advanced Technology Attachment Packet Interface). ATAPI enabled Enhanced IDE to support alternative storage devices, such as CD-ROM and tape drives, using the same physical and electrical interface as standard ATA hard disks. This specification defines a standardized method for interfacing non-hard disk devices utilizing the existing IDE computer interface and cabling. It is compatible with existing IDE hardware without changes or additional cables. An ATAPI device could co-exist with a hard disk on a single channel, although it would have to be a slave. The co-existence would also cause problems with 32-bit disk access in Windows for Workgroups 3.11.

ATAPI basically converted IDE from a computer register based architecture to one that was based on more modern packet based transport. Three new IDE commands are used to control this protocol (Table 74).

Table 74. ATAPI-Inspired Enhanced IDE Commands and Opcodes

Command	Opcode	Description
ATAPI Soft Reset	08$_H$	Perform a soft reset on the device.
Packet Command	A0$_H$	Perform a SCSI command.
ATAPI Identify Device	A1$_H$	Locate ATAPI devices.

A soft reset is a software-based reboot, without interruption to power. A soft reset can be locked out; that is, a system can be crashed so badly that it will not respond to a soft reset request. In this case, a user might escalate to a hard reset, where the computer is turned off, then on.

The packets were logically formatted by deriving SCSI counterparts. So in the end, ATAPI basically runs SCSI-2 commands across IDE wires. The specification also includes a few commands specific to CD-ROM drives to select speed, play audio, or determine if the drive is ready.

The ATAPI standard was championed by many BIOS, CD-ROM and drive vendors, and has been forwarded to the ANSI committee as SFF 8020 Rev 1.2. ATAPI has become so prevalent in 1995 that many CD-ROM drives are either available only in ATAPI or available in ATAPI first.

ATAPI requires BIOS extensions to send ATAPI Identify Device commands at startup to locate ATAPI devices. Transfers can occur in either PIO or DMA data transfer modes.

Basic ATAPI operation

A typical ATAPI operation integrates SCSI-like protocols with ATA protocols.

1. Initialize task file and issue Packet Command.
2. Wait for INT, write SCSI command packet bytes using PIO.

3. Wait for INTRQ, read byte count from cylinder register, transfer bytes.
4. Wait for INTRQ, read status byte, DRQ set to 0 to end command.
5. If there is an error, read error register.

ATAPI registers

The following are the changes to IDE Task File registers that are used for accessing ATAPI drives. They are all part of the Task File Register through which all communications take place. This register is at memory location 1F0 on PCs.

 Registers are temporary hardware storage areas that assist with the speedy transfer of arithmetic/logical operations within the CPU.

Table 75. *ATAPI Registers*

Register	Location	Details
Data Register	1F0	Exchange data between host and device.
Error Register	1F1	Contains Media Change and End of Media flags.
Interrupt Reason	1F2	Why an interrupt was generated. Indicates what emulated SCSI phase we are in.
Reserved	1F3	Reserved.
Byte Count Reg	1F4	Transfer size in bytes.
Byte Count Reg	1F5	Transfer size in bytes.
Drive Select	1F6	LUN to select.
ATAPI Status ATA Cmd	1F7	Drive/Controller status.
Dev Control Reg	3F6	Same as ATA.
Features Register	3F7	Indicates DMA mode for data transfers.

Although ATAPI allows SCSI packets to cross the bus, there is no support for SCSI's command queuing, multiple logical units, and disconnect/reconnect because there's no way to tell which device on the bus generated an interrupt.

ATAPI CD-ROM Mode Pages

The SCSI-2 specification defines additional mode pages for use by CD-ROM devices. ATAPI adds to this list. CD-ROM Capabilities & Mechanical Status Page (2A$_H$) contains information on the capabilities of the CD-ROM drive including:

- Speed
- Volume levels
- Modes supported
- Audio commands

ATAPI tape Mode Pages

The SCSI-2 specification defines additional mode pages for use by tape devices. ATAPI adds to this list. Capabilities & Mechanical Status Page $(2A_H)$ contains information on the capabilities of the tape drive including:

- Media support
- Speed support
- Transfer rates
- Buffer sizes

ATA-3

Looking to improve upon the Enhanced IDE specification, PC vendors came together again in 1995 to propose a new and improved specification known as ATA-3 to support 32-bit operating systems such as Windows 95 and NT. Western Digital advocated a similar Enhanced IDE 95/96 specification. The ATA-3 architecture was designed to be flexible and modular, abstracting the physical interface from the transport mechanism and command sets. Many vendors would like ATA-3 to add support for multitasking operating systems, support that would involve major changes to system BIOS and disk drive firmware. These changes could limit its compatibility, however.

ATA-3 supports the following:

- Drives as large as 137 GB
- Data transfer rates of 16.6 MB/s via Mode 4 PIO or Mode 2 DMA
- Devices such as disk, tape, CD-ROM and CDR

Future speeds above 16.6 MB/s will take place only with DMA. With transfer rates so fast, cable quality and length become ever more important. Cables must be shorter than Enhanced IDE's 18-inch cables. Cable insulation may need to be fabricated from Teflon®. The specification recommends source and receiver termination à la SCSI and rise-time control to help reduce ringing on the ATA bus at speeds of over 15 MB/s.

Teflon insulation provides a more constant impedance than standard PVC. In really fast data transfers, that means better signal integrity, leading to fewer errors on a cable in which the conductors are placed very closely together.

ATA-3 also adds a password security system to prevent unauthorized access and a self-monitoring, analysis and reporting technology (SMART). SMART helps protect user data from predictable degradation in drive performance.

ATA-3 is also designed to fix a major loophole in the ATA-2 specification that forces the speed of each device to run only as fast as the slowest device on that channel. If a CD-ROM was attached to a channel with a hard disk, the hard disk would be forced to run at CD-ROM speeds. This is because the host only sees one data port with a single set of transfer rate timings.

Table 76 lists the new Commands added by ATA-3.

Table 76. *ATA-3 New Commands and Opcodes*

Command	Opcode	Description
Smart	$B0_H$	Self monitoring, analysis and reporting.
Security Set Password	$F1_H$	Set a security password.
Security Unlock	$F2_H$	Remove security lock.
Security Erase Prepare	$F3_H$	Prepare to erase drive.
Security Erase Unit	$F4_H$	Erase drive thoroughly.
Security Freeze	$F5_H$	Freeze drive operation.
Security Disable Password	$F6_H$	Disable security password.

ATA-3 should be compatible with ATA-2 devices. It's likely to be finalized in 1996.

 See "Appendix A: Additional Information Sources" on page 311 for additional sources of information on ATA.

Other Drive Interfaces

FIPS-60

FIPS-60 (Federal Information Processing Standard 60) is also known as IBM's 370-OEM interface. It provided for very fast transfers up to 5 MB/s and cable lengths over 100 meters. It has been extensively used in IBM's System 370, 3080 and 3090 mainframe families.

SMD-E and SMD-H

In the late 1980s, Storage Module Device (SMD-E and SMD-H) was, until SCSI's rise to prominence, the preferred interface for drives used with high-end server applications, such as minicomputers and workstations. It was developed in the mid-1980s by Control Data Corporation's Storage Module Drives branch. Its separate control and data cables complicate daisy-chaining, limiting the number of attachable devices to four. Unlike SCSI, SMD uses a separate controller board for the disk controller, which contains all the intelligence. The least expensive interface for eight-inch drives, SMD-E transfers data at about 3 MB/s. SMD drives can store more 2 GB, with a fast average seek time. Its large form factor (8- and 14-inch) and heavy power consumption, however, make it unpopular in the PC world.

IPI

IPI (Intelligent Peripheral Interface) is the successor to the block multiplexer channel, or OEM channel, popularized by IBM in the 1960s. It offers parallel 16-bit data transfer, rather than OEM's eight-bit transfer, and can be split into two eight-bit buses to work like the OEM channel. IPI's dual ports allow from one to eight devices to be connected on one port, and from two to 16 in pairs using both ports. It is largely limited to the mainframe world, typically on 8- and 14-inch drives. It offers read-ahead capability and is extremely fast for large-data transfers. IPI has bus phases, but with the host as the sole bus master. Unlike SCSI, only one control signal can change during transition from one phase to another. IPI uses nine control lines and transfers data at 80 Mb/s along cables that can be as long as 125 meters. It is designed for hard disk drives only.

IPI-2 is capable of transfer rates of 36 to 72 Mb/s, and is best when transferring very large blocks of data. Costlier than SMD, ESDI or SCSI, IPI-2 is a device-level interface, lacks intelligent features, and has no error correction. It offers fast seek times, a storage capacity of over 2 GB, and uses a single interface cable that can be easily daisy-chained. It has emerged as the performance interface of the 1990s for workstations.

IPI-3, also known as HPPI (High Performance Parallel Interface), is a parallel interface enabling 800 or 1,600 Mb/s data transfers over 32 or 64 twisted-pair copper wires, or on fiber-optic cable. Fiber cabling can be up to 10 kilometers in length, while the other cabling can be up to 36 meters in length. Developed out of work at the Los Alamos National Lab, it is intended for supercomputing applications. It allows multiple block transfers via a single command execution, but can transfer data in only one direction at a time.

6

All About Expansion Buses

Buses are pathways between the CPU, memory and I/O components in computers. Most computers do not come with adequate built-in interfaces for high-performance I/O. To run high-performance storage products on these computers, users must typically add expansion cards. Computer expansion cards (bus cards) play an important role in the performance of storage solutions. The performance of these cards is directly related to the robustness of the particular expansion bus. In this section, we will examine some of the more important computer buses.

For buses to become industry standards they must include the following critical features:

- Open standard, designed to be built upon rather than obsoleted
- Expansion compatible
- High performance
- Easy to use
- Flexible
- Inexpensive

NuBus

Figure 79. NuBus SCSI expansion card

NuBus is the IEEE Standard for a simple, 32-bit, backplane bus (NuBus, IEEE Std P1196-R1990). It was introduced with the Macintosh II in 1987. It was

Apple's expansion bus of choice for about 8 years. MIT, Apple and Texas Instruments helped create the bus. Apple's version deviated from the standard in that its cards were 4 × 13 inches instead of 11 × 14 inches. Apple also adjusted the specification by allowing non-master request interrupts and adding a power failure warning line.

NuBus featured the following:

- Autoconfiguration without dip switches
- 32-bit architecture
- 10 MHz bus clock
- Support for multiple processors
- Fair arbitration
- Bus mastering
- Block mode transfer support

A bus clock is an electronic circuit that regulates the synchronization of the flow of information through the bus. Bus mastering allows the bus card to pass data directly into memory, freeing the CPU to perform more useful functions. (The CPU would otherwise act as an intermediary between the card and memory.)

Some cards were accessed through a software manager called the Slot Manager. Others could be activated transparently through the use of a configuration ROM. Each vendor of cards would register its board with Apple and in return receive a unique board ID number.

For more information on the Slot Manager, see *Inside Macintosh Volume V*.

Early Macintosh II systems had a problem with 32-bit addressing of NuBus memory space. This prevented cards with ROMs mapped into the top 16 MB of space from being seen. A motherboard swap fixed the problem.

NuBus promised maximum theoretical data transfer rates of 40 MB/s, but due to chip limitations, effective data transfer actually took place at much slower speeds. The original NuBus implementation did not support block mode data transfers, limiting performance to under 5 MB/s.

NuBus block mode data transfers allow large blocks of data to be transferred quickly before releasing the bus. They require only one arbitration for the bus.

The Quadra family added support for block mode data transfers from the card to the motherboard, effectively doubling data transfer rates. NuBus data transfers can be performed between the card and main memory or from NuBus card to NuBus card. Card to card transfers significantly benefited from block transfers, allowing data to bypass main memory. Entries in the declaration ROM of each NuBus card told the system whether the card supported block transfers and the maximum number of transfers it supported.

 As the Macintosh evolved, its data transfer rates escalated. Table 77 illustrates the performance gain ushered in with each new Macintosh model. Note, however, that the step between the Quadra 840AV and the PowerMacintosh family was, at best, a step sideways.

Table 77. *Evolution of Macintosh Data Transfer Rates*

Macintosh Model	Maximum Data Transfer Rate
Macintosh II Family	3.7–4.5 MB/s
Quadra Family	5.5–9 MB/s
Quadra 840AV	15–18 MB/s
PowerMac Family	12–15 MB/s

Some machines had up to six NuBus Slots, others as few as one. The maximum per the specification was 14. A wide variety of cards are available with a NuBus interface:

- Video cards
- Digital video capture cards
- DSP accelerators
- SCSI accelerators
- Serial port cards
- RAM cards

Some cards were so sophisticated that they drew more than the allotted 13.9 watts per card and pushed the computer's power supply to the limit.

NuBus-90, introduced with the Quadra family, doubled the bus clock to 20 MHz. Data transfer rates with NuBus-90 could reach about 80 MB/s burst, or about 20 MB/s sustained. This new protocol mainly sped up data transfers between two NuBus-90 compliant cards. It didn't speed up data transfers to the motherboard. NuBus-90 was not widely supported, and only a few NuBus-90 compliant cards were ever produced.

The Quadra 840AV with its MUNI NuBus chip had the fastest NuBus performance of all Macs.

MUNI stands for Macintosh Universal NuBus Interface. This bus offered the following features:

- Support for the full range of NuBus master/slave transactions with single or block moves.
- Support for the faster data transfer rates to and from the CPU bus.
- Support for NuBus '90 data transfers between cards at a clock rate of 20 MHz.
- Provision of first-in, first-out (FIFO) data buffering between the CPU bus and accessory cards.

PowerMacs were more limited in NuBus performance due to the absence of the MOVE16 instruction on the PowerPC processor. A work-around known as the PBBlockMove Extension was created to maximize performance of NuBus cards in PowerMacs. NuBus cards only worked on the Macintosh, a small market, so they were typically priced much higher than PC type cards.

The Move16 instruction is a 68000 instruction that moves 16 bytes of data very quickly.

Some machines, such as the Centris 610, Centris 660AV and PowerMac 6100, could accommodate only smaller, seven-inch NuBus cards.

ISA

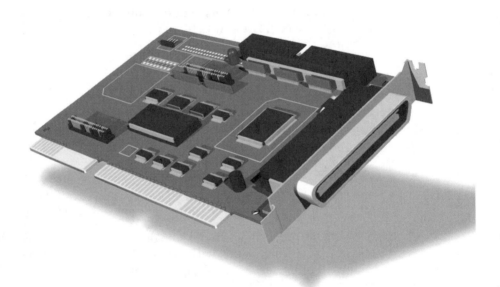

Figure 80. *16-bit ISA SCSI card*

The ISA expansion bus has become one of the most popular computer buses. ISA stands for Industry Standard Architecture. It was introduced with the original IBM PC and IBM PC XT in the early 80s. Almost any type of card is available in the 62-pin ISA form factor. The original version ran at 4.77 MHz and had 8-bits of data and 20-bits of addressing range. ISA supported both DMA and PIO.

A later version, introduced with the IBM AT, ran at 6 MHz and had a 16-bit data bus and 24-bits of addressing range. It added 36 contacts to the ISA connector. On the AT, bus mastering was supported for the first time.

The transfer rate it offered was 3 to 5 MB/s. Later IBM ATs ran the bus at 8 MHz. AT compatibles from third parties with processor speeds up to 16 MHz later ran the bus at up to 8.33 MHz, the ISA maximum. A couple of vendors even over-clocked the bus to 10 or 12.5 MHz, causing lots of card incompatibilities. Its biggest limitations included the need to use jumpers to configure cards and its use of 24 bits for addressing up to 16 MB of expansion space. With such low data transfer speeds, it made no sense to offer anything but 5 MB/s SCSI-1 or SCSI-2.

MicroChannel

IBM designed its proprietary MicroChannel architecture (MCA) in 1980. It was developed along with the IBM PS/2 to improve upon and replace the aging ISA bus. IBM gave up on backward-compatibility with ISA in an effort to create a new bus designed for 32-bit processors and multitasking operating systems, such as OS/2.

MCA cards were available in 8-, 16-, and 32-bit data types, with the addressing range fixed at the full 32 bits. The main slot was contained in a 90-contact connector. Additional connects were used by 16- and 32-bit cards. These were located in front of the 8-bit connector. MCA provided for configuration without jumpers. It provided 8-, 16-, or 32-bit operation at speeds up to 10 MHz, capable of transferring 20 MB/s. Real data rates ranged in more like the 8 to 10 MB/s range. Later versions included a streaming data procedure feature that boosted data transfer rates up to 80 MB/s with 64-bit data procedures.

MicroChannel fully supports DMA and bus mastering. In fact, several CPU accelerators have been designed this way. However, this bus proved to be unpopular because it was found only on IBM machines and a few clones. Limited distribution was due to high licensing costs.

This bus continues on in IBM's RS/6000 workstation line powered by POWER and PowerPC processors.

EISA

EISA stands for Enhanced Industry Standard Architecture. It was designed to supersede the ISA bus, yet retain full compatibility with ISA. PC-compatible vendors developed EISA as an answer to IBM's MicroChannel bus. EISA ran at the ISA standard 8.33 MHz clock rate and allowed bus masters to be supported. EISA extended ISA to 32-bit operation and sped burst data transfer rates up to 33 MB/s (these would be DMA burst type C transfers). Its sustained rate was closer to 8 MB/s.

EISA allowed for automatic adapter configuration without DIP switches. Each adapter came with a .cfg file. The EISA Configuration Utility used this to automatically configure the card so that it did not conflict with other cards.

EISA was only popular in the Intel-based server arena. This was due to high costs. It used a high-density 188-pin edge connector that was similar in size to ISA. EISA allowed old ISA cards to plug and run. Later versions of EISA allowed for enhanced master burst (EMB) data transfers of up to 66 or 133 MB/s by using both edges of clock signals to issue data transfers.

VESA Local Bus

The ISA bus became a serious limitation with the advent of Windows, multimedia and other technologies that required megabytes of information per second. The need for high-volume, high-performance data transfer was particularly apparent with graphical software applications. The Video Electronic Standards Association (VESA) Local Bus (VLB) was designed to interface the Intel 80486 high speed processor bus to a local high-speed expansion bus.

It ran at the processor speed and provided for high-speed, 32-bit data transfers. Version 1.0 ran at either 40 or 66 MHz. Version 2.0 ran at 50 MHz. Version 1.0 provided for data transfers up to 133 MB/s, while 2.0 provided for up to 160 MB/s. Version 2.0 supported write-back caching and 64-bit addressing, which allowed for data transfer rates up to 267 MB/s.

Write-back caching keeps track of what information in the cache has been modified by the microprocessor. This is done by marking modified information with a "dirty bit." When displaced from the cache, all the information with dirty bits is written to primary memory. It's likely that the term "dirty bit" was coined to denote a tag that marked information that needed to be "cleaned out" (written) to the disk or to memory.

VESA cards were 16-bit ISA cards with an additional connector to form a 124-pin VESA standard edge connector. Up to three cards were supported in each system. DMA was not supported as VLB allowed for direct transfers into main memory. The main problem with this bus is that it was X86 CPU specific and operated at the CPU's speed, making it impractical for universal applications. VLB initially was very popular with the advent of the 80486 processor. When PCI shipped with Pentium processors, VLB slowly died off.

For sources of more information on VESA Local Bus, see "Appendix A: Additional Information Sources" on page 311.

PCI

Figure 81. *Certified PCI local bus trademark*

PCI (Peripheral Component Interconnect) is a system standard that defines a high performance interconnection method between plug-in expansion cards, integrated I/O controller chips, and a computer's main processing and memory systems. It was originally designed by Intel in the early 1990's as an alternative to other proposed peripheral expansion buses.

PCI was patented by Intel, but they agreed to license it openly and make it royalty-free.

PCI is now governed by a consortium of industry partners known as the PCI Special Interest Group (PCI SIG). This body of computer systems manufacturers, peripheral vendors, component suppliers and software companies is organized for the following purposes:

* To insure compatibility and interoperability across the PCI standard
* To continue to refine the specification to increase throughput

The PCI SIG runs PCI-compliance test workshops every quarter, ensuring that all cards operate in all machines.

Figure 82. *PCI SCSI card*

The first release of the specification—the PCI Local Bus Specification—became available in June 1992. A second release (2.0) was published in April 1993. Version 2.1 was published in 1995 and offered the following:

- 66 MHz clock speeds
- 264 MB/s data transfer rates
- Card bus support
- New latency rules to improve performance
- User-definable configuration mechanism

Other PCI-related specifications soon followed:

- PCI to PCI Bridge
- PCI BIOS
- PCI Multimedia Design Suite
- PCI Mobile Design Guide

PCI was initially difficult to implement because it required special chips with output buffer drivers that had both minimum and maximum AC currents (as opposed to traditional DC current). It also allowed only one load per bus slot, making ASICs the only feasible interface to the bus. A computer typically would have only two or three PCI slots. Adding more would require expensive

PCI bridge chips or additional PCI peer bus chips that join separate PCI buses together logically.

 ASIC stands for application-specific integrated circuit. ASICs are computer chips developed for specific functions. These are used in a wide-range of devices, such as video machines, microwave ovens and security alarms.

The PCI family includes multifunction chips that provide two distinct features (Ethernet and SCSI) on a single chip.

PCI features

PCI is loaded with high-performance features including the following:

- 32-bit bus bandwidth with a compatible 64-bit and/or 66 MHz upgrade path
- Electrical signals of 5 volts (3.3 volts later)
- Bus clock rate of 33 MHz
- Up to 132 MB/s burst transfer rate over the 32-bit bus

 Sustained rates are much lower.

- Full PCI bus master and slave support
- Supports either a 6.875-inch (known as Short Card form factor) or a 12.283-inch (known as Standard Card form factor) card size
- PCI Local Bus Specification, Revision 2.1 (1995)
- Operates independently of any particular microprocessor design
- ISA style mechanical bracket
- Edge card connection into the motherboard
- Recommended use of plug-in card expansion ROM

A PCI burst transfer is defined as a single PCI bus transaction with a single address phase followed by two or more data phases. The PCI master arbitrates for ownership of the bus, then issues a start address and transaction type during the address phase. The target device latches this start address into its address counter and increments the address from data phase to data phase.

Table 78 lists and describes the commands that pass between the CPU and the PCI interface and indicates which entity initiates the command.

Table 78. *PCI Commands and Initiators*

PCI Command	Initiator	Description
I/O Read, I/O Write	CPU	Used to transfer data between the CPU and the Target's I/O memory space.
Configuration Read, Configuration Write	CPU	Used to transfer data between the CPU and the PCI target's Configuration registers during computer initialization.
Memory Read, Memory Write	CPU or PCI Master	Used to transfer data between the PCI Master and the Target's memory space.
Memory Read Line	CPU or PCI Master	Used by the PCI Master to transfer a cache line of data from the PCI Target's memory space. Much faster than Memory Read.
Memory Read Multiple	CPU or PCI Master	Used by the PCI Master to transfer more than one cache line of data from the PCI Target's memory space. This is the mode to use when transferring lots of data.
Memory Write and Invalidate	CPU or PCI Master	Used by the PCI Master to transfer one or more complete cache lines of data to the PCI Target's memory space. The faster type of Memory Write command.

On PCI, the fastest performance is achieved with data transfer commands that transact aligned data to and from cacheable memory regions in data chunks the size of CPU cache lines.

Although PCI promised 132 MB/s data transfer rates, initial implementations on chips such as the Intel Mercury and Neptune were limited to much less. Later implementations, such as the Intel Triton and Orion, handled the faster 70 MB/s PCI streaming bursts (Table 79). Limitations were due mainly to PCI controller chips. Early chips could not handle PCI's high-performance bursts.

Table 79. *Maximum Data Transfer Rates of Intel Chipsets*

Intel PCI Chipset	Maximum Data Transfer Rate
Mercury, Saturn	30 MB/s
Neptune	40 MB/s

Table 79. *Maximum Data Transfer Rates of Intel Chipsets (Continued)*

Intel PCI Chipset	Maximum Data Transfer Rate
Triton	70 MB/s
Orion	70+ MB/s

Some chips did not support multiple-byte data transfers or did not optimally support the cache line size or invalidation technique of the CPU. Memory bandwidth limitations also hampered PCI performance. Data from a card needs to be put into memory, and if the memory subsystem speed is slow, the data transfer rate will be limited.

Read and write performance to and from the PCI bus were often different. PCI performance was also hampered by the fact that buses were clocked at rates slower than the 33 MHz standard. It was easier to clock the PCI bus as a divisor of the CPU's system bus.

- Pentium systems that ran at 75 MHz had system buses running at 50 MHz and PCI buses clocked at half that rate (25 MHz).
- Pentium systems that ran at 60, 90, 120, 150 or 180 MHz had system buses running at 60 MHz and PCI buses clocked at half that rate (30 MHz).
- Pentium systems that ran at 66, 100, 133, 166 or 200 MHz had system buses running at 66 MHz and PCI buses clocked at half that rate (33 MHz).

PCI has become the bus of choice on most PCs and most recently on the Apple Macintosh. Digital Equipment's Alpha line of workstations has also adopted PCI. Even their CPU has an on-board PCI interface, the first implementation of 64-bit PCI found in this line.

Macintosh PCI

1995 will be remembered as the "Year of Confusion" for many people: Macintosh users, resellers and even industry insiders. With the recent introduction of Apple's Power Macintosh with PCI family and the dawning of the Mac™ OS clones—both PCI and NuBus—the Macintosh market offers consumers such a wide array of choices that making sure your purchase delivers real value requires significant contemplation and research.

In high-end markets where Apple has the leading position—digital video, color publishing, digital pre-press and multimedia—the requirements for mass storage in performance, capacity and cost are dramatically influenced by the implementation of PCI on the Power Macintosh.

Apple's SCSI interface by itself yields very low performance for the Macintosh's high-end markets. As with the NuBus machines of the past, it will be the third-party vendors who provide high-performance, Fast and Wide SCSI-2 cards and disk arrays to meet the speed and capacity needs of digital video, color publishing, digital pre-press, multimedia and networking. These cards and arrays allow users to realize the full potential of their solutions—something Apple's on-board SCSI interface prohibits.

 Higher-performing storage interfaces, such as Fast-20 (also known as Ultra SCSI), Fiber Channel and SSA, will offer bandwidths with up to 100 MB/s sustained data transfer rates—over 10 times the performance of Apple's built in SCSI interface.

Only with PCI on the Power Macintosh, and the performance gain PCI provides, will users be able to maximize the benefits of the current high-performance SCSI interface—Fast and Wide SCSI-2—and realize the benefits of the new coming technologies for storage.

Performance gains are evident when you compare FWB's SledgeHammer 7000 Fast and Wide SCSI-2 RAID solution on the Power Macintosh 9500 (PCI) and on the Power Macintosh 8100 (NuBus):

- On the Power Macintosh 9500, this array attains sustained data transfer rates of 33 MB/s.
- On the Power Macintosh 8100, this same array sustains a rate of only 15 MB/s.

To sort out PCI's impact on mass storage, we'll explore the following topics:

- What is PCI and why did Apple adopt it?
- What is the impact of PCI on Power Macintosh and how will you benefit?
- What are the implications for performance on the Power Macintosh?
- What are the issues of compatibility for hardware and software?
- How will the entrance of many "Mac-clone" companies affect you?

 This section was written under the assumption that you are a reasonably knowledgeable user of the Macintosh or Power Macintosh platform.

Apple based its Power Macintosh with PCI family on Version 2.0 of the PCI specification, like the majority of companies that have implemented the Intel PC platform. The entire Power Macintosh with PCI family—the 7200, 7500, 8500 and 9500—fully conforms to this industry standard.

The second generation of Power Macintosh computers containing PowerPC microprocessors uses PCI buses to communicate with both internal I/O chips and plug-in expansion cards. Both 601- and 604-based Power Macintosh systems utilize the PCI bus architecture.

Four key reasons went into Apple's decision to replace its aging NuBus architecture with PCI:

1. Apple wants to offer a widely-adopted industry standard so that it can market its computers in a way that promotes commonality with other platforms while allowing Apple to market the differentiated benefits of the Macintosh experience.

2. Since PCI is an industry standard, Apple hopes to attract a more widely varied pool of cards for different solutions.

3. Apple hopes the cost of PCI products will be lower than comparable cards on the NuBus as more developers offer their products for the Power Macintosh with PCI family.

4. The addition of PCI gives the Power Macintosh platform a tremendous boost in performance over the NuBus. This will eventually open up additional markets to Apple for applications that need the added performance that only PCI can deliver.

In the past, Apple has used NuBus as its expansion bus for both Macintosh and Power Macintosh machines. With the advent of the Power Macintosh with PCI, Apple is moving from a semi-proprietary expansion bus (the NuBus) to one with much greater industry acceptance (PCI). Apple can assure its compatibility with other computer manufacturers through it compliance with the PCI standard. Apple plans to differentiate its robust architecture—with its unmatched application richness—from Intel Pentiums with PCI running Windows 3.1 or Windows 95.

PCI provides a needed standard in the computer industry. Because the PCI bus uses the same architecture and protocols to communicate with I/O chips and expansion cards, it reduces the cost and complexity of computer hardware. It allows Apple, and other systems manufacturers, to provide high-speed expandability at minimum cost.

The key features of Apple's PCI implementation include the following:

- 32-bit bus bandwidth with a compatible 64-bit and/or 66 MHz upgrade path

- Electrical signals of 5 volts

- Bus clock rate of 33 MHz, compared to only 10 MHz for Apple's fastest NuBus

- Up to 132 MB/s burst transfer rate over the 32-bit bus

- Full PCI bus master and slave support

- Either 6.875-inch (known as Short Card form factor) or 12.283-inch (known as Standard Card form factor) card sizes
- Supports Open Firmware Boot Specification (IEEE1275-1994) for booting cards in an OS-independent environment
- PCI Local Bus Specification, Revision 2.0
- Operates independently of any particular microprocessor design
- ISA-style mechanical bracket
- Edge-card connection into the motherboard
- Recommended use of plug-in card expansion ROM, allowing true Macintosh plug-and-play
- Macintosh PCI Performance

The first implementation of PCI on the Power Macintosh with PCI utilized the Apple-designed BANDIT chip. Its performance varied depending on the PCI transaction.

Table 80 and Table 81 illustrate that data transfers performed at the cache line size of 32-bytes result in the highest performance.

Table 80. Macintosh PowerPC to PCI Data Transfer Rate

Transaction	Size (bytes)	PCI Performance	Parallel Processing Chip Instruction
Write to PCI	4	20 MB/s	Integer Store
	8	40 MB/s	FP Store
	32	85 MB/s	PCI Copyback
Read from PCI	4	11 MB/s	Integer Store
	8	20 MB/s	FP Store
	32	40 MB/s	PCI Copyback

Table 81. *Macintosh PCI Master to Memory Data Transfer Rate*

Transaction	Size (bytes)	PCI Performance	PCI Command
Write to Memory	4	20 MB/s	Mem Write
	8	35 MB/s	Mem Write
	32	80 MB/s	Mem Write & Inv
Read from Memory	4	10 MB/s	Mem Read
	8	15 MB/s	Mem Read
	32	30 MB/s	Mem Read Line/M

Open firmware

You may have heard the term "Open Firmware" used in reference to Apple's PCI implementation (it is also sometimes called "Open Boot"). It refers to PCI's independence from any particular operating system.

Open Firmware was originally developed as Open Boot by Sun Microsystems. It debuted in 1988 with the original Sun SparcStation workstation. It provides a way of booting a computer system that is independent of both operating system and processor. Its native language is interpreted by the computer and is based on the programming language Forth. Open Firmware drivers are written in a Forth variant known as FCode.

During the Open Firmware process, startup firmware in the Power Macintosh's ROM:

1. Searches the PCI buses and generates a data structure that lists all available peripheral devices.

   This data structure also stores the peripheral support software, such as FWB's Hard Disk ToolKit™ device driver, provided by each PCI expansion card.

2. Finds an operating system (for example, Mac OS System 7.5.2 on the Power Macintosh with PCI) in ROM or on a mass storage device.

3. Loads it and starts it running.

The operating system does not need to be Mac OS, though with the Power Macintosh it is. Hence, it is possible for PCI-compatible Power Macintosh computers to operate PCI peripheral devices using either Macintosh or third-party system software. In short, all Mac OS-compatible computers (Mac clones) can be used with the PCI bus.

This is comparable to what Supermac and Power Computing have done with NuBus.

Any operating system that is compatible with the Power PC chip used in the Power Macintosh will be compatible with the Power Macintosh with PCI.

Open Boot provides Apple's PCI bus with the following features:

- Auto-configuration of devices on startup
- Flexibility in system software
- Wide industry acceptance

Open Boot also increases the flexibility of PCI on PCs using Intel chips by not requiring use of the system BIOS. This differs from previous expansion buses used in the Intel world—ISA, EISA, MCA and VLB—where BIOS code is necessary to successfully utilize cards in the bus.

This offers no advantage to the already easy-to-use architecture of the Power Macintosh, and it does not exempt the card from needing a Power Macintosh-specific device driver to be fully functional.

The establishment of the PCI bus standard offers real benefits to the Power Macintosh and to users at large:

- Additional ease-of-use
- Future expansion
- Overall lower cost

These benefits allow for incredible performance gains over NuBus. They make the Power Macintosh with PCI platform the solution for the 90s.

The performance gain PCI offers users on all Power Macintosh with PCI platforms is the most significant advantage over NuBus-based machines and PCI machines running Windows or Windows 95. PCI delivers unmatched performance gains for digital video, color publishing and multimedia environments, particularly when coupled with the power of the PowerPC 604 chip (used in the Power Macintosh 9500 and 8500), increased native System software and 604-optimized application packages.

Mass storage is one of the key beneficiaries of the increased bandwidth and throughput of PCI. A dramatic illustration of this improvement in performance is the comparison of a Fast and Wide SCSI-2 disk array on the Power Macintosh 9500 with the fastest NuBus machines available (Figure 83).

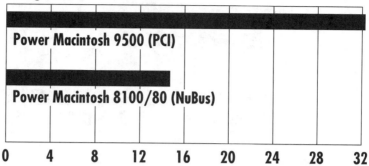

Figure 83. *PCI and NuBus transfer rates using Benchtest*

 In Figure 83, the bars indicate sustained data transfer rates in MB/s. Two JackHammers™ were used. All testing was done with the latest System software for each platform, 5 MB transfer size and Hard Disk ToolKit™ Benchtest 1.7.5. Longer bars indicate faster performance.

As Figure 83 illustrates, an FWB SledgeHammer 7000 II RAID solution on the Power Macintosh 9500 achieves a sustained data transfer rate of over 33 MB/s. This is more than twice the performance of the fastest NuBus Power Macintosh—the 8100/80—and almost twice the performance of Apple's fastest NuBus Macintosh, the Quadra 840AV.

 The 840AV is the fastest of all NuBus machines, Macintosh or Power Macintosh.

Remember, the example in Figure 83 is with today's RAID and mass storage technology. As mentioned earlier, with new higher-performing storage architectures—which started appearing in the last part of 1995 and are continuing to develop and debut throughout 1996—the increased power they offer will be realized only on Power Macintosh with PCI. NuBus machines cannot match the performance of these interfaces.

While artificial benchmarks are useful, Macintosh users want to know:

- "What can this really do for me?"
- "How will this increase my real productivity?"

Results for real-world applications, such as Adobe PhotoShop™, impressively demonstrate that PCI performance gains are not confined to artificial benchmarks.

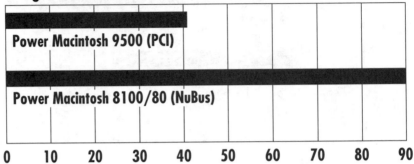

SledgeHammer 7000FMF II

Figure 84. PCI and NuBus transfer rates using Adobe Photoshop™

Figure 84 illustrates transfer rates achieved while using Adobe Photoshop™ to open a 100 MB TIFF on the SledgeHammer 7000 FMF II for PCI. All testing was done with the latest System software and Photoshop 3.04; 32 MB of RAM was allocated to Photoshop; primary and secondary scratch disk preferences in Photoshop were set to disk array; and Photoshop and the TIFF file were launched from disk array. Shorter bars indicate faster performance.

PCI's performance gain extends to real-world applications for real-world uses. While Figure 84 focuses on color publishing, the benefit of PCI on the Power Macintosh extends to any application and/or hardware peripheral that involves significant PCI bus activity. For example, digital video card vendors were limited by the throughput of NuBus to video compression of 4:1. With PCI, these same vendors feel they can deliver 2:1 compression, and perhaps uncompressed video—virtually impossible on NuBus. Similar performance enhancements will be seen by users of multimedia, pre-press and network applications. Overall, the Power Macintosh with PCI family sets new standards for price/performance value in the desktop computer arena.

While PCI is an industry standard, Power Macintosh users should not be lulled into the belief that all products designed to work on PCI for the Intel platform will work in the Power Macintosh. PCI compliance is only the first step to successful integration of a third-party card with Power Macintosh.

For example, a card that is fully PCI compliant but does not support Open Boot may work fine on a Pentium with PCI, but will not work on a Power Macintosh. Even if a card fully supports Open Boot, it still requires a Macintosh device driver. In the case of storage, a PCI card must have a Macintosh disk device driver, such as FWB's Hard Disk ToolKit™ or RAID ToolKit™, in order to operate properly for mass storage applications. Additionally, that device driver must be compliant with SCSI Manager 4.3.

 The SCSI Manager is that part of the Apple System software that controls the interaction of SCSI peripherals and the Mac OS.

Apple has instituted a compatibility program to let customers know which products meet the minimum level of Power Macintosh with PCI compatibility.

- This program **DOES NOT** guarantee you the fastest, best engineered or most suitable product for your application.
- However, it **DOES** indicate that the product will work in the Power Macintosh with PCI family.

Apple requires vendors who participate in the program to submit cards to Apple for compatibility testing. If the cards are deemed compatible, the vendor is allowed to use the "Designed for Macintosh with PCI" logo in its marketing materials and advertising (Figure 85).

Figure 85. *Apple's certified PCI trademark*

 A PCI compatibility rating from Apple indicates compatibility only. Apple does not check for optimal performance, good Macintosh technical support or synergy with Macintosh applications.

For the consumer, the Apple PCI logo is a valuable signal that the product meets the minimum level of Power Macintosh with PCI compatibility and is worth considering.

PCI cards introduced a new method of installation. In the NuBus era, a Eurocard connector on the bottom edge of the card tightly mated to another connector on the motherboard. For Power Macintosh with PCI, this has been replaced with the use of edge connectors on the card that install into a slot on the motherboard. Although this is a PCI industry standard, it is, unfortunately, too easy for cards to seat incorrectly in the motherboard slot. To address this problem, Apple created a system that keeps a card in its slot by firmly locking the ISA-style fence into the machine's backplane plastic. Additionally, all the Power Macs with PCI have a locking mechanism that gently secures the cards from the top. Very few PCI implementations feature these useful innovations.

The entrance of many PC companies into the Macintosh market through PCI will create additional confusion for users already wary of the many choices available. These companies are unproven entities on the Macintosh platform, though several have established leadership positions on Intel platforms. Some of these companies are serious about Macintosh and want to offer excellent products. Others have no idea what Macintosh users expect or want in their products and just see the advent of Power Macintosh with PCI as a means to enter a new market with the same expansion bus interface. Only time will tell which PC companies can successfully deliver "real" Macintosh products on the Power Macintosh with PCI platform.

Probably the most important question you need to ask yourself is "What do I expect from a company whose products are to be used in my Power Macintosh with PCI?" Once this is answered, you can determine if a PC company has products that meet your expectations. For instance, what users expect to see in any Macintosh product is thorough documentation and excellent technical support. Thorough documentation is often only included in the best products on the PC side, and users have learned not always to expect high-quality technical support.

Other key questions users should ask about PC companies selling Power Macintosh PCI solutions include the following:

- What is the true level of Macintosh compliance I will receive?
- What help will I get in the integration of their PCI solution with my Macintosh applications and the Mac OS?
- How well will they engineer their products to work cooperatively with other Macintosh PCI cards and software products?

Many PC companies will be entering the Macintosh market via PCI. What remains to be seen is whether they can meet the higher expectations that Macintosh users have of technical support, documentation, integration, OS compliance and synergy with complementary hardware and software.

Some of the PC companies will learn the Macintosh way and offer customers robust, quality PCI solutions. Others will just throw their current PC products at the Macintosh. If you are shopping for these products, you will need to be just as aware and selective as you have been in the NuBus era and not be swayed by wild claims of incredible performance at incredibly low prices.

PCI for Power Macintosh brings to the Macintosh platform the real power needed for today's demanding applications. Coupled with the next generation of PowerPC chips and System software, PCI provides high-end users the performance they demand to continue to push the envelope.

For sources of more information on PCI, see "Appendix A: Additional Information Sources" on page 311.

PCI Mezzanine Specification

The PC Industrial Computer Manufacturers Group (PICMG) was established in 1994 to develop a standard for a low-end, passive-backplane CPU board that could incorporate PCI.

A passive backplane is a board that exists merely to pass signals; no processing takes place.

This group created the PCI Mezzanine card (PMC). The standard specifies the physical implementation of PCI as a mezzanine card. These cards generally fit on top of the industrial CPU board. PMC allows general purpose CPU boards to be customized for specific applications. These cards adhere to PCI 2.0 specifications. Standardization creates an industry of add-on boards that can leverage low-cost chips used for PCs.

PCMCIA

PCMCIA stands for Personal Computer Memory Card International Association. This group was founded in 1989 and consists of about 400 members from the computer industry. This popular specification was created to standardize expansion cards for portable computers. The cards are credit card sized, 85 × 54 mm modules.

The original 1.0 specification, released in 1990, was targeted at memory cards. A later 2.0 specification in 1991 added support for I/O cards and introduced three thicknesses of cards—Type I, II and III:

- Type I cards are 3.3 mm thick.
- Type II are 5 mm thick.
- Type III are 10.5 mm thick.

PCMCIA release 2.01 allows for ATA storage cards (Flash ATA and ATA hard drives), I/O cards (such as fax, ethernet and SCSI), and memory cards (RAM, ROM, flash). This specification basically mapped the 40-pin IDE interface to the 68-pin PCMCIA connector. This is a 5 V interface that supports 16-bit, 8 MHz operation through its 68-pins.

PCMCIA defines a software layer known as card and socket services. This software handles the insertion and removal of PCMCIA cards. It sets up the PCMCIA bus chip on the computer and configures the PCMCIA card to manage its I/O ports and interrupt usage. The biggest challenge with PCMCIA has been software compatibility. This has caused some cards to be incompatible with certain computers. Hot-swapping of cards has also been problematic. Cards should be removable and insertable on the fly at any time.

The latest version of PCMCIA is known as the CardBus or PC Card 94 bus. It specifies a new mode that allows PCI devices to be packaged like PCMCIA cards and be plugged into similar sockets. It is a 32-bit, 33-MHz bus, marrying PCI protocols to PCMCIA 3.0 electrical specifications. This supports 3 V operation, bus mastering, DMA and both 20- and 33-MHz operation. CardBus utilizes the same Card Information Structure (CIS) as PCMCIA cards. For the first time, cards such as video capture, 100 Mb Ethernet and Ultra SCSI could be created.

 For more information on PCMCIA, see "Appendix A: Additional Information Sources" on page 311.

7

Storage Software

Many utility software packages are currently available that are designed to maximize the usefulness and performance of storage peripherals. Chapter 7 provides an overview of some of these products and gives some reasons why you might find them useful.

Formatter Software

Figure 86. *FWB's Hard Disk ToolKit™*

Formatter software is utility software designed to set up hard disks for use on a computer system. These utilities can be simple or complex.

The Macintosh requires formatter software to format, partition and install a SCSI driver on disks before they can be used by the operating system. There are several makers of formatter software, including Apple and FWB.

Apple's formatter software is called Drive Setup. It's a no-frills formatter that works on both IDE and SCSI drives. However, it works only on Apple hard drives. Other formatters, such as FWB's Hard Disk ToolKit, offer all the basics of Apple's software, work on virtually every SCSI hard drive, and contain advanced features, such as password protection, encryption, Device Copy, SCSI Configure, and extensive drive diagnostics.

Formatter software adds support for removable-media drives to the Macintosh operating system in the form of a System Extension. The Extension loads a driver into memory that watches and provides for media insertion and removal.

PCs typically utilize formatter software bundled with the operating system. IDE drives on PCs do not need to be formatted. They are partitioned by operating system utilities such as DOS's FDISK or Windows NT's Disk Administrator. SCSI drives are usually formatted by software included with the SCSI host adapter. There are several formatter programs that provide additional diagnostics and compatibility for IDE and SCSI drives. Some also provide support for multiple operating systems on a single drive.

RAID Software

Figure 87. FWB's RAID ToolKit

RAID software is used to create a software-based array out of several drives. Some RAID levels increase the performance of drives, while others provide fault tolerance. This software generally runs on top of any industry-standard host adapter.

 An array is a collection of drives, connected and configured so as to act and appear as one drive. Software-based arrays are created with installed software packages. Hardware-based arrays are created through logic built into a controller chip.

Disk striping or RAID 0 is very popular on the Macintosh. Users that require the utmost in throughput use software such as FWB's RAID ToolKit to stripe multiple drives together into a high performance disk array. Apple includes a utility called AppleRAID with its Workgroup Servers that creates a more limited RAID set.

NOTE To learn more about RAID, see "What Is RAID?" on page 61.

Disk striping is slowly gaining popularity on PCs. FWB's RAID ToolKit for Windows provides striping for Windows for Workgroups 3.11 and Windows 95. Windows NT has built-in RAID 0 striping. Windows NT Advanced Server has built-in RAID 5 support.

CD-ROM Software

Figure 88. FWB's CD-ROM ToolKit

CD-ROM drivers are software routines that enable the operation of a CD-ROM drive connected to a computer. They also map industry-standard CD formats to native operating system structures, making it possible to mount a variety of disc formats on a wide range of operating systems.

On the Macintosh, there are several CD-ROM driver packages. Apple includes CD-ROM drivers for its CD-ROM drives. As with its hard disk drivers, Apple's CD-ROM drivers only work on their drives. Third-party products, such as FWB's CD-ROM ToolKit™, provide drivers and acceleration for a wide variety of CD-ROM drives on the Macintosh. Part of Apple's system software includes translators for the various CD-ROM formats that map them to the Macintosh operating system.

Windows 95 includes integral support and caching for most SCSI and IDE CD-ROM drives, so third-party drivers are not needed. Translators for several CD-ROM formats are also included.

Tape Backup Software

Tape Backup software is used to perform backups and restores to tape or DAT drives. These drives are known as sequential access devices because the stored data can be accessed only in a linear sequence—the tape has to wind or unwind and pass across the stationary tape head to position data for reading or the tape for writing. Most sequential access devices do not show up as mounted volumes on the Desktop and require tape backup software to access the media. Advanced backup packages allow for network backups to servers through the use of backup agents.

The Macintosh operating system does not have any built in support for tape backup. It relies on third-party tape backup software to operate tape drives.

Windows 95 includes integral tape backup software for some tape backup drives. The selection of functions is limited as is the support list. Only a few popular IDE and SCSI tape drives are supported. There is no support for 8 mm, DAT or Travan. Other tape backup software can be used through the ASPI manager interface.

Compression Software

Compression software is used to extend the capacity of drives. Compression utilizes algorithms that reduce the amount of storage needed to store a given stream of data. These algorithms exploit redundancy and disk allocation units. Compression software buys extra space, but at the price of performance. Data must be compressed before it is written and uncompressed before it is read. Compression complicates the recovery of data from a malfunctioning drive. Compression will usually buy you from 20 to 40 percent more space, not the 100 percent increase some programs claim.

There is no compression built into the Macintosh System 7.5 operating system. However third-party utilities are available for adding compression.

Windows 95 includes support for compression of disk drives. The Windows 95 Plus Pak adds a 32-bit version of the compression program.

Figure 89. FWB's HSM ToolKit™

HSM is software that automates the process of migrating files to less expensive storage. It is designed to manage mass storage devices and repositories.

The growth of information stored on-line over the last 10 years is unprecedented. More users are accessing complex applications, creating large data files and downloading more information than ever before. Over the next five years, both users and administrators will struggle with straining storage capacities.

You can add more disk space and archive unused files, but the costs associated with these strategies can be staggering. Within an enterprise, installation and maintenance of a single disk drive costs four to five times the price of the equipment. Archiving alone burdens users and administrators alike with productivity losses.

This has created the need for real storage management tools. With HSM, as a disk becomes full or as files age, they can be moved to optical or tape media to create free space on primary storage. HSM works continuously and is completely transparent to users. HSM delivers significant cost and time savings while boosting data access with near limitless storage.

Managing data storage: the hidden costs

Most computer users don't spend much time thinking about data storage management. Nevertheless, it is a significant cost center for computer-integrated businesses. It can also be quite expensive for home users. Studies have shown that managing two gigabytes of data over a one-year period costs the average business about $7,000. This is the time spent administering and servicing the device, restoring or recovering lost data, and all the other activities that go into maintaining an MIS—it does not include the cost of the disk drive. The primary objective of HSM is to save money by lowering storage hardware and support costs.

There are currently three primary techniques for addressing the dilemma of soaring storage requirements (Table 82).

Table 82. *Three Common Techniques for Storage Management*

Solution	Disadvantage
Buy more hard drive storage	• Expensive. A 1 GB GB disk drive can cost from $.25 per MB to $2 per MB for RAID storage. • Costly to install. System down-time, parts, and labor can double the cost of adding a disk drive. • Costly to maintain. Increasing capacity increases backup, restore, troubleshooting, repair and administration costs.
Manually delete files	• Time consuming. Manually grooming a disk can cost $10-$100 per hour for high paid end-users. • High risk. Many users will delete important data or application files. • Inefficient. Some users will not delete enough files.
Archive files off-line	• Time consuming. Like manual deletion, manual archiving is costly to perform. • Inefficient. Finding and restoring archived data is labor intensive and can become a tremendous burden as archived data grows.

Too often, users choose to add disk drives to address a capacity problem. But, even as storage prices fall, the exponential growth in the number and size of application, image and data files will continue to outpace the ability to add more storage cost-effectively. Much of this problem could be eliminated if "inactive" data could be stored elsewhere but still be accessible.

A large portion of information stored on a typical server could be moved to secondary storage. It is HSM's job to manage this process intelligently and retrieve these files when needed.

On-line, off-line, and near-line storage

Storage for applications and data can be broken down into three broad categories:

* On-line

- Off-line
- Near-line

Table 83 explores these storage options.

Table 83. *On-line, Off-line and Near-line Storage*

Application	Description
On-line • RAM ... $15–$50 MB • Array ... $2–$5 MB • Disk ... $.50 MB	On-line storage is storage media that provides virtually immediate access to your needed applications and data. Hard disks and system memory are the most common types of on-line storage.
Off-line • Tape ... $.10–$.50 MB • CD-ROM ... $.01–$.15 MB	Backup tapes are a good example of Off-line storage. This data cannot be accessed without a user physically placing the media in the computer or drive.
Near-line • Optical Cartridge ... $.40–$1 MB • Optical Jukebox ... $.20–$2 MB	Near-line storage manages the middle ground: faster than off-line but more economical than on-line. The category comprises technologies such as magneto-optical disks and network servers.

Archiving, backup and HSM

There is significant confusion over the role of Archiving and Backup in an HSM system. These activities are an essential part of any storage management program and should be performed hand-in-hand with HSM.

Archiving

Archiving is the transfer of infrequently used data files from primary storage to less expensive media—usually tape or removable disks of some sort. The files are preserved for future use, but are essentially off-line. The expensive primary storage space made available by the removal of the files can then be used for more pressing matters.

Judicious archiving can save a considerable amount of money by reducing the requirements for hard-disk capacity. On the Macintosh, archiving can be done manually by dragging files to secondary storage and erasing files in the Finder. However, for many users it will be more efficient to partially automate the process with archival software.

While archiving is good at minimizing the hardware costs of data storage, it is of no help in the case of drive failures, viruses, theft, or such disasters as fire, flood, and earthquake. This is because archiving alone only maintains a single copy of any data file.

Backup

Backup is a process that creates duplicate copies of data files. If the original files are lost or damaged in some way, they can be restored from the duplicates. Regular backup is an essential part of a comprehensive data security strategy.

Several software packages currently offer robust backup features on the Macintosh. Selection of an HSM package should include careful evaluation of the various compatibility issues between HSM and your backup utility software to ensure preservation of current investments in software and hardware.

HSM

Archiving and backup are important processes in data storage management. However, they don't provide a complete solution. To achieve that, HSM should be included in the mix.

HSM provides the following storage-management benefits:

- Prevents out-of-disk space conditions
- Lowers data management costs
- Improves data accessibility

Hierarchical storage management software automatically moves infrequently used data to less expensive storage devices. Unlike archiving, however, it moves the data to storage that is maintained on-line and leaves a trail as it does so, such as an alias file in the original file's location. You can use this trail to retrieve data automatically when you need it. Typically, the entire process is transparent to the user. Accessing files on the primary hard drive is virtually identical to accessing files that have been moved by HSM.

HSM architecture

HSM solutions typically employ three levels of hierarchy:

- Primary storage
- Secondary storage
- Tertiary storage

Primary storage typically consists of fast Winchester drives or disk arrays. Secondary storage typically consists of slower, higher-capacity drives or removable cartridge devices. Tertiary storage typically consists of a much slower tape device.

How HSM works

HSM is designed to automatically move (migrate) and retrieve (demigrate) files based on a set of rules and filters defined by the user. These user-defined rules allow HSM to compile a list of "migration candidates." This list contains the files that will be moved off-line to secondary storage.

- Rules determine where, when and which files are migrated or demigrated.
- Filters provide additional guidelines that prevent some files from migrating.

Once a user determines what rules and filters should be in effect, the software acts automatically, based on those determinations. The user can intervene at any time to change the rules and filters.

- The Watermark Rule governs how much empty space should always be available on the primary storage device (the source). For example, if the "high watermark" is set to 80 percent and the "low watermark" is set to 70 percent, whenever the source becomes more than 80 percent full, data will be migrated until the used capacity on the source is below the low watermark.
- The Cobweb Rule monitors when a file was last accessed (not just modified). Last-access date is a good indicator of whether or not a file needs to be kept on primary storage. Files not accessed for 90 days are less likely to be needed in the future.

You can use both the Watermark and Cobweb rules together. When you do, HSM first selects unused files based on the aging criteria, then checks to see if any additional files need to be migrated, based on the defined watermark threshold.

- Filters prevent certain files or folders from becoming candidates for migration. For example, you wouldn't want your System Folder migrated to another drive. A filter would prevent that. Other filters might keep applications, certain file types or specific files from being migrated.

Migration movement of candidate files takes place in several steps:

1. Once a file has been selected for migration and the user-defined migration time is at hand, HSM copies the file to a secondary storage device that has been designated as the destination.
2. HSM verifies that the copy is identical to the original file.
3. After a successful verification, HSM deletes the original file and replaces it with an alias or "pointer" bearing the same name as the original file.

When you access a migrated file through its alias or pointer, it may be demigrated immediately or "tagged" for retrieval at the next scheduled migration.

If immediate demigration is selected, there may be a slight delay as HSM moves and opens the file.

The best HSM solutions are easy to configure and transparent to the end-user. Nevertheless, these systems always inform the user if a recall is in progress and allow cancellation of the process if system response time is impaired.

File compressing during migration is a growing trend in HSM applications. The higher capacity offered by compression is well worth the additional delay experienced when accessing infrequently used files.

Back-up software and other utilities that scrutinize files on disk can unknowingly force simultaneous demigration of files from the hierarchy. It is important that you select an HSM application that can differentiate between true file access and access by another probing application.

The benefits of HSM

HSM reduces the cost of data storage by automatically and transparently moving infrequently used files to less expensive storage media. However, the files remain online. Furthermore, aliases are left behind with the exact names and locations of the moved files. This means that, as far as the user experience goes, it's as if the files had never been moved. HSM provides similar cost savings to archiving, with better data access time.

Archiving, backup and HSM are related, but not identical. They are all components of a well-planned data storage management system. Used together, they can ensure data integrity, reduce storage costs, and maintain easy access to data. The best solutions are easily configured and operate transparently to the end-user. With a little planning, HSM can be implemented to solve the storage dilemma in an intelligent and cost-effective way.

Hierarchical Storage Management software, such as FWB's HSM ToolKit, is available from third-party vendors of Macintosh software.

Several vendors on the PC offer HSM software. Versions are available for single users as well as network file servers.

CD-R Mastering

CD-R mastering software is used to create compact discs. The software formats data into forms that adhere to industry standards for data interchange. Data sources could be files, disks, or even other CD-ROMs. A user has the capability to produce data discs, hybrid data discs, audio discs, video-CDs, or even CD-Extra discs. The main task of CD-R mastering software is to ensure that there is a continuous stream of data from the source drive. Any hiccups in data will create a flawed disc.

CD-R mastering software is built into neither the Macintosh nor the PC operating systems. Third-party solutions for CD-R mastering are available for both platforms.

Disk Benchmarks

Disk benchmark utilities are used to measure disk performance. There are several types of benchmarks, each measuring its own set of criteria. These utilities are useful in measuring performance gains when adding new drives or software.

The leading benchmark utilities for the Macintosh are FWB's BenchTest and Ziff-Davis' MacBench. BenchTest is a low-level disk benchmark program, measuring many important low-level characteristics of drives. MacBench is a file-system level benchmark program. It's good at measuring real-world performance of drives used for office-oriented applications.

The most popular benchmarks for the PC are the Ziff-Davis Benchmark suite. Ziff's PCBench, WinBench, and Winstone measure real-world and artificial performance of disk subsystems and the computer. They are good at mirroring typical office application performance.

Other popular benchmarks include CoreTest for measuring burst transfer and sustained data rates in DOS, and Drive Rocket for measuring many different transfer rates under DOS. DiskPerf and VidTest, on Microsoft's Development Platform CDs, are good benchmarks for Windows 95 and NT operating systems. They perform benchmarks for large data transfers, mirroring high-end video, and color publishing applications.

8

Troubleshooting

Many things can happen to create errors and crashes on your storage device, including:

- Power surges or outages
- Viruses
- System errors

These errors can corrupt data the computer uses to keep track of the contents of the drive. Depending on what data has been corrupted and how badly it has been corrupted, the result can be barely noticeable or could render your hard drive unusable.

What follows are lists of common problems, probable causes and recommended actions. If the proposed solutions fail to correct the problem, contact the technical support department of your peripheral's vendor.

General Troubleshooting

Problem: Drive Not Seen on SCSI bus		
Symptoms	**Possible Causes**	**Recommended Actions**
Can't see a drive on-line.	No power to drive.	Check to be sure the drive is plugged into a "live" power source.
	Incorrect cabling; improper termination.	• Make sure only the first and last device are terminated. • Make sure that total cable length doesn't exceed the SCSI maximum (3 meters for SCSI-2). • Make sure the cables are plugged in securely. • Make sure all cables are securely mated together. • Make sure Pin 1 is correct on all internal ribbon cabling.
	Drive has hardware problem.	• Use a utility to scan the bus. If you can't see the drive, it may have a hardware problem. • Make sure the drive was spun up when the computer was turned on. • Check the drive's power cord and power supply.
	SCSI ID problems.	• Make sure no two devices are set to the same ID • Make sure that no devices are set to ID 7.
	SCSI host adapter problem.	Make sure the SCSI host adapter is properly seated in its slot. Make sure that all settings on the SCSI host adapter are accurate.
With internal and external drives connected to a SCSI card, none of the drives will mount or show up on the card's SCSI bus.	Card termination not removed.	When both internal and external drives are connected to a SCSI card, terminators should be removed or disabled from the card. Please refer to your SCSI card's manual for details.

Problem: Formatting Problems

Symptoms	Possible Causes	Recommended Actions
Can't format a drive.	• Incorrect cabling. • Improper termination.	• Make sure only the first and last device are terminated. • Make sure that total cable length doesn't exceed the SCSI maximum (3 meters for SCSI-2).
	Incorrect interleave.	Make sure you format the drive with an interleave that is supported. (Optical discs come preformatted with a 1:1 interleave—tracks are etched into the platter and can't be reinterleaved. If you choose to reformat an MO disc with FWB's Hard Disk ToolKit, select the default.)
	Format software times out.	Get an updated formatter that can format bigger drives.

Problem: Spinup Problems

Symptoms	Possible Causes	Recommended Actions
The drive doesn't spin up and the LEDs don't light up.	No power or a blown fuse.	• Make sure the power supply can produce enough power for the drive. • Check and replace the power cable. • Make sure the outlet is active. • Check the drive's fuse. If it is burnt, replace it with a fuse having the same specifications. Make sure the fuse is the fast-blow type. If the problem continues or the fuses repeatedly blow, you may have a power supply problem; contact technical support of your drive's manufacturer.
Drive doesn't spin up to a "ready" state.	Controller card is bad.	Scan with a SCSI utility, if the drive is not ready, it may need repair or replacement.

Problem: Spinup Problems		
Symptoms	**Possible Causes**	**Recommended Actions**
With a new drive installed, the drive will not spin up, or does not spin up reliably.	Hard drive draws more power than the computer's power supply can give.	Certain internal hard drives tend to use the power that is reserved for cards in order to spin up. In addition, some cards require power beyond the limit for a single card, and end up tapping into the power reserved for other cards. The only solutions are: • Get a drive that will work within your computer's power limits. • Remove the offending card (or cards) that exceeds the power limitation. OR • Install the peripheral into a computer with a more robust power supply.
	Jumper settings are wrong.	Check your settings against the drive documentation.

Macintosh Troubleshooting

Mac boot process

The Macintosh has a complicated process for starting up the machine. Knowing more about the process will allow users to troubleshoot problems they have booting in the future and understand better how the Macintosh works.

For information on the PC boot process, see "PC boot process" on page 307.

1. The Macintosh is powered on and performs a test of RAM and other motherboard components. Motherboard video is initialized.

2. The Mac ROM initializes all NuBus or PCI cards, causing drivers to be loaded from these cards. Video card drivers are loaded first, then drivers from other cards.

3. If Command-Option-C is pressed, the Mac will attempt to boot off its CD-ROM drive. (On Macintoshes introduced from 1995.)

4. If Command-Option-TAB is pressed, the Mac will attempt to boot off its floppy drive.

5. It checks for bootable floppies in the floppy drive.

6. The Mac looks at its parameter RAM (PRAM) to see if a device has been chosen in the Startup Device control panel. Once drivers for all block devices that can be found are loaded, the value stored in PRAM is compared with those of each drive in the drive queue. When the correct drive is found, it is mounted and the chosen folder (if any) is sought.

7. The Mac then looks at the Startup Device's partition map and loads a SCSI driver for the Startup Device from its Apple_Driver partition.

8. If no Startup Device is set or if the Startup Device is missing, the Mac scans the first SCSI bus it encounters and looks for bootable drives from the highest SCSI ID to the lowest ID.

9. The SCSI driver is called to mount volumes of type Apple_HFS found in the drive's partition map and to read boot blocks in from the first volume.

10. All other SCSI devices have their drivers loaded and are mounted.

11. Compatibility of the current System file and the computer is checked.

12. The SCSI driver is called to read the System in.

13. Startup screens are displayed if present.

14. Welcome to Macintosh is displayed.

15. If the Mac requires a System Enabler, the Enabler is read in.

16. MacsBug, if present in the System Folder, is loaded.

17. The Mac loads all System Extensions, Chooser Extensions and Control Panels that have Extensions embedded in them.

18. The Macintosh launches any Startup applications and loads the Finder to bring up the Desktop.

Macintosh problems and recommended actions

If the following recommended actions fail to correct your system problems, reformatting the drive and reinstalling a clean System Folder may do the trick.

 Remember that formatting will erase all data on the disk.

Make sure that the replacement System Folder is not corrupted and has no special System Extensions in it. If you cannot solve the problems, call the technical support department of your peripheral's vendor for assistance.

Happy Mac problems

Problem: Happy Mac Problems		
Symptoms	**Possible Causes**	**Recommended Actions**
The Happy Mac appears briefly, then disappears, and a floppy disk icon appears with a question mark in the middle of it.	No power to boot drive.	Check to be sure your boot drive is connected to a "live" power source.
	• Bad boot blocks. • Corrupted System files. OR • Corrupted disk data structures.	• Run a disk recovery program. • Reinstall the Apple System Software. • Update the driver on the hard drive.
Happy Mac flashes on and off, and the drive does not boot.	The boot blocks or System files have become corrupted.	• Run a recovery program • Reinstall the Apple System Software.
Happy Mac appears but the drive seeks repeatedly before booting.	A "dirty" shutdown, due to a bomb or power outage. All data structures were not properly updated before shutdown. The Mac sees this upon start-up and reverifies these structures.	None needed, once the Macintosh has verified the structures. You may want to run Apple's Disk First Aid to verify that the disk is in good condition. Use Restart to reboot the computer and Shutdown to turn off the computer instead of simply turning off the machine.

Sad Mac Problems

The sad Mac appears when the Macintosh fails one of its diagnostic tests on start-up. The characters below the sad Mac indicate what has gone wrong. For the Macintosh Plus and earlier, if the first two characters are "0F," there is a software problem. Any other two characters indicate a hardware failure. For the Macintosh SE and later, if the first four characters are "000F," the problem is software, and the last four characters indicate the specific problem. Typically, this is caused by damaged Apple System Software.

The error codes can be found in Inside Macintosh or in some public domain programs.

Problem: Sad Mac Problems		
Symptoms	**Possible Causes**	**Recommended Actions**
The Macintosh crashes with a SCSI accelerator installed.	Possible card conflict.	Try reconnecting the card's devices to the native Macintosh's SCSI port. If the problem remains when no drives are connected to the card, contact your card vendor.
	Parameter RAM corrupted.	Zap PRAM. PRAM is parameter RAM that is backed up by a battery on the Macintosh's motherboard. • If you're using System 7 or newer, restart and hold down the Command, Option, "P" and "R" keys until you hear the startup sound again. • If you're using System 6, hold down the Command, Option, and Shift keys while selecting Control Panel from the Apple menu, and click OK on the resulting dialog box. This will clear the parameter RAM, and should allow normal operation. You may need a utility such as TechTool to clear all PRAM.
	Corrupted driver.	Reinstall the driver.

Problem: Drive Problems		
Symptoms	**Possible Causes**	**Recommended Actions**
Multiple icons appear on the Desktop for the same drive. If you have partitioned your drive, there should be a separate icon for each partition that is mounted, but no more.	SCSI ID conflict.	• Make sure that no two SCSI devices share the same SCSI ID, and that the ID numbers range between zero and six (seven is reserved for the Macintosh). • Make sure cabling and termination are OK.
	Failed SCSI ID switch.	Have an authorized service provider replace the switch.

Problem: Drive Problems		
Symptoms	**Possible Causes**	**Recommended Actions**
The drive does not mount.	There are many software or hardware possibilities.	• Make sure your drive is properly connected to the Macintosh, properly terminated, and has a "live" power source. • Check the SCSI ID of the drive as well as any other devices on the SCSI bus. • Use your formatter software to test the media and update the driver. • Make sure any SCSI cards are seated securely in their slots.
	Parameter RAM corrupted.	• If you're using System 7 or newer, restart and hold down the Command, Option, "P" and "R" keys until you hear the startup sound again. • If you're using System 6, hold down the Command, Option, and Shift keys while selecting Control Panel from the Apple menu, and click OK on the resulting dialog box. This will clear the parameter RAM, which is RAM that is backed up by a battery on the Macintosh's motherboard.
Why can't I see my drive in my formatter?	Multiple SCSI buses exist. If you are using a Quadra 900/950 with a PowerMac Upgrade Card or running SCSI Manager 4.3 extension (part of System 7.5 and newer) on a PowerMac 8100, PowerMac 8150, or PowerMac 9150, you have 2 (two) SCSI buses. The internal drive is usually on Bus 0 (internal). The internal CD-ROM drive, any drives in the second drive bay, and all external devices are usually on Bus 1 (internal/external).	To see these devices you need to select another SCSI bus.
	SCSI ID conflict.	Check the SCSI IDs of all attached devices.
	Bad drive (dead controller).	Repair drive.
	Bad cable leading to drive.	Replace cable.

Problem: Drive Problems		
Symptoms	**Possible Causes**	**Recommended Actions**
The drive starts to mount, but then crashes. This could have many causes.	Damaged System File.	Boot off another disk by holding down Command-Option-Shift-Delete at startup.
	The hard disk's System Folder or the SCSI drivers may have been corrupted by a system crash or virus.	Replace the System Folder on the hard disk first by booting initially off a floppy disk and reinstalling using the Installer. If the problem persists after reinstalling the System Folder, use your formatter software to update the drivers on the hard disk.
	Multiple System Folders on the drive.	Make sure you have only one System and Finder pair on your drive. Find any extra ones using Find File, and delete them. If you try to remove an active System/Finder, you will get an error indicating that it is in use. Remove all inactive System and Finder files.
	The Desktop file may be corrupt.	Rebuild the invisible Desktop file: 1. Hold down the Command (Open Apple key) and Option keys while the Macintosh is starting-up. 2. A dialog box will ask you if you want to rebuild it. Click OK. This does not damage your data, but does remove any file comments.
	The Desktop file may be too big. With System 6.X, disks with Desktop files larger than about 275 KB would cause resource manager problems.	• Upgrade to System 7. OR • Partition the drive.
	The Finder may not have enough memory. Under System 6.X MultiFinder, the Finder is normally allocated 160 KB. You can see how much memory it is using by bringing up "About The Finder" from the Apple menu.	• Increase the Finder's memory partition by doing a Get Info on the Finder. Try allocating 256 KB or more. OR • Upgrade to System 7.
	Too little system heap space. Under System 6.X, especially when many INITs or System Extensions are loaded, you may need to increase heap space.	Use a utility program, such as Heapfixer, to increase this system setting.

Problem: Drive Problems		
Symptoms	**Possible Causes**	**Recommended Actions**
	The directory on your hard disk may be damaged.	Repair the directory with Apple's Disk First Aid. Use a recovery program or restore the data from previous backups. Use a low-level bad block scan program to search for bad blocks.
	A virus may have infected your hard disk.	Check your hard disk with a virus detection and eradication program.
A "Disk is full" message appears when the disk is not full.	• You may have large invisible or temporary files. • The directory may be corrupted. • You have attempted to access a large volume on a machine that does not support large volumes.	Run a recovery program or Disk First Aid.
The drive mounts but cannot be used as a start-up disk.	• Bad boot blocks on the disk. • System Software on the drive. • A hardware problem with the drive.	• Make sure drive is marked as start-up device in the control panel. • Check the hardware connections. • Reinstall the System software. **NOTE:** The Macintosh Plus will only start up off the device with the highest SCSI ID number.
A dialog box appears saying "This disk is unreadable. Do you want to initialize it?"	Corrupted data structure on the disk.	**Do not click on OK**; this will erase the data on the disk. Run a disk recovery program.
	Blind data transfers are not supported. In Blind Data Transfer mode, the CPU allows the SCSI chip to oversee transfers, freeing the CPU for other tasks. The CPU checks in only once before a block of data is transferred, requiring constant timing of the computer rather than a polling method, where the CPU would have to check for a Request/Acknowledge handshake with every byte transferred. The polling method requires more CPU time, so blind transfers complete much faster.	You should turn blind transfers off under the following circumstances: • The device is not fast enough to keep up. • The device has irregular timing with the SCSI chip. • When using Daystar™ or other third party CPU accelerators that are incompatible with blind SCSI transfers.
A dialog box appears saying "This disk needs minor repairs. Do you want to repair it?"	The invisible Desktop file has become corrupted due to abrupt shutdown.	Click OK. The Macintosh will rebuild the Desktop file.

Problem: Removable Media Problems		
Symptoms	**Possible Causes**	**Recommended Actions**
The drive does not mount.	Incorrect SCSI ID, faulty cabling, no termination, or an inappropriate cartridge.	• Make sure the cabling and SCSI ID of the drive are correct and secure. • Make sure the bus is properly terminated. • Make sure the cartridge is formatted for the Macintosh and contains valid data. • If you have not installed your formatter's extension in your boot drive's System Folder, and you booted up without a cartridge in the drive, you need to mount the cartridge by running your formatting software, or from within a Control Panel based mount utility.
	Bad or missing driver.	Reload the device driver that came with your removable media drive.
	Damaged cartridge.	The media may be damaged (particularly if dropped). Do not insert a damaged disc into the drive because it could damage the drive heads.
Light is flashing in the front of drive without media inserted.	Hardware problem.	If termination and cabling are correct, the drive may have a hardware problem. Contact the drive manufacturer.

Problem: File Oriented Problems		
Symptoms	**Possible Causes**	**Recommended Actions**
Errors reading or writing files in the Finder; "Some files couldn't be read/written and were skipped" message.	• Cabling or termination problems. • Bad blocks on the media.	• Check for proper cabling and termination. • Use HDT's Primer to test the drive for bad blocks and to remap them or reformat the drive. • Try reformatting and erasing grown defects.

Problem: File Oriented Problems		
Symptoms	**Possible Causes**	**Recommended Actions**
A file cannot be opened from within an application.	• The file is corrupted. • The application is the wrong version for the file. • The file type code is incorrect.	• Check the Get Info box on the file. Reinstall the application. • Check the application for version compatibility.
The parent application cannot be opened by double-clicking on the file icon.	• The Desktop file is corrupted. • The application is corrupted or missing. • The file's type code is inconsistent with the application or its bundle information is erroneous.	• Reinstall the application. • Rebuild the Desktop file.
A file cannot be thrown away or the trash cannot be emptied.	• The file or folder is busy, locked, or protected. • There is an invisible file in the folder. • The directory is corrupted.	• Close and unlock the file or folder. • Use HDT Util to unprotect the file or folder. Rebuild the Directory. • Restart and try throwing it away again. • Run recovery program.
A folder cannot be renamed.	• A locked disk. • The Directory is corrupted.	• Unlock the disk. • Run a disk recovery program.
A folder takes a long time to open.	• Too many files in folder. • The Desktop file is corrupted.	• Reorganize the folder hierarchy. • Rebuild the Desktop file.
Programs bomb when launched.	Corrupted application or extension conflict.	• Reinstall the application. • Reboot and turn off all extensions by holding down the shift key while starting up.
	Damaged Preferences file.	Find the program's preferences file, usually in the Preferences folder; delete it and relaunch the program.
	Damaged Font file.	Isolate damaged font by moving the Fonts folder out of the System Folder and putting Fonts back in one at a time.
The icons appear and then disappear or become generic icons.	The Desktop file has become corrupted.	Rebuild the Desktop file by restarting and holding down Command and Option keys.
A file or folder disappears.	The directory has become corrupted.	Run Disk First Aid or a recovery program.
Files and folders appear with garbage names.	Cabling and or termination problems.	Immediately **TURN-OFF** the computer and check cabling.

Problem: File Oriented Problems		
Symptoms	**Possible Causes**	**Recommended Actions**
Multiple icons appear on the Desktop for the same drive. If you have partitioned your drive, there should be a separate icon for each partition that is mounted, but no more.	SCSI ID conflict.	Make sure that no two SCSI devices, including any SCSI cards, share the same SCSI ID. Make sure that none of the devices uses ID 7, which is reserved for the host.
Cannot delete a file.	File is locked or in use.	Make sure file is not locked or open by a program. 1. Boot without extensions. 2. Drag file to the trash. 3. Hold the Option Key down when Emptying Trash.

Problem: System Bomb		
Symptoms	**Possible Causes**	**Recommended Actions**
The Bomb System Error Dialog box appears.	This can be caused by many software problems including conflicts with an extension, too little system heap, or another application.	Attempt to restart the system. If the bomb continues, check for free system heap space, disable System Extensions, and reinstall the software. Heap space is a memory pool that is used by the Macintosh operating system to store system data. **NOTE:** System error code descriptions are available in public domain programs or in Inside Macintosh books from Apple.

PC Troubleshooting

PC boot process

The PC has a complicated process for starting up the machine. Knowing more about the process will allow users to troubleshoot future boot problems and to develop a better understanding of how the PC works.

 For information on the Macintosh boot process, see "Mac boot process" on page 298.

1. The PC is powered on and the BIOS performs a test of RAM and other motherboard components.

2. Video cards are initialized and the default video mode is enabled.

3. The machine looks at its CMOS setting to determine if any system drives (IDE, ESDI, ST-506) are in the computer.

CMOS stands for Complementary (symmetry) metal-oxide semiconductor. It is a memory chip that permits many components to be packed together in a very small area. The main characteristics of CMOS chips are low power consumption, high noise immunity and slow speed.

4. The BIOS initializes all cards, causing drivers to be loaded from these cards and banners to be displayed.

   If SCSI cards are encountered, the SCSI card's BIOS will scan their buses and allocate INT13 numbers for any usable drives.

5. The machine checks for bootable floppies in the floppy drive.

6. If a system drive is found, the PC will attempt to boot from it.

   If no system drives are in the system, the PC will attempt to boot from the first SCSI host adapter card it encounters.

7. Using the INT13 interface, the startup drive will be examined to see if it has a valid boot sector.

A valid boot sector consists of two components: boot loader code and a partition information table.

8. If the startup drive has a valid boot sector, the BIOS will execute the boot loader code contained in the boot sector.

9. The boot loader examines the partition table for an active, or bootable, partition. The first sector of that partition contains operating system-specific boot code and operating system-specific partition information.

10. The partition boot code is executed and proceeds to load in whatever operating system is present on that partition (for DOS, this would be the hidden files IO.SYS and MSDOS.SYS).

PC problems and recommended actions

If the following recommended actions fail to correct your system problems, reformatting the drive may do the trick.

Remember that formatting will erase all data on the disk.

If you cannot solve the problems, call the technical support department of your peripheral's vendor for assistance.

Problem: PC Problems		
Symptoms	**Possible Causes**	**Recommended Actions**
Cannot see a new drive.	Drive is not set up correctly.	• IDE drives must be set up using the ROM based Setup program. SCSI drives usually do not need to be allocated in the Setup program. • Make sure cables are plugged in the right way.
	Drive is set to wrong SCSI ID.	Some SCSI Host Adapters require drives to be set to SCSI ID 0, the next drive to 1, and subsequent drives in sequence.
Disk Boot Failure Cannot find system files Invalid Partition table Invalid Drive Specification Error loading operating system	Damaged operating system.	Boot off emergency boot disk and update operating system on drive using the SYS command.
	Invalid CMOS settings.	Use your BIOS Setup utility to reconfigure your drive. You should write all these CMOS settings down so that you can re-enter them if they get corrupted.
	Damaged Master Boot Record or partition table.	Run a disk recovery program.
	DOS boot record is missing.	Run FDISK to make the partition active.
Missing Operating System	Damaged boot block.	Run a recovery program to repair the block.
General failure reading drive C:	Defect on disk.	Run a disk test program such as SCANDISK to map out bad blocks.
Drive is running very slow	File fragmentation	Run a disk optimizer program to clean up your disk.
Lost Clusters Found on drive.	Entries in the file allocation table (FAT) cannot be found on any FAT chains.	Use CHKDSK or SCANDISK to convert them to files and fix the directories.
Cannot boot off a drive.	Incorrect BIOS settings	Make sure no drives are configured in your BIOS. These system drives boot before any drives are present on host adapters. Devices present on host adapters are booted from in order of their Device Number on the PCI bus. Place devices that are bootable in lower number slots.

Problem: PC Problems		
Symptoms	**Possible Causes**	**Recommended Actions**
Drive connected but not ready.	Drive was not fully spun up when it needed to be.	Turn on the drive before turning on the computer. Set a delay in your host adapter's scanning routine.
SCSI Bus scan hangs.	A device does not support synchronous data transfers or SCSI parity checking.	Disable synchronous transfers and/or parity for the device in question.
Inserting a new card causes the computer to hang during initialization.	Card is incompatible with motherboard or other cards.	Make sure that there are no conflicting IRQ, DMA, memory address, or I/O port settings. See if an updated BIOS is available for card or other cards.
Operating system does not see removable media changes.	Removable media drivers not loaded.	Disable BIOS support for removable drives and use driver based removable support.

Appendix A: Additional Information Sources

Web Sites

Industry or Organization	Web Site Address
Fiber Channel Association	http://www.Amdahl.com/ext/CARP/FCA/FCA.html
Fiber Channel Loop Community (FCLC)	WWW: http://tachyon.rose.hp.com/fclc
IEEE 1394 Trade Association	http://www.austin.apple.com/1394web_pages/1394_TA.html
PCI	http://www.teleport.com/~pc2/pcisigindex.html
	http://www.intel.com/product/tech-briefs/pcibus.html
SCSI-2 Rev 10L on-line in HTML	http://abekas.com:8080/SCSI2/
SSA Industry Association	http://www.ssaia.org/
VESA Local Bus	http://www.vesa.org /
X3 Standards Committee home page	http://www.x3.org/
X3T10 Home Page	http://www.symbios.com/x3t10/

FTP Sites

Industry or Organization	FTP Site
ATA FTP Site	fission.dt.wdc.com Directory: /pub/standards/ata/
Fibre Channel documents FTP Site	ftp.network.com
FCSI Fibre Channel Profiles FTP Site	playground.sun.com
SCSI Anonymous FTP Site	ftp.symbios.com Directory: /pub/standards/io/

I/O Interface Reflectors (mailing lists):

The following table lists information about several electronic mailing lists that you can "join." To join a list:

---

1. Write to the address in the **To Subscribe or Unsubscribe ...** column. (Use the same address to request removal from a list).

2. Type the information in the **Subject** column in the e-mail subject line.

3. In the body of a subscription message put:
   [*subscribe* **or** *unsubscribe*] [*keyword*] [*your e-mail address*]

All of the majordomo and listserv reflectors are automatic. Be sure to use the format listed in Step 3.

On the reflectors using majordomo, your e-mail address is optional. If you include it and it doesn't match the address in the e-mail headers, there will be a delay while humans verify your e-mail address.

To post a message, send it to the address in the **To Post a Message ...** column.

These lists are often called Reflectors or Exploders because mail sent to one address gets sent to everyone on the list (causing a small explosion of mail activity).

Subject	To Subscribe or Unsubscribe ...	To Post a Message ...	Keyword
ATA	majordomo@dt.wdc.com	ata@dt.wdc.com	ata
ATAPI	majordomo@dt.wdc.com	atapi@dt.wdc.com	atapi
CD-Recordable	majordomo@dt.wdc.com	cdr@dt.wdc.com	cdr
Disk Attach	majordomo@dt.wdc.com	disk_attach@dt.wdc.com	disk_attach
FC Class 4	majordomo@northyork.hp.com	fc-class4@northyork.com	fc-class4
FC IP Prot.	majordomo@think.com	fc-ip-ext@think.com	fc-ip-ext
FC Isoch.	majordomo@northyork.hp.com	fc-isoch@northyork.hp.com	fc-isoch
Fibre Chan.	majordomo@think.com	fibre-channel-ext@think.com	fibre-channel-ext
HIPPI	majordomo@think.com	hippi-ext@think.com	hippi-ext
IDETAPE	majordomo@dt.wdc.com	idetape@dt.wdc.com	idetape
IEEE P1394	bob.snively@eng.sun.com	p1394@sun.com	n/a (human)
IPI	majordomo@think.com	ipi-ext@think.com	ipi-ext
MultiMedia	majordomo@dt.wdc.com	mmc@dt.wdc.com	mmc
PCMCIA	listserv@cirrus.com	pcmcia-gen@cirrus.com	pcmcia-gen
SCSI	majordomo@symbios.com	scsi@symbios.com	scsi
SFF	bob.snively@eng.sun.com	sff_reflector@sun.com	n/a (human)

Subject	To Subscribe or Unsubscribe ...	To Post a Message ...	Keyword
SSA	majordomo@dt.wdc.com	ssa@dt.wdc.com	ssa
STA SCSI Trade Assn.	majordomo@symbios.com		star
System Issues	majordomo@dt.wdc.com	si@dt.wdc.com	si
10bit	majordomo@dt.wdc.com	10bit@dt.wdc.com	10bit

American National Standards Institute (ANSI)

If you wish to contact ANSI, write or call:

ANSI
1430 Broadway
New York, NY 10018

Phone: (212) 642-4900

ANSI documents are published by

11 West 42nd Street
13th Floor
New York, NY 10036

Sales Department: (212) 642-4900

The SCSI Trade Association

STA was formed in 1995 and is dedicated to the following ends for parallel SCSI:

- Promote increased use.
- Promote better understanding.
- Shape the evolution.

For more information about SCSI or the STA contact:

Joe Molina, Technology Forums LTD
13 Marie Lane
St. Peter, MN 56082-9423

Phone: (507) 931-0967
Fax: (507) 931-0976

e-mail: tforums@ic.mankato.mn.us

Source for Additional Fiber Channel Information

The Fiber Channel Loop Community (FCLC)
P.O. Box 2161
Saratoga, CA 95070

Phone: (408) 867-1385
Fax: (408) 741-1600

Source for Additional PC Card Standard Information

The PC Card Standard is published by
Personal Computer Memory Card International Association
2635 North First Street, Suite 209, San Jose, California 95131

Source for Additional PCI Information

PCI Special Interest Group
PO Box 14070
Portland, Oregon 97214

Phone (US): 800-433-5177
Phone (international): 503-797-4207
Fax (all): 503-234-6762

Source for Additional PCMCIA Information

International Headquarters
2635 North First Street, Suite 209
San Jose, CA 95131

Phone: 408-433-CARD (2273)
Fax: 408-433-9558

BBS: 408-433-2270

Source for Additional SFF Information

SFF documents are published by

SFF
14426 Black Walnut Court
Saratoga, California 95070

Fax: 408-741-1600

Source for Additional X3T10 Information

X3T10 Bulletin Board System: 719-574-0424

Appendix B: Suggested Additional Reading

This section contains a list of storage-related publications that provide more information on particular topics.

A Case for Redundant Array of Inexpensive Drives (RAID), Patterson, David A; Gibson Garth; Katz, Randy H.1987.

ANSI Standards
ST506 X3.170-1990
ATA CAM X3.221-1994
ATA X3.279-199x
ATA-2 Draft Specification
ATA-3 Draft Specification
SCSI X3.131-1986
SCSI-2 X3.131-1993
American National Standards Institute.

Basics of SCSI, Ancot Corp1993.

Computer Technology Review, West World Productions Publication, ISSN 0278-9647, 1990–1995.

Conner CFA810A/CFA1080A Product Manual Revision A, Conner Peripherals, May 1994.

Designing Cards and Drivers for the Macintosh Family, 3rd Edition, Addison Wesley Publishing Company.

Designing PCI Cards and Drivers For Power Macintosh Computers, Apple Computer, 1995.

Electronic Engineering Times, CMP Publications, 1993–1995.

Fast Track to SCSI, Prentice Hall, ISBN 0-13-307000-X.

Hard Disk Secrets, Goodman, John M., IDG Books, ISBN 1-878058-64-9.

Inside Macintosh: Devices, Addison Wesley Publishing Company, ISBN 0-201-62271-8, 1995.

Introduction to Redundant Array of Inexpensive Drives (RAID), Patterson, David A; Gibson Garth; Katz, Randy H., 1987.

Quadra 630 Computer Developer Note, Apple Computer, 1993.

SCSI Bench Reference; SCSI Tutor, ENDL Publications, 1991, ISBN 1-879936-11-9.

SCSI Interconnection Guide Book, AMP, 1993.

SCSI-3 Documents, Global Engineering Documents, 1995.

Small Form Factor documents, SFF, 1993.

The Book of SCSI: A Guide for Adventurers, No Starch Press, ISBN 1-886411-02-6.

The Hard Drive Encyclopedia, Alting-Mess, Adrian, Annabooks, ISBN 0-929392-10-8.

The RAIDbook, A Source Book for Disk Array Technology, RAID Advisory Board, 1994.

The SCSI Bus and IDE Interface, Schmidt, Friedhelm, Addison-Wesley Publishing Company, ISBN 0-201-42284-0, 1995.

The SCSI Encyclopedia, Endl Publications, 1991.

What is Fibre Channel, Ancot Corp, 1994.

Glossary

1394

FireWire. A low- to medium-speed bus intended for desktop PC implementations. It appears that 1394 will be used mainly in consumer audio/video products, set-top (cable) boxes, scanners and printers.

2,7 RLL

A version of Run-Length Limited recording that allows from two to seven consecutive zero bits. This results in a 50 percent increase in drive capacity over standard MFM.

See also Run-Length Limited and MFM.

3,9 RLL

A version of Run-Length Limited recording that allows the run length of the zero string to range from three to nine. This method, also called Advanced Run-Length Limited (ARLL), permits a 100 percent increase in drive capacity over standard MFM.

See also Run-Length Limited and MFM.

Ablative WORM

A method of writing to a CD that changes the physical properties of the media in a way that cannot be undone. The "ablative" in "ablative WORM" refers to the creation of permanent pits in the media surface. WORM stands for write-once read-many.

Absolute Filter

Filters that prevent particles bigger than a certain size from contaminating a hard disk. They usually have a filtering ability of several tenths of a micron. At the same time, they allow outside air into the sealed area of the drive to equalize pressures and temperatures in accordance with changes in the external environment.

Access Time

The time period from issuance of a command to access a single sector to the time when the disk drive's head reaches the sector. Access time can represented by the following formula:

$$Seek\ Time\ +\ Latency\ +\ Time\ to\ Read\ a\ Sector\ =\ Access\ Time$$

ActiveAudio™

A type of Enhanced CD. ActiveAudio is one of the approaches developers have taken to solve the problems that occur when you combine digital and audio data on one CD-ROM. ActiveAudio information is organized in this way: digital data occupies the silence preceding track 1 (so-called track 0). Audio data occupies track 1 and up.

Active Backplane

A backplane that provides multiple drives with power and data connections even when some drives are pulled out or plugged in on the fly. This is necessary for a hot-swappable drive. Without an active backplane, plugging in a drive while the system is operating could kill the SCSI bus and hang the computer.

Active High Signal

Signals along the bus that are asserted when the signal strength is above a certain voltage, which is typically over 2.5 volts (plus or minus a five percent margin).

Active Low Signal

Signals on the bus that are asserted when the voltage falls below a stated level, which is typically under 0.4 volts.

Active Negation

Circuitry that drives the signal line high when it is negated. Driving the lines high ensures that Request and Acknowledge signals are clearly recognized.

Active Termination

Termination that attempts to address impedance mismatches by compensating for voltage. With active termination, a voltage regulator provides about 24 milliAMPs of current into each asserted SCSI line over a considerable range of terminator power values.

Actuator

See Head Actuator.

Address

The ID number of a device on the SCSI bus, or of a block of data in storage.

Advanced RLL

The 3,9 RLL technique, where the run length of the zero string can range from three to nine. This method permits a 100 percent increase in drive capacity over standard MFM.

See also Run-Length Limited and MFM.

AEN

Asynchronous Event Notification. A protocol that can be used to inform processor devices that an asynchronous event has occurred. Instead of the initiator polling, the target would notify the initiator.

AIFF

Audio Interchange File Format. It is a full-featured audio file specification that allows many programs on multiple platforms to share standards for audio storage. Electronic Arts published the AIFF specification in 1985. It started as a digital music instrument specification. Over the years it has been enhanced to provide compressed digital sound (AIFC).

Algorithm

A step-by-step problem-solving procedure that has only one starting point and one finishing point. In computing, it is the process of defining a set of instructions so that a program can be written to find the solution to a given problem.

The word comes from the name of an early proponent, Muhammad ibn-Musa *al-Khwarizmi*.

Alias

A small "marker" file that points the Mac OS to the real file. Aliases are commonly used to organize the

Macintosh Desktop. On larger volumes, where larger allocation blocks are used, an alias can be as big as 4 KB, 8 KB, 16 KB, or more.

Allocation Block Size

The allowable size of units of information in which data is organized and stored on a disk by the operating system. Blocks are of fixed size, with the most common being 512 bytes. They are stored contiguously, with space between adjacent blocks on the same track.

Analog

Information that is highly variable and has a direct, proportional relationship to the thing it describes. For example, information that describes current wind velocity or temperature.

ANSI

The American National Standards Institute. ANSI is a private, nonprofit membership organization that performs two functions: it coordinates the United States' voluntary consensus standards system, and it approves American National Standards. ANSI ensures that a single set of non-conflicting American National Standards are developed by ANSI-accredited standards-developers, and that all interests concerned have the opportunity to participate in the development process. These requirements for due process have resulted in a high level of confidence and credibility and broad acceptance for American National Standards. But it is important to remember that ANSI does not develop standards. Rather, it provides the means for determining the need for standards, ensures that qualified organizations develop those standards, and coordinates standards approval. If you wish to contact ANSI, write or call: ANSI, 1430 Broadway, New York, NY 10018; (212) 642-4900.

Arbitration

An optional phase required for multiple-host systems. If supported, it is a protocol by which SCSI devices gain control of the bus.

Areal Density

A measure of disk capacity in bits per square inch. It is calculated by taking the number of bits per inch that can be written to and read from each track, and multiplying that by the number of tracks per inch that can be packed onto the disk.

Armature

The supporting framework for a drive head.

Array

A linked group of small, independent drives used to replace larger, single drive systems.

ARLL

Advanced Run-Length Limited. See 3,9 RLL.

ASIC

Application-specific integrated circuit. ASICs are computer chips developed for specific functions. These are used in a wide-range of devices, such as video machines, microwave ovens and security alarms.

ASPI

Advanced SCSI Programming Interface managers are software programs that enable the storage software, SCSI device drivers, your host adapter, and your SCSI devices to communicate with each other. ASPI managers are written for a specific operating system, such as DOS, and a specific family of host adapters.

Assert

Usually assert means to send a control signal. However, for two control signals, Control/Data (C/D) and Input/Output (I/O), it means selecting one or the other.

Asynchronous

A method of data transfer that requires a Request/Acknowledge handshake for the movement of every information byte.

The asynchronous mode is the data transfer default. It is in effect at power-up, after a Bus Device Reset message, and after a hard reset condition.

AT

Advanced Technology. Sometimes used to mean IDE, Integrated Drive Electronics interface.

ATA

Advanced Technology Attachment. Sometimes used to mean IDE, Integrated Drive Electronics., although ATA specifically references an implementation of IDE designed for the AT bus (either ISA or EISA).

ATA-2

Advanced Technology Attachment-2. Another name for Enhanced IDE.

ATA-3

Advanced Technology Attachment-3. Designed to support 32-bit operating systems such as Windows 95 and NT. The ATA-3 architecture was designed to be flexible and modular, abstracting the physical interface from the transport mechanism and command sets. ATA-3 supports the following:

- Drives as large as 137 GB
- Data transfer rates of 16.6 MB/s via Mode 4 PIO or Mode 2 DMA
- Devices such as disk, tape, CD-ROM and CDR

ATA Manager

Provides the interface between the ATA software (operating system drivers or application programs) and hardware (chip).

ATAPI

Advanced Technology Attachment Packet Interface. Part of Enhanced IDE, this specification defines a standardized method for interfacing non-hard disk devices utilizing the existing IDE computer interface and cabling.

Attention Condition

A condition on the SCSI bus that results when the initiator signals the target that it has a message ready.

Auto Compensator

A mechanism within a drive that regularly conducts seek tests and adjusts the movements of the head actuators accordingly.

Autolocking

Autolocking physically locks a parked drive head over a designated landing zone on the disk, preventing any head movement.

Autoparking

Upon power loss, the drive heads are automatically pulled by a spring to a safe position on the disk—the landing or parking zone.

AV

A marketing designation given to computers that are equipped with special hardware and software to facilitate audio, video and related types of production.

Average Seek Time

The time in milliseconds to do all possible seeks on the drive divided by the number of seeks possible.

Backplane

The section of a computer system board into which other boards are plugged.

Back up, Backup

v. To make duplicates of files on a separate medium; *n.* the duplicated data.

Backward Compatibility

Design that takes into account compatibility requirements for earlier models and builds support for those requirements into later generations. The result is a new product that can still be used on an old product platform.

Bandwidth

The range of frequencies that can pass along a cable or communications link.

Benchmark

A standard used to compare computer systems or programs, usually in relation to speed, reliability and accuracy.

Bernoulli Drive

A drive with a 5.25" cartridge containing a flexible disk that spins within a cushion of filtered air.

Bernoulli Effect

An effect that is observed when the velocity of a fluid over a surface is increased and the pressure of that fluid on the surface decreases. In the instance of Bernoulli drives, the fluid involved is air. The reduced air pressure draws the disk toward the read/write head.

Binary Data

Data that is represented as 0 or 1.

BIOS (Basic Input/Output System)

Software coded into computer chips for various purposes. The BIOS on the motherboard of a computer is the special program used to boot and control the computer. Most host adapters include an on-board BIOS that initializes the SCSI Bus, runs bootup diagnostics, and performs other functions.

Bit

Bit is a contraction of "binary" and "digit." All computer information is represented as a unique combination of the binary digits 0 and 1, which are also called "ons" and "offs."

Bit Cells

Magnetic domains created through RLL encoding. They are one-third smaller than those used in MFM encoding.

Bit-Based Striping with Parity

An array of disk drives that transfer data in parallel, while one redundant drive functions as the parity check disk. Another term for RAID level 3.

See also Byte-Based Striping with Parity.

Blind Data Transfer

Data transfer that forgoes request/acknowledge handshakes and thus is much faster than regular data transfer. Blind transfer is used during programmed I/O when SCSI DMA hardware is not available.

Block

The smallest "chunk" of memory accessed or transferred by the disk drive. Usually 512 bytes in size, it can be larger in multiples of 512. The number of bytes in a block is the same as block size.

Block Descriptor

Specifies the logical block length for the drive, including the following:

- Density code, which is the density of the medium—usually used only for tape drives
- Number of logical blocks on the medium in the density code
- Block length, which is the length in bytes of each logical block described by the block descriptor

The rest of the data consists of one or more mode pages.

BLER

Block error rate. A measurement of how many errors are detected in the error correction code (ECC) blocks on the media.

Block Mode Data Transfer

See NuBus Block Mode Data Transfer.

Block Multiplexer

A processing standard that allows multiple peripherals to intercommunicate at the same time. It became so popular that the federal government made it a processing standard (FIPS 60).

Also called the OEM channel.

Blown Session

A CD-ROM recording session that is disrupted such that the recorder cannot complete the writing of a disc or track, rendering the recording medium—a writable compact disc—unusable.

Blue Book

A standard that defines a way of combining audio and data on a disc in such a way that the audio may be played on any consumer CD player, while both the audio and the data can be enjoyed on a computer with a compatible CD-ROM drive.

Boolean Function

A switching function in which the function and each of its independent variables may have only two possible values.

Boot Block

Part of the Macintosh HFS partition (although other operating systems place similar information in the first block of the drive platter). The boot blocks on each HFS partition occupy blocks zero and one. They are filled in with data when a System Folder is copied into the partition. The boot blocks contain the following:

- Information that allows the system to start up from the System Folder
- Information on the maximum number of open files
- The name of the debugger
- The names of system files

Bootstrap, or Bootstrapping

A trigger (command code or signal) that allows a device to start-up without outside aid.

Boot-up

The loading of the operating system of a computer into RAM. It is typically an automatic loading procedure issued by the ROM chip.

Buffer

A temporary storage area for data being transferred from one place in the computer system to another. When accessing a single sector, the controller may read the entire track and store it in a buffer.

Buffer Underrun

In CD recording, when the device supplying the data does not get data to the recorder fast enough.

Burst Data Transfer Rate

The fastest that data can be moved at one instance under optimal

conditions, which means data transferred from cache.

Bus

A means of transferring information, usually referring to a set of wires.

Bus Arbitration

How devices vie for control of the bus during an optional bus phase.

Bus Clock

An electronic circuit that regulates the synchronization of the flow of information through the bus.

Bus Condition

A condition on a bus that affects all attached devices and cannot be ignored. It is a critical operation mode and thus overrides other lines. There are two bus conditions:

- Attention
- Reset

Bus Device Reset

A message sent to reset the operation of a specific device.

Bus Free Phase

The bus is empty; no one is riding. This is SCSI's starting point at power-up, after a Reset, and where it returns when a command is completed.

Both the Busy and Select signals must be negated for a defined period of time before this phase is entered.

Bus Mastering

A feature included with some bus cards that allows a card to pass data directly into memory, freeing the CPU to perform more useful functions. (The CPU would otherwise act as an intermediary between the card and memory.)

Bus Phases

Communication across the SCSI bus is divided into stages known as phases. There are eight possible bus phases:

- Bus Free
- Arbitration
- Selection
- Reselection
- Command
- Data-In/Out
- Status
- Message-In/Out

Bus Reset

A method of clearing and consequently stopping all action on the SCSI bus and returning to a known, free state.

Bus-Based Hardware Disk Array

Arrays that are controlled by a RAID host adapter that resides in the computer. These are typically PCI-based boards that include multiple SCSI channels to drives and a RISC-based processor.

Buswidth

The number of bits that can travel simultaneously (in parallel) across a bus.

Butterfly Test

A diagnostic test that is useful for finding media errors.

Byte

A group of eight bits. The basic unit of information.

Byte-Based Striping with Parity

An array of disk drives that transfer data in parallel, while one redundant drive functions as the parity check disk. Another term for RAID level 3.

See also Bit-Based Striping with Parity.

Cable Extender

A cable that functions as an extension cord. They can be attached to one another (male-female), to a System cable, and to a Peripheral Interface Cable.

Cable Impedance Mismatch

Condition created when two or more cables retain different impedances, resulting in signal reflections that adversely impact system performance.

Cache

Similar to buffer but more configurable. Cache can reside in RAM or on the drive's controller. It is used to store and quickly transfer recently used data.

Caddy

A plastic tray with a hinged lid and metal shutter used as a carrier for CDs and CD-R discs in some readers and recorders. The caddy helps ensure proper alignment of the disc and aids in keeping CD-R discs clean prior to writing.

Call

A request or instruction from the initiator or target.

Call Chain

A complicated sequence of continuous calls.

The call chain represents the many layers through which calls pass and the levels at which they are translated—in effect, readied for the next level.

In a call chain, each step is distinct and self-contained. This is the result of purposeful intent by good engineers. If an aspect of the call chain is improved, only the layer affected needs to be changed.

CAM

Common Access Method. A software interface for attaching SCSI peripherals. CAM describes a layered architecture with a transport layer on top (XPT). The single XPT vector calls to one or more SCSI interface module (SIM) layers. Each SIM controls a single host bus adapter (HBA).

CAM's major goal is to provide one interface across all hardware platforms to ease software development for every new system.

Canister Drive

A hard drive and its entire head assembly in a rigid cartridge module that plugs into a "mother" unit. The removable part contains the platter and read/write head. The mother unit contains a power supply and may contain a hard drive controller for communicating with the computer.

Capacitance

A value expressed as the ratio of a quantity of electricity to a potential difference.

Capacitor

An electric circuit element used to store charge temporarily, consisting in general of two metallic plates separated by a nonconducting medium.

Catalog Tree

A data structure that tracks the location of and statistics for all files and folders on the disk.

CCS

See Common Command Set.

CD Bridge

A compact disc format used for Kodak Photo CDs and Video CDs. Many readers support the format but it has not yet become important globally. Software support and demand for discs in these formats has not yet fully developed. The standard for PhotoCD was created and is enforced by Kodak. Standards are proposed, but not in place.

CDB

See Command Descriptor Block.

CD-DA

Compact Disc Digital Audio. The format used for conventional audio CDs. It is readable on all audio CD players and most CD-ROM readers, as well as a wide variety of other multimedia devices.

CD-E

CD-ROM Erasable. A proposed standard for creating a rewritable compact disc. Unlike CD-R, CD-E discs can be reused many times. It uses a special drive and media to provide erasability. The discs that are created can be used in many modern CD-ROM drives, but not all, because erasable platters reflect less light than the platters shipping now.

CD-E Drive

These drives, along with specialized mastering software, allow users to write, erase and rewrite to erasable compact discs.

CD-Extra

CD-Extra is one of the approaches developers have taken to solve the problems that occur when you combine computer and audio data on one CD-ROM. CD-Extra takes a multisession approach: Audio data occupies session 1. Computer data occupies session 2.

See also Blue Book.

CD-G (CD Graphics)

Compact disc format used for Karaoke CDs. The format is readable on many devices, but most of them are consumer audio components. While the discs may be readable on CD-ROM drives, special software is required to see the graphics.

CD-i (CD-interactive)

Compact disc format developed by Philips for use in home entertainment systems and multimedia applications. Like CD+G, many readers support this format, but there are few computers or applications that allow the discs to be used. The "Green Book" standard defines this format.

CD-R (CD-Recordable)

Compact disc technology that enables writing to recordable compact discs. Data is written to a specially made

disc by activating a dye embedded in the disc. This dye changes the reflection of the laser in the same way a pit does on a compact disc.

CD Recorder

These drives, along with specialized mastering software, allow users to make their own compact discs.

CD-ROM (Compact Disk-Read-Only Memory)

Data is stored as pits on the CD platter's surface. The pits are read by a laser in the CD ROM drive. The data can be read. Data cannot be erased. New data cannot be added.

CD-ROM Drive

A read-only drive that uses a laser beam to read large amounts of data from compact discs.

CD-ROM XA

CD-ROM Extended Architecture. Compact disc format that allows the interleaving of data and audio for smoother playback of multimedia content. It is readable only on XA compatible drives. Most drives sold after 1991 are XA compatible.

Central Processing Unit, or CPU

The brains or "central switching station" of any computer.

Chassis

The outer protective enclosure of a hard drive or peripheral.

Check Disc

In CD mastering, a disc created before the master, used to check the quality, organization and functionality of the recorded material before a master disc is created.

Chip

An integrated circuit etched into a small slab of silicon. The circuits act as either transistors, resistors or capacitors.

Chip-on-Board

Chip technology that reduces the required real estate by eliminating standard packaging (the black plastic square you see on circuit boards) and attaching to the circuit board directly. The chip is often then covered with a dense polymer that provides protection against environmental rigors.

Clean Room

A room kept virtually free of contaminants, used for laboratory work and in the production of precision parts.

CMOS

Complementary Metal-Oxide Semiconductor. A memory chip that permits many components to be packed together in a very small area. The main characteristics of CMOS chips are low power consumption, high noise immunity and slow speed.

COB

See Chip-on-Board.

Cobalt-Nickel Alloy

A medium for data storage, used to improve densities and provide better reliability.

Coercivity

A measurement of a magnetic material's ability to withstand demagnetizing. Materials that are very hard, such as steel, tend to have high coercivity.

Command Complete

The only message supported by all SCSI devices. Command Complete is sent by the target to the initiator to indicate that:

- It has executed the command (or a series of linked commands).
- A valid status has been sent to the initiator.

Command Complete is neutral. It is up to the status byte to indicate whether or not the command was completed successfully.

Command Descriptor Block

A six-, ten-, or twelve-byte data structure residing in the computer's memory that contains the command code and other information needed by a target to execute a command.

Command Linking

A feature that allows two or more SCSI commands to be linked together. If a linked flag is set in the CDB, the completion of one command triggers the execution of the following command, saving arbitration time.

Command Overhead

The time needed for a computer's command to be interpreted and acted upon by the controller.

Command Phase

The bus phase in which the target requests command information from the initiator.

Common Access Method

See CAM.

Common Command Set

A comprehensive de facto standard for commands. CCS defines the following:

- Data structures for Mode Select and Mode Sense commands
- Defect management of the Format command
- Error recovery procedures
- Numerous other command functions

CCS was the beginning of SCSI-2, but it is only for disk drives.

Compression

A procedure in which data is transformed by the removal of redundant information in order to reduce the number of bits required to represent the data. This is done by representing strings of bytes with code words.

Connectivity

The degree to which a system allows for connecting different devices to it to operate together as a whole system.

Connector

A plug with either or both male (pins) or female (holes) connections at either or both ends, used to connect devices to each other, cards to motherboards, canisters to backplanes, and so on, and to pass signals into or out of these components.

Contingent Allegiance

A state in which targets reject commands until an error status on the bus is cleared.

Controller, or Controller Board

Circuitry, usually built into a drive, that interprets signals between the host and the peripheral. It acts upon these signals, thus providing the device with "intelligence."

Controller Chip

A chip that controls one or more I/O channels.

Control Signals

Signals that direct communications and determine bus phases. There are nine control signals:

- Control/Data
- Input/Output
- Select
- Busy
- Message
- Request
- Acknowledge
- Attention
- Reset

CPU

See Central Processing Unit.

CPU Cache

Cache that resides on or near the CPU.

Crash

When the computer fails and the drive stops working.

Cyanine

One of the two types of dyes used in the production of CD-R discs. On a CD-R disc, rather than a physical pit or depression in the groove, a dye is used to change the reflection of the laser in the same way that a pit would. This dye is activated by a laser beam of a somewhat higher intensity than that used to read data. The use of this dye allows discs created by a laser to be just as readable on conventional CD readers as discs created by a stamper.

See also Phthalocyanine.

Cyclic Redundancy Check

One of the pieces of information in a typical data sector. It is a method of checking for data transmission errors through the use of a mathematical algorithm.

Cylinder

In multi-platter hard disk drives, tracks of equal radius on different platters form a virtual cylinder.

Cylinder Switch Time

One of the influences on data access time. It is the amount of time it takes to move from one track to another.

Daisy Chain

Multiple devices connected to each other, where the SCSI bus is dependent upon each device to pass signals along.

DAO

Disk-at-Once. Also known as uninterrupted write. It is a writing method in which the entire disc is written in one uninterrupted session.

Data cannot be added to the disc later.

Data Error

Any discrepancy between recorded data and recovered data.

Data Transfer Rate

A measure of how quickly data is supplied to the computer from the peripheral device.

DAT Drive

Digital Audio Tape drive. A tape drive that uses helical scan magnetic recording tape to store data in a fashion similar to audio tape recorders, only the information is usually stored in digital form.

See also Digital Data Storage.

Data Block

The smallest contiguous area that can be allocated for storage of data. In UNIX, this is 8 KB. In Macintosh and DOS, this is 512 bytes or multiples of 512 bytes.

In DOS, this unit is referred to as a cluster.

Data Bus Line

The lines on a SCSI bus dedicated to transmitting data signals.

The SCSI bus is composed of up to 50 lines, depending on the electrical specification used, of which 18 are signal lines. Nine transmit data signals, and nine transmit control signals. The rest are connected to ground, except for number 25, which is left open.

Data Density

A measurement, which can be in tracks-per-inch, of the amount of data that can fit on a given media surface.

Data Pattern Test

A diagnostic test that is useful for finding media errors. A pattern is written to disk, then read back and compared with what should be there. The pattern is changed, and the process is repeated. This way, it becomes obvious if there are any disk areas that are not converting from 1s to 0s as they should.

Data Redundancy

Some form of ongoing data duplication, often associated with a RAID architecture, that provides a fairly high level of protection against unrecoverable loss of data.

Data Signals

Data, command, status, message and SCSI ID information transmitted over data signal lines.

Data Striping

RAID level 0. An array of drives transferring data in parallel. The data is spread out among the drives one segment at a time. The multiple drives appear to the user as one large, fast drive.

Data Track

On magnetic media, the invisible magnetic "grooves" upon which data is physically stored. Instead of one continuous track, as on a vinyl record, data tracks form distinct concentric circles that emanate from the center of the platter out to the perimeter.

Data Transfer Modes

Data transfer occurs in either one of two modes, or protocols:

- Asynchronous
- Synchronous

The mode used is determined by the SCSI chip and via messages between the initiator and target, usually after a bus reset.

Data Transfer Rate

The rate at which data is transferred from a storage medium to the computer. Two rates of transfer are commonly measured:

- Burst data transfer rate
- Sustained data transfer rate

Data Underrun

See Buffer Underrun.

Data-In/Out Phase

The Data-In Phase allows the target to ask for data to be sent from the target to the initiator. In the Data-Out Phase, the target asks to receive data from the initiator. Data is transferred in either the asynchronous or synchronous data transfer mode.

DDA

Direct Disk Attach Profile. In Fibre Channel architecture (FC-4), a protocol used to attach drives to the computer.

DDM

See Driver Descriptor Map.

DDS

See Digital Data Storage.

Decompression

Reversal of the compression software algorithm to return data to its original size and condition.

De Facto Standard

Standards set by users over time, rather than by an agency.

Defragment

To reorder the files on a platter so that all the sectors of each file are contiguous. This results in improved access times. (See Fragmentation.)

Device Driver

The software program that translates commands between the computer's operating system and the storage I/O interface.

Device-Independent

Operating at the systems level and not requiring specific customization to run.

Differential

An electrical signal configuration where information is sent simultaneously through two sets of wires in a cable. The information is interpreted by the difference in voltage between the wires. Differential interfaces allow cable lengths up to 25 meters.

Compare with single-ended.

Differential Backup

A combination of an initial full backup and then subsequent backups of all files that have changed since the last full backup (not just the changed parts of those files).

Digital

Describes information that is stored as binary digits (bits), either zero or one.

Digital Audio Extraction (DAE)

The transfer of audio information from a CD-ROM drive to a computer system though a SCSI cable. DAE is capable of producing an exact copy of the digital information contained on the CD.

Digital Data Storage

A standard format for 4 mm tapes using helical scan recording. It was developed by Hewlett-Packard and Sony to replace the audio cassette. It has subsequently found homes in both pro-audio and computer areas.

Digital Signal Processor

A processor that speeds the calculation of floating point operations. Among its many applications, floating point arithmetic is used for graphics (in 3-D rendering), imaging, speech synthesis and recognition, audio mixing and numerical processing.

Direct-Access Device

Any device that provides direct access to non-sequential blocks of data. (See Sequential-Access Device.)

Disc-at-Once

CD-R disc writing method in which the entire disc is written in a single session. Data cannot be added to the disc later. This method produces discs that are compatible with all CD-ROM drives, and is used for electronic publishing, audio or any other application where compatibility is crucial.

Diode

A non-linear, two-terminal device that is the simplest semiconductor used in electronics. It acts as a one-way valve, letting current flow through it in one direction while blocking current flow in the other.

DIP Switch

Dual In-line Package Switch. DIP switches are usually found on internal circuit boards. They are used to set some of a device's operational parameters.

Directory

A list of all the files and groups of files stored on a disk. Usually includes the type and name of a file, its size and its creation or modification date.

Disconnect Capability

A capability of most SCSI peripherals to leave the bus, complete a time-consuming operation, and then return.

Disk Array Controller Board

A board with built-in logic for setting up and maintaining a RAID array.

Disk Drive

The physical components necessary to transfer data to and from the recording medium.

Disk Duplexing

Using one drive to duplicate the read/write moves of another. This creates an identical copy of the original. It is accomplished through a dedicated set-up that has two drives and two separate drive interfaces and host adapters, each with its own power supply. Data is both read from and written to both drives.

Disk Mirroring

A single disk controller is connected to two drives. All controller activity is performed twice—first to one drive, then the other.

DLT Drive

Digital Linear Tape drive. Tape Drives use magnetic recording tape to store data in a fashion similar to audio tape recorders, only the information is usually stored in digital form.

DMA (Direct Memory Access)

A mechanism that allows for the transfer of streams of data to or from a computer's main memory without the use of the host microprocessor.

DMA may require setup by the host software. After initialization, DMA automatically sequences the required data transfer and provides the necessary address information.

DMA Controller

Direct Memory Access Controller. A microprocessor dedicated to handling Direct Memory Access. It is usually incorporated into the device controller and operates without depending on the host CPU.

Doubled Embedded Servo

Placing servo information at the beginning and middle of a disk sector.

Double-Density Recording

Another term for Modified Frequency Modulation.

Drive Channel

A communication path to the drive, capable of transmitting data.

Drive Controller

Circuitry that provides the hardware interface between the disk drive and the computer, sending and receiving signals. It interprets the computer's signals and controls the operations of the disk drive.

Driver Descriptor Map

The first data read from a Macintosh. It contains the following:

- The number of blocks on the device
- The block size
- The number of drivers
- The location and size of the first driver

Driver Partition

The disk partition that contains a device's driver.

Drum Storage

Early IBM drives that were shaped like drums, had heads that touched the platters, and held very little data.

The IBM RAMAC 350, in 1956, stored 5 MB with 20-inch disks and had a 600 ms access time. A one- year lease cost about $35,000.

DSP

See Digital Signal Processor.

Dual Channel SCSI

A system with two SCSI controllers, allowing twice as many connected devices as single channel. In regular dual-channel SCSI, you can have up to 16 devices on the bus. In Wide dual-channel SCSI, you can have up to 32.

DVD

Digital Versatile Disc. Also sometimes referred to as Digital Video Disc. A new standard that provides for up to 4.7 GB of storage on a 120-mm, CD-ROM-sized optical disc.

Edge Connector

A connector with flat, metal contact points that mate with like contact points in connection ports, such as motherboard slots or cable ports. They were designed to eliminate the vulnerability to bends and breaks inherent in pin connectors.

EDPT

Enhanced Drive Parameter Table. A parameter table used on PC compatibles that contains two sets of drive parameter information. The first set is called CHS, for cylinder, head, sector. It provides a straight translation of BIOS cylinder, head and sector information, without reducing the number of heads supported from 255 to 16.

The second set translates the cylinder, head, sector information into a 28-bit logical block address à la SCSI.

EISA

Enhanced Industry Standard Architecture. It was designed to supersede the ISA bus, yet retain full compatibility with ISA. EISA ran at the ISA standard 8.33 MHz clock rate and allowed bus masters to be supported. EISA extended ISA to 32-bit operation and sped burst data transfer rates up to 33 MB/s. Its sustained rate was closer to 8 MB/s.

EISA allowed for automatic adapter configuration without DIP switches.

Embedded Servo

Servo data is embedded on the platter between the tracks in the form of magnetic bursts. This is also known as wedged servo.

Encoding

The protocol by which data is written to the hard disk platter. Encoding provides timing marks for the head and a shorthand form of the data, which increases the platter's capacity.

Enhanced IDE

A storage interface that allows support of four IDE devices when two IDE channels are present. The primary channel is designed for high-speed hard disks, whereas the low-speed secondary channel is designed for non-hard disk devices, such as CD-ROM and tape drives. Allows support of drives up to 8.4 GB in capacity. Logical block addressing allows for the increase in capacity potential. Support for multiple-block transfers is included.

Error Correcting Code (ECC)

Additional data stored on the drive to help correct an error before the drive exhausts its allowable number of retries.

Errors, Hard Data

Data loss through physical damage to the hardware, usually the surface of the recording medium, which may not be recoverable. Hard errors are permanent and thus are likely to be repeatable.

Errors, Soft Data

Data misreads or miswrites due to poorly written software or viruses, which may not be repeatable. Soft errors can usually be recovered through reread attempts or a recovery program.

ESDI

Enhanced Small-Device Interface. An improved ST-506 interface developed in the mid-1980s and championed by Maxtor. ESDI doubled ST-506's data transfer rate and allowed for selective reformatting of tracks. Otherwise, mechanically and electronically it was virtually identical to ST-506. It was device-specific and only used for hard disk drives, mostly those with very large capacity. It offered a maximum capacity of about 1 GB.

Exabyte (EX)

An exabyte equals 10^{18} or 1,000,000,000,000,000,000 bytes.

Exabyte is also the name of a manufacturer of tape drives.

Exclusive Or (XOR)

A Boolean function that sets a parity bit to 1 if and only if either of the compared data bits is 1, but not both.

Expansion Card

An add-in card that typically enhances system features. Typically, cards provide additional connection ports and/or increase I/O performance.

Extended Partition

Separate logical partitions that can be up to 8 GB in capacity. There can be lots of extended partitions because they include their own partition tables.

Extents Tree

A data structure on the Macintosh that tracks the location of and statistics for all files and folders on the disk.

External Hard Drive

A hard drive in its own chassis that is connected to a host computer with a cable.

Fast ATA

Seagate and Quantum's version of EIDE, but without some of the extensions, like large capacity and ATAPI support. It was designed to minimize the need to enhance system BIOS.

Fast SCSI

Fast SCSI uses the standard 50-pin connector to double the maximum data transfer rate to 80 Mb/s in fast synchronous mode. (Up to 10 mega-transfers per second.) It does this by cutting synchronous transfer timings in half. However, this works only with modern SCSI chips, which were not used in the Macintosh for many years, but are available through third-party add-ons.

Fast SCSI is used in only the data-in/out phase.

Performance improvements for sustained data transfer rates increase as follows:

- Fast SCSI-2: 10 MB/s (8-bit narrow)
- Fast/Wide SCSI-2: 20 MB/s (16-bit wide)
- Fast-20 SCSI/Ultra: 20 MB/s (8-bit narrow)
- Ultra Wide SCSI: 40 MB/s (16-bit wide)

Fast/Wide SCSI

Part of both the SCSI-2 and SCSI-3 specification. Fast/Wide SCSI allows for the support of 16 devices on a single-channel bus (32 on a dual-channel), a 20 MB/s data transfer rate, and 16-bit wide data transfers. Typically a 68-pin connector is used with Fast/Wide SCSI, although a 50-pin can be used.

See also Fast SCSI.

Fast-20 SCSI

Part of the SCSI-3 specification. Also referred to as Ultra SCSI. Fast-20 SCSI allows for the support of 8 devices on a bus, a 20 MB/s data transfer rate, and 8-bit data transfers. A 50-pin connector is used with Fast-20.

See also Fast SCSI.

FAT

See File Allocation Table.

Fault Tolerance

The ability of a system to continue to perform its function (possibly at reduced performance), even when one of its components has failed. Fault tolerance is often provided by equipping a system with extra instances of components whose failure would cause the system to fail.

FC-AL

See Fibre Channel Arbitrated Loop.

Ferric Oxide

Used for 40 years as the primary medium for data storage. A floppy's surface is covered with rust-oxidized iron particles held in place with a binding agent (typically plastic).

Fibre Channel Arbitrated Loop

An architecture geared towards connecting large scale host computers to storage subsystems and network hubs. The loop structure enables the rapid exchange of data from device to device.

Fibre-Optic Cable

Cable made of plastic or glass fibre that is designed to transmit information at very high frequencies, requiring infrared or visible light as the carrier.

Field Rate of Return (FRR)

One of the calculations used to determine Mean Time Between Failures. FRR only relates to the failure rate of the installed base, not the average life span of each drive. with FRR, an MTBF of 1,000,000 means that out of 10,000 drives, you can expect one drive to fail every 100 hours.

File Allocation Table

A table that keeps track of the locations of blocks in which the operating system has written data to a disk.

File Data Area

The space on disk where data is stored in allocation block-sized chunks.

File Manager

A software library typically located in ROM that manages I/O flow to and from files.

FIPS-60

Federal Information Processing Standard 60. It is also known as IBM's 370-OEM interface. It provided for very fast transfers up to 5 MB/s and cable lengths over 100 meters. It has been extensively used in IBM's System 370, 3080 and 3090 families.

FireWire

See 1394.

Firmware

An often-used microprogram or instruction stored in ROM. Usually refers to the ROM-based software that controls a drive.

Flag

In a Mode Page, a flag is a bit (either on or off) that tells the drive how to respond to a situation.

Flash Memory

A type of electrically erasable, programmable ROM (EEPROM) that can be programmed by the computer or the device it is connected to. It can also refer to a nonvolatile memory system.

Floptical Drive

A drive that marries optical and magnetic technology. The servo data is perforated into the disk. The magnetic data is located in between optical grooves.

Forced Perfect Termination

Developed by IBM, FPT uses a resistor/diode network to pull current up until the diode threshold is crossed. The diode then maintains the voltage at the desired level.

Form Factor

The physical diameter of a drive's platter.

Formatting

The process of preparing a disk for use. The drive maps the disk into blocks, sectors, and tracks. Bad blocks are marked and placed on a defect list.

FPT

See Forced Perfect Termination.

Fragmentation

With use over time, the sectors of a file are written in different areas across the platter's surface. This slows access time.

Frequency Modulation

Timing mechanisms correlate a platter's constant speed with the distance traveled to yield a precise calculation of the head's position over the platter.

Frequency Modulation was the first timing mechanism used. It needed every other magnetic domain to represent a clock pulse. This method had the disadvantage of using half of a disk's storage capacity just for the timing information.

FRR

See Field Rate of Return.

Full-Height

A drive with a housing unit that is 3.25-inches high. It houses 5.25-inch form factor drives.

g

A measurement value. A g is equivalent to the pull of earth's gravity. Device shock ratings are measured in g's.

Giant Magnetoresistance Head (GMR)

The heir-apparent to the Magneto-Resistive head. The GMR may permit magnetic recording in the tens of gigabits per square inch and data rates in the tens of megabytes per second. This new technology has sensitivity in the greater-than 3000 microvolt per micron of track width range.

Gigabit

1024 Megabits or 1,073,741,824 bits.

Gigabyte (GB)

1024 Megabytes or 1,073,741,824 bytes.

Green Book

One of the "color-book" standards for CD recording, in this instance CD-interactive (CD-i). CD-i is used for some home entertainment systems. Philips, which developed the standard, has been the most vocal proponent of this technology. Like CD-G, many readers support the format, but there are few computers or applications that allow the discs to be used.

Green Drive

Environmentally correct drives that support conscientious features like:

- Low-power sleep mode
- Deep sleep mode
- Power management
- Lower power requirements

The EPA estimates that a system that powers down during inactivity could save the user $70 to $90 a year.

Grown Defects List

Created during formatting, it is a list of the bad areas on a disk made available to the controller so that it knows not to write data to them.

Half-Height

A drive with a housing unit that is 1.625-inches high. It houses 3.5- and 5.25-inch form factor drives.

Handshake

The SCSI Request/Acknowledge handshake signifies completion of a data transfer between the target and host across the SCSI bus.

Hard Disk Drive

A data storage device that employs one or more rigid disks as the storage medium.

Hard Drive Cache

Cache that resides on the hard drive's controller board.

Hard Reset

The Reset condition kicks every device off the bus.

A Hard Reset:

- Knocks out all commands in process

- Drops all SCSI device reservations (for disconnects and command queuing)
- Returns all operating modes to their default conditions

This condition is asserted on the Reset signal line and goes out to all devices.

Compare with Soft Reset.

Hardware-Based Disk Array

An array where the drives are connected to a RAID controller board installed inside the disk array chassis. The host computer recognizes the RAID controller board as the SCSI storage device, and not the drives connected to it. Read and write commands sent from the computer are processed by the RAID controller board, which in turn sends the appropriate read and write commands to the drives.

HBA

See Host Bus Adapter.

HDA

See Head Disk Assembly.

Head

See Read/Write Head.

Head Actuator

The physical device (a type of motor) that moves the armature and thus the read/write head(s) across the surface of the hard disk platter.

Head Disk Assembly

An assembly that includes magnetic disks, magnetic heads and an access mechanism, all enclosed in a container.

Head Drift

A diminishment of the positioning accuracy of the drive head due to wear-and-tear.

Header

The first data contained in the Mode Parameter List, which is sent by the initiator to the drive during the Data-Out Phase. It contains the following:

- What type of storage medium, if any, is used in the drive

  A setting of zero for the medium type, which is the default, indicates that the medium is nonremovable.
- The length in bytes of all Block Descriptors

Head Gap

In magnetic head/disk assemblies, most heads consist of an iron core with 8 to 30 coil turns of wire banded around it. There is a gap in the core through which a magnetic field passes. This is the head gap.

Head Parking

When a drive is turned off, the read/write head is moved to a specified location on the disk that is not used for data storage - the landing or parking zone. Most modern drives have an autopark function.

Head Switch Time

The time, measured in microseconds, it takes to switch from one read/write head to another in a read or write operation.

HFS

See Hierarchical File System.

HFS Partition

A Macintosh partition that contains structures to help the Macintosh operating system boot the computer and locate information on files and folders. This data structure is set up when initializing the partition for the Macintosh within the hard disk setup utility program. The following data structures are written to disk:

- Boot blocks
- Volume information block (VIB)
- Volume bitmap
- Extents tree
- Catalog tree
- File data area

Hierarchical File System

The file system used by the Apple Macintosh for storing files and folders on a hard disk.

High-Density Connector

Defined in the SCSI-3 specification, high-density connectors pack the pins more tightly, and are 1.44 inches wide and a quarter-inch thick.

High-Level Formatting

Formatting performed by the operating system to create the root directory, file allocation tables and other basic configurations.

High-Level Interface

A sophisticated interface level that describes a nonphysical abstraction (a logical perspective) that can be manipulated with software.

Holographic Memory

A variation of conventional holography. Two laser beams are focused in the system at different angles and optically interfere on a light-sensitive film. One beam carries the data, which can be either a representation of the digital data stream or a pictorial image. By using a scanner to change the angle or position of the other beam, multiple views of the image are recorded. Thousands of these holograms can be recorded on a single piece of film.

Host

The computer—specifically, its central processing unit (CPU) and SCSI chip.

Host Bus Adapter

Also known as a SCSI adapter or a SCSI host bus adapter. Circuit, card, or device that translates between a computer's "native" bus architecture and the SCSI specified bus architecture.

Hot Spare

In some RAID subsystems, an extra drive that is fully spun up but will be used only if one of the other drives fails.

Hot-Swappable Drive

A drive in a canister, shuttle or carrier that can be removed and plugged in while the system is running.

Hot-Swappable Power Supply

Hot swap capability allows you to swap out the inoperable power supply with an operable spare while the system continues to run. Hot swappable power supplies should be used in conjunction with uninterrupted power supplies and power conditioners to ensure a continuous flow of power during swaps.

Housing Unit

The rigid enclosure that contains the mechanism and controller. It is the foundation to which all other parts are connected. It needs to be rigid so that components within the drive are not hurt on installation or during operation. Most housing units are made from aluminum alloys.

HPPI

High Performance Parallel Interface. This is another name for IPI-3. It is a parallel interface enabling 800 or 1,600 Mb/s data transfers over 32 or 64 twisted-pair copper wires, or on fiber-optic cable. Fiber cabling can be up to 10 kilometers in length, while the other cabling can be up to 36 meters in length. Developed out of work at the Los Alamos National Lab, it is intended for supercomputing applications. It allows multiple block transfers via a single command execution, but can transfer data in only one direction at a time.

HSM

Hierarchical Storage Management. HSM is a concept that creates a hierarchy—a layered structure—of your storage capacity. At the top of this hierarchy is your fastest-but most expensive-storage device. At the bottom, your slowest, least expensive device.

IC

See Integrated Circuit.

IDE

Integrated Drive Electronics or Intelligent Drive Electronics. IDE incorporates controller hardware onto the disk drive, which results in significant parts reduction and cost savings. IDE combines the physical and electrical protocols of ST-506 with the speed of ESDI. IDE drives can be "directly" plugged into a computer's expansion bus.

IEEE

Institute of Electrical and Electronics Engineers. An ANSI-accredited body of scientists and engineers that promotes standardization and provides expertise to ANSI on matters relating to electrical and electronic development.

Impedance

The total opposition offered by a component or circuit to the flow of an alternating or varying current.

Incremental Backup

Creating data security through duplication. With an incremental backup, a software utility reads whatever information has been added to the hard drive during that work session and copies it to a secondary storage medium.

Incremental Recording

A recording method in which data can be added to a CD-R disc in segments. There may be, but does not have to be, interruptions in the data flow between segments. Data can be added using track-at-once (TAO) or packet writing and single session or multisession recording. These discs are Orange Book compliant.

Inductive Head

A read/write head that consists of an iron core with 8 to 30 coil turns of wire banded around it. There is a gap in the core through which a magnetic field passes. The field is induced by the coil of wires wrapped around the iron core, depending on the direction current is flowing in the coil.

Initialization

The process of laying down the directory information that the operating system needs to locate files and folders. Usually destroys only directory information, not the actual data, so that recovery programs can still recover files from initialized disks.

Initiator

A SCSI device, usually the computer—or more specifically its SCSI chip—capable of initiating an operation. In multiple-host systems initiators (hosts) may also be targets.

Input/Output (I/O)

The communication flow between the Mac and its peripherals.

Inside Mac IV and V

Technical manuals provided by Apple. Also used to denote partitioning schemes.

Integrated Circuits, or Chips

An IC performs a host of electronic functions. One IC replaces many discrete transistors. Because it resides on a silicon chip, these ICs are referred to as "chips."

Intelligent

Refers to a device capable of processing commands on its own.

Interface

The go-between that provides a common basis for communication between two otherwise incompatible devices.

Interleaving

The ordering of sectors on a track so that the next sector (in the file being read or written) arrives at the read/write head just as the computer is ready to access it. (See Latency.)

INT13 BIOS

The standard software interface method for accessing a PC hard disk.

Intelligent Peripheral Interface

The successor to the block multiplexer channel, or OEM channel, popularized by IBM in the 1960s. It offers parallel 16-bit data transfer, rather than OEM's eight-bit transfer, and can be split into two eight-bit buses to work like the OEM channel. IPI's dual ports allow from one to eight devices to be connected on one port, and from two to 16 in pairs using both ports. It is largely limited to the mainframe world, typically on 8- and 14-inch drives. It offers read-ahead capability and is extremely fast for large-data transfers.

Interoperability

Connecting different devices to operate together as part of a system.

Interrupt

A momentary suspension of processing caused by a deliberate instruction to the microprocessor.

Intersector Gap

Data on a track sector that separates the preceding sector from the next sector.

Intrasector Gap

Data on a track sector that separates the sector ID information from the data track. Data follows this gap.

I/O

Input/Output. Refers to the sending and receiving of data from the CPU to attached peripherals, such as CD-ROM and external hard disk drives.

IPI

See Intelligent Peripheral Interface.

IRQ

Interrupt Request. Refers to the lines in a computer that carry hardware interrupt signals to the processor on a personal computer.

ISA

Industry Standard Architecture. An expansion bus introduced with the original IBM PC and IBM PC XT in the early 80s.

Isochronous

Having the capability of dedicating a fixed slice of bandwidth to a particular peripheral, such as video.

ISO 9660

ISO is an acronym for the International Standards Organization. ISO 9660 is an established international standard file structure for CD-ROM discs adopted by ISO.

Jukebox

A large chassis that contains multiple optical cartridges, tapes, or CD-ROM discs that get shuffled around by a mechanical device.

Jumper

A small plastic-covered metal connector used to connect pairs of pins on a circuit board. Jumpers are used to set device parameters, such as the SCSI ID.

KB/s

Kilobytes per second.

Kb/s

Kilobits per second.

Kerr Effect

The Kerr effect states that when a polarized light is reflected off a metal surface in a magnetic field, the polarity of the light is rotated clockwise or counterclockwise, depending on the field's polarity. The drive detects this rotation and interprets it as data.

Kilobit (Kb)

One thousand bits (actually 1024 bits).

Kilobyte (KB)

One thousand bytes (actually 1024 bytes).

Landing Zone

A data-free "safe" area on a disk, set aside for parking the drive head.

Laptop

A small, portable personal computer.

Laser Diode

A laser that generates an infrared or visible-light beam.

Latency

The time, in milliseconds, it takes for the spinning platter to bring around the desired sector to where the read/write head can access it. Does not include head positioning time. It is one of the factors of access time.

LBA

See Logical Block Address.

Level 2 Cache

Cache that is external to the CPU.

LIMM DOW

Light intensity modulation method direct over-write. In optical drives, LIMM DOW allows data to be written in a single pass.

Logical Block

Data is grouped in standard sizes known as logical blocks. 512-, 1,024-, and 2,048-byte blocks are common.

Logical Unit Number (LUN)

The numerical representation of the peripheral's address. A SCSI device's address can have up to seven LUNs.

Logical Unit

A physical or virtual device that is addressable as a target.

Logical

An abstract representation of something that physically exists.

Loop Architecture

An architecture geared towards connecting large-scale host computers to storage subsystems and network hubs.

In a loop architecture, the preferred approach is to attach disk drives directly to a backplane, rather than daisy-chaining them together.

Low-Level Formatting

The electronic equivalent of a detailed street map, written on a hard disk. Electronic markings are made on the disk that tell the controller the locations of cylinder/head/sector addresses, servo tracking information and data start/stop points.

Low-Level Interface

Specifications for the wiring, electrical operations and physical connections in an interface standard.

LUN

See Logical Unit Number.

Magnetic Domain

The area on a platter that contains one bit of data.

Magnetic Flux

The magnetic exchange between the read/write head and the platter, which allows the head to write and read data.

Magneto-Optical Drive

Devices that use a high-powered laser to write to a disc and a low-powered laser, which does not heat the disc significantly, to read a disc.

Magneto-Resistive Head

Thin conductive strips that detect magnetic domain transitions by measuring magnetic effects on the resistive element within the head.

This element changes its resistance as its angle of magnetization changes.

Mainframe

A large and fast central computer. The term "mainframe" originally referred to the metal framework that housed the computer circuits, but it came to mean the entire computer. Typically, a mainframe is defined by function rather than by size. It describes a computer that handles all of an organization's processing needs.

Master

When two devices or systems are in such a relationship that one of them has control over the other:

- The controlling device is the master.
- The controlled device is the slave.

MB/s

Megabytes per second. Equal to 8 Megabits per second.

Mb/s

Megabits per second. Equal to 1/8 or 0.125 Megabytes per second.

MCA

See MicroChannel Architecture.

MCM

See Multichip-Module.

Mean Time Between Failures

A vendor-supplied rating that indicates the longevity of a drive. Often referred to by its initials MTBF.

Mean Time to Repair

Amount of time it takes a trained repairman to repair a device.

Media

In hard disks, another term for the platter, but more specifically the magnetic coating that covers the platter. The surface of the platter that holds the data.

Media is also the term used for the recording surface of all drive technologies, such as MO, CD-R and Phase Change Optical.

Megabit

One thousand kilobits (actually, 1024 Kb). Abbreviated as Mb.

Megabyte

One thousand kilobytes (actually, 1024 KB). Abbreviated as MB.

Message-In/Out Phase

A SCSI bus phase. During the Message-In Phase, the target may request to send a message to the initiator.

The Message-Out Phase is invoked by the target only in response to an Attention condition generated by the initiator. It can be generated at any time.

Metallurgy

The science that deals with extracting metals from their ores and making useful objects from them.

MFM

See Modified Frequency Modulation.

MicroChannel Architecture

An IBM-designed proprietary architecture, developed in 1980 to improve upon and replace the aging ISA bus.

Microcontroller

A chip that controls input/output channels.

Micron

A unit of length equal to one-millionth of a meter (10^{-6}).

Microvolt

One-millionth of a volt (10^{-6}).

Millisecond (ms)

One-thousandth of a second. In computing, this measurement is often used to specify the access time of a hard disk drive.

Miniport Driver

A hardware-specific translation layer that abstracts the I/O architecture of the host adapter. It initializes and configures the adapter, starts I/O, verifies the adapter state, and resets the SCSI bus.

MIPS

Million Instructions Per Second. A measurement of the speed of execution of a computer's CPU.

Mirrored Cache

A method of using duplicate caches in which a mirror image of the first cache is stored in the second, providing 100 percent duplication. If the first cache fails, the second one takes over in a way that is transparent to the user.

Mirroring

Writing data to two drives simultaneously. (See RAID.)

Mode Page

A device's behavior, or "mode," is determined by its operating parameters. These mode parameters are grouped into related pages that are numbered for easy reference. A mode page is the minimum unit that can be specified by the Mode Select or Mode Sense Command. A page consists of multiple parameters, which must be specified whenever a page is invoked.

Mode Parameter List

A list that specifies device parameters and is sent by the initiator to the drive during the Data Out Phase. The Mode Parameter list contains the following:

- Header
- Zero or more Block Descriptors
- Mode pages

Modified Frequency Modulation

Timing mechanisms correlate a platter's constant speed with the distance traveled to yield a precise calculation of the head's position over the platter.

Modified Frequency Modulation is where timing information is encoded onto its own track. During the original low-level formatting process of an MFM drive, the synchronization bytes—magnetic data that marks location and time—are added. MFM is also known as double-density recording because it results in twice as much data storage as the original FM.

Motherboard

The primary circuit board in a computer. It contains such components as expansion slots, the CPU, memory and device controllers.

Mount

To appear as a drive letter on PCs or on the Desktop on Macintoshes.

Move16

An instruction inherent in model 68000 microprocessors that moves 16 bytes very quickly.

MPEG

Motion Picture Experts Group, and the algorithms endorsed by that group. Both MPEG-1 and MPEG-2 provide configurable compression for video data. They allow content producers to control the amount of data required by the video portion of their media, sacrificing visual quality for greater compression. MPEG-2 offers better quality than MPEG-1. It allows both backward and forward motion video, but results in larger file sizes.

MTBF

See Mean Time Between Failures.

MTTR

See Mean Time To Repair.

Multichip Module

A small, high-speed, high-density, multi-function, multi-layer chip designed to provide the greatest amount of processing in the smallest amount of space.

Multiple-Host System

A system that has more than one computer connected to the SCSI bus.

Multisession Recording

A CD made with at least two sessions, where the boundary between the sessions also forms a boundary between tracks. Each session is recorded as a contiguous, spiraling string of data, one session following the other. The boundary between the lead-out of one session and the lead-in of the next is a small bit of smooth, unmarred CD surface.

Multivolume/Multisession Recording

A format where each session appears as a separate volume of data.

- On a PC, different volumes can be displayed as different drive letters.
- On a Mac, different volumes can be displayed as different icons.

This is the most common type of multisession disc.

MUNI Chip

Macintosh Universal NuBus Interface. This bus offered the following features:

- Support for the full range of NuBus master/slave transactions with single or block moves.
- Support for the faster data transfer rates to and from the CPU bus.
- Support for NuBus '90 data transfers between cards at a clock rate of 20 MHz.
- Provision of first-in, first-out (FIFO) data buffering between the CPU bus and accessory cards.

Negate

To withdraw a control signal or indicate its absence.

Network Server

A computer attached to a network that stores applications, databases, data, and other tools and information used in common by people connected to the network. A server's multiple-access capability is made possible through software that contains multitasking and multi-user support.

Nibble

A half-byte, or four bits, of data.

Noise

Reflected or distorted signals or voltages on the bus.

Nonproprietary

Refers to a device that implements shared or open technology and can communicate with other devices using the same technology. (See Proprietary.)

Nonproprietary Standard

An open standard that is not owned by any enterprise and is therefore not subject to licensing fees by developers who create products to that standard.

Nonvolatile

Content, such as data or memory, that is retained after power is removed.

Notch

Each section or a range of the logical unit with a different number of blocks per cylinder. Also known as a zone.

Notebook

A small, portable computer that typically weighs six pounds or less. A notebook is usually smaller than a laptop.

ns

See nanosecond.

NuBus

A Macintosh expansion bus whose technology was originally developed by MIT in the 1970s and enlarged upon by IEEE in the mid-1980s. NuBus boards support multiple processors and bus mastering and are self-configuring (eliminating the need to set board parameters with DIP switches).

NuBus accelerates system performance and enables you to expand your system by adding cabling ports.

NuBus Block Mode Data Transfer

Allows large blocks of data to be transferred quickly before releasing the bus, with only one arbitration for the bus.

OEM

Original Equipment Manufacturer. OEM applies to a product that is manufactured by one enterprise then sold to another, where it is bundled and sold with the purchasing enterprise's own products.

Offset

The Request/Acknowledge offset sets the maximum number of Request signals that may be sent

before a corresponding Acknowledge signal is received.

One-Third Height

A housing unit that is 1-inch high. It houses 2.5- and 3.5-inch form factor drives.

On-Going Reliability Test

One of the techniques manufacturers use to produce MTBF ratings. Manufacturer's randomly select drives at the plant and test them. ORT is useful in combination with combined life expectancy and FRR to determine MTBF ratings on older drives.

Opcode

The first byte of a command. The first three bits encode the command group (6-byte, 10-byte, 12-byte, vendor-unique and reserved), and the next five encode the command.

Open Boot

See Open Firmware.

Open Firmware

Open Firmware was originally developed as Open Boot by Sun Microsystems. It debuted in 1988 with the original Sun SparcStation workstation. It provides a way of booting a computer system that is independent of both operating system and processor.

ORT

See On-Going Reliability Test.

Overhead

The incidental command processing time that is necessary to complete a task.

Packet Writing

A method of writing to a compact disc. A packet is a logical group of data. A disc can hold up to 9,500 packets, space permitting.

Paddle Card

A nickname for an IDE host adapter card.

Palmtop

A very small computer, conceivably small enough to fit in the palm of a hand. Usually their storage capacity is minimal, and applications are built in.

Pancake Motor

A brushless, direct-drive (no gears or belts), direct-current (DC) electric motor that drives the spindle in an HDA. This model resides below the spindle and is called a pancake motor because of its flat shape.

Parallel Architecture

In a parallel architecture each byte (eight bits) is sent simultaneously using separate lines.

Parallel Backplane Bus

A backplane with connectors for peripherals that conduct parallel, 8-bit data transfers.

Parallel Data Transfer

Data bits travel simultaneously along eight parallel wires in the cable. (Also see Serial Data Transfer.)

Parallel Disk Array

Another way of referring to RAID level 3. RAID level 3 is an array of disk drives that transfer data in parallel, while one redundant drive functions as the parity check disk.

Parallel Port

A connector port that allows all eight bits of a byte to be transferred at once.

Parameter

Configuration values for the operation of a logical unit. Parameters are sent across the bus in blocks called pages. Some pages pertain to all devices, while some are only for specific classes.

Parameter RAM

A LUN has three copies of its parameters: the current, the default and the saved. The current parameters are those with which the device is currently functioning. These reside in RAM. This is the parameter RAM.

Parity

A method of checking the accuracy of binary numbers. SCSI uses odd parity, which means that the sum of all ones in a number plus its parity bit will always be odd.

Parity Bit

An extra bit, added to a number, used for checking the accuracy of binary numbers.

Parity Check Disk

A disk in an array used exclusively for storing parity information.

Partial Response Maximum Likelihood

A technique used by a read/write head in a drive mechanism for detecting data. Instead of spacing out analog peaks as in peak detection, digital filtering is used to compensate for signal overlap. After filtering, the scheme identifies what are the likeliest sequence of data bits written to the media.

Partition

A portion of a storage area allocated to a particular use or user.

Partition Map

A map detailing the layout of the medium, which the operating system and drivers use to find partition locations.

Follows the Driver Descriptor Block (block 0) on a formatted disk and contains the following information about all partitions on the disk:

- Name of the partition
- Processor type
- Type of partition
- Partition status
- Partition size
- More

Each partition's information occupies one block. The partition map can vary in size from a few to hundreds of blocks. After the partition map come the partitions in sequence.

Partition Table

Part of the Master Boot Block. Partition tables store information on the location, starting point, ending point and size of each partition on a hard disk.

Passive Backplane

A board that exists merely to pass signals; no microprocessing takes place.

PBC

See Port Bypass Circuit.

PCI

Peripheral Component Interconnect. A system standard that defines a high performance interconnection method between plug-in expansion cards, integrated I/O controller chips and a computer's main processing and memory systems. It was originally designed by Intel in the early 1990's as an alternative to other proposed peripheral expansion buses.

PCMCIA

Personal Computer Memory Card International Association. A joint effort of various special interest groups aimed at setting a standard for memory cards used in PCs. PCMCIA cards add improved computer memory capacity or enhance connectivity to external networks and services.

Peak Detection

Data is detected in hard drives typically with a technique known as peak detection. It involves detecting data at high speeds, using a data-encoding method that spaces the signal during reads. The analog detection circuits can then scan each peak in series.

Peer-to-Peer Interface

An interface in which all devices on a bus are treated as equals in terms of their capability to communicate directly with other devices on the bus.They share the processing and control of the exchange.

Peripheral

An optional input/output device that connects to a computer's CPU. Typical peripherals include mass-storage devices, CD-ROM drives, printers and modems.

Peripheral Interface Cable

A cable that makes it possible to daisy chain SCSI devices, one after the other, up to a total of seven, not including the computer.

This cable has two (male-male) 50-pin connectors. It is referred to as a 50-50 cable.

Personal Digital Assistant (PDA)

Hand-held electronic computerized devices that assist a user to become better organized in terms of administrative and telecommunications tasks. Apple's first PDA was the Newton.

PFA

See Predictive Failure Analysis.

Phase Change Optical Drive

A drive that records by using a laser to change the physical nature of the disk from amorphous to crystalline. Phase change drives write in one pass, unlike MO drives, which write in two.

Phthalocyanine

One of the two types of dyes used in the production of CD-R discs. On a CD-R disc, rather than a physical pit or depression in the groove, a dye is used to change the reflection of the laser in the same way that a pit would. This dye is activated by a laser beam of a somewhat higher intensity than that used to read data. The use of this dye allows discs created by a laser to be just as readable on conventional CD readers as discs created by a stamper.

See also Cyanine.

Physical Path

The channel taken by SCSI communications.

PIO

See Polled In/Out.

Platter

The rigid disk that is used for storing memory on hard disk drives.

Plug-and-Play Specification

Created by Intel, Microsoft and Compaq to make it easier to add adapter boards into PCs. It was primarily designed to make the allocation of interrupt, DMA and I/O port addresses automatic when using ISA-based cards. (Previously you had to manually adjust jumpers.) It also mandated the need for self-resetting terminator power fuses and for a special SCSI icon on the back of the adapter. To be implemented, the Plug-and-Play standard required additions to the computer BIOS.

Pointer

Information in the Command Descriptor Block that tracks the execution of command information. There are two types of pointers to keep track of command, status, and data transfers:

- Current (or active)

- Saved

Polled I/O

The transfer protocol employed by IDE, where data transfers are handled by a processor. PIO transfers are "blind" because there is no synchronizing handshaking.

Polling Method

See Normal Mode.

Port

A connector on a computer or peripheral device used for sending and receiving data (I/O).

Port Bypass Circuit

In Fibre Channel Architecture, the logic that enables devices to be removed or inserted without disrupting the operation of the loop. In addition, the PBC logic can take drives off-line or bring them back on-line by sending a command to any device to remove it from loop operation or reinstall it onto the loop.

POST

Power On Self-Test. The sequence of diagnostic checks that a device runs on itself as it starts up.

Power Management

An energy-saving feature. It is the ability of a system to recognize when it has been inactive for a (usually) user-specified amount of time, and consequently to spin down.

Power Spike

A momentary, sharp surge in voltage.

Power Supply

Converts alternating current (AC) coming through the power cord into direct current (DC) that most computers' integrated circuits require. Regulates and delivers voltages at designated levels to specific locations. The power supply contains a variety of filters that smooth voltage irregularities and provide an electrically clean, consistent power source.

PRAM

See Parameter RAM.

Predictive Failure Analysis

A technique for predicting when a drive will die. PFA records and reports suspicious levels of activity, such as many recoverable errors, many retries or slowing performance.

Prefetch

Similar to buffering, except prefetching can read ahead to the next track. These larger reads get more data ready for the CPU's next request, thus speeding up access time.

Primary Partition

The first active partition on the disk. Boot files are always stored on a primary partition. On any disk there can be only four primary partitions. Older DOS versions could support primary partitions of up to 32 MB.

PRML

See Partial Response Maximum Likelihood.

Proprietary

Vendor-unique technology or devices that are incompatible with other products in the industry.

Protocol

A strict set of rules that govern the exchange of information between computer devices.

Pseudo-DMA Mode

Pseudo-Direct Memory Access Mode. An operating mode in which the Macintosh SCSI chip oversees data transfer, letting the CPU tend to other tasks. This is also known as the Blind Data Transfer method because the CPU checks in just once, before a block of data is transferred, and then turns things over to the SCSI chip. Blind transfers are much quicker than the polling method because larger chunks of information-blocks—as opposed to a byte—are transferred at a time.

Punch Card

A card punched with holes that, along with the lack of holes, represented binary data.

QIC Tape Drive

A quarter-inch tape drive that uses magnetic recording tape to store data in a fashion similar to audio tape recorders, except the information is stored in digital form.

RAB

RAID Advisory Board. An association of suppliers and consumers of RAID-related products and other organizations with an interest in RAID technology. The goal of the RAID Advisory Board is to foster an orderly development of RAID technology and to introduce RAID-related products into the marketplace.

RAID

Redundant Array of Independent Disks. A typical RAID unit contains a set of disks that appear to the user as one large storage volume. It is unlike a single drive in that it provides improved system performance delivered in the form of either dramatically increased data transfer speeds, various levels of data security, or both.

RAID Controller

A microprocessor that contains the logic and command control to oversee the creation and maintenance of a RAID architecture.

RAM (Random Access Memory)

Temporary memory usually found on single in-line memory modules (SIMMs) on the motherboard of the computer. RAM is lost when power is turned off.

RAM Buffer

Space allocated in RAM for temporary storage. Large-capacity RAM buffers are useful in CD recording to prevent data underrun.

RAM Chip

Random Access Memory chips whose storage capacities are determined by their number of built-in electronic switches.

Read-Ahead Cache

A variant of the read cache, where an entire track of data is read and stored in cache when a single sector of that track is requested. This allows all further transfers within the track to come from cache.

Read Caching

Read caching utilizes more RAM than track buffering, but it uses the RAM more efficiently. Usually there is enough RAM to store several tracks worth of data. Each time a disk request is made, the cache algorithm checks to see if it's in RAM cache. If the data is in RAM cache, it is returned right away. If the data is not in RAM cache, it is read from disk, copied to the cache, and transferred to the host. Read data remains in cache until the cache is full. When it is full, there are different methods of selecting which data should be replaced with new data. Methods include:

- A random entry
- The least recently used
- The oldest entry

Read/Write Channel

A group of circuits that transfers the data off the platter. These circuits read the sector header information to ensure that the data being read or written is the data that is desired. They also amplify signals to ensure they are strong enough to record information. They must be extremely fast to handle the transitions between looking at sector information and reading or writing the data into the sector in the same rotation. Read/write channels are often the limiting factor in drive performance.

Read/Write Head

The disk drive's electromagnet, directed by the controller, that creates and reads magnetic

information on the surface of the platters.

Real Estate

The limited, and therefore extremely valuable, space on a hard disk platter, a controller board, an HBA, or inside an external device chassis.

Red Book

Standard for normal audio CD. Refers to the specifications for the compact audio disc format developed by Philips and Sony. It is the standard format of commercial audio CDs. When a disc conforms to the Red Book standard, it will usually have "digital audio" printed beneath the disc logo.

Reflection

A signal that reaches the end of the line and improperly flows back towards the device. This situation is remedied with proper termination.

Register

A temporary hardware storage area that assists with the speedy transfer of arithmetic/logical operations within the CPU.

Removable Cartridge Drive

One or more hard drive platters in a self-contained rigid case that can be removed from the main drive unit.

Removable Drive

A hard drive and its entire head assembly in a rigid cartridge module that plugs into a "mother" unit. Also called a canister drive.

Reselection Phase

In Arbitrating systems, the phase in which a target is reconnected to the bus after having disconnected to perform a time-consuming task.

A target device asserts the Reselection signal and its own ID number. It gets reconnected if the bus is free or the target's SCSI ID has a priority higher than another device that is asserting the Select signal.

Reset Condition

A condition that kicks every device off the bus. It is caused when a SCSI device asserts the Reset control signal. A Reset condition may occur at any time, forcing the bus into the Bus Free Phase. Targets may go through a complete power on self test (POST) sequence and clear out pending or current operations.

Retries

When you hear drives seeking the head hard (a hard seek usually makes a cha-chunking noise), it's probably because retries are occurring. Retries cause the head to seek back to track zero and retry the data access. A drive will try this multiple times. The number of times is defined in a SCSI drive's Mode Page 1 settings.

RISC

Reduced instruction set computing. It is the successor of CISC, complex instruction set computing. A microprocessor commonly used in professional workstations as well as PCs. The RISC chip is 75 percent faster than CISC. It incorporates over a million transistors and processes data 64 bits at a time.

RLL

See Run-Length Limited.

ROM (Read-Only Memory)

Permanently stored data in the computer memory. Also refers to storage media that may only be read (not erased or written to.)

Rotational Position Locking (RPL)

A drive feature that causes synchronization of drive spindles, so the spinning of multiple disks can be coordinated. This is critical for faster transfer rates in disk arrays.

RPM

Rotations per minute. In drives, the measurement of the rotational speed of the platter.

Run-Length Limited

A data compression encoding scheme borrowed from the world of mainframe computers to increase a drive's storage capacity beyond MFM.

SAF-TE

SCSI Accessed Fault-Tolerant Enclosures. A specification, started by Conner, for a standard method of communicating with fault-tolerant enclosures. It defined a set of SCSI commands used to check the status of fans, power supplies and temperature. A small computer with its own SCSI ID essentially monitors the enclosure and tells the computer how it's doing.

SASI

Shugart Associates System Interface. The forerunner of SCSI. SASI was intended as a low-cost, peer-to-peer interface.

S-Bus

Sun Microsystem's high-performance expansion bus for sparc-based workstations. The S-Bus runs data transfers at 70 MB/s or faster and offers I/O configurations that can sustain mainframe-like I/O rates. The S-Bus supports Fibre Channel Loop Architecture.

SCA

Single Connector Attachment. A high-density connector that carries every type of signal passed along a SCSI bus, including SCSI ID, LED and spindle synchronization information.

SCAM

SCSI Configured Auto-Magically. A protocol that allows a host adapter to set the SCSI ID number of devices on the SCSI bus, preventing ID conflicts, and to set termination automatically.

Scatter/Gather

Refers to reading logically contiguous blocks of data from a disk and storing them at discontiguous host computer memory addresses (scatter) and writing data from discontiguous host computer memory addresses to consecutive logical block addresses on a disk (gather).

SCSI

Small Computer Systems Interface. A standard interface via which computers and their peripherals communicate with each other.

SCSI BIOS Boot ROM

Used to initialize the SCSI chip on startup and to support the transparent operation of the adapter under DOS through the standard INT13 BIOS interface.

SCSI Bus

A facility, developed according to SCSI specifications, for transferring data between several devices located between two end points, with only one initiator and one target being able to communicate at a given time.

The SCSI bus provides high-speed, parallel data transmission and is typically used to connect hard disks, tape backup drives, scanners and printers to the host computer.

SCSI Disk Mode

Allows an internal hard disk to be mounted and used as an external drive by another Macintosh.

SCSI Host Adapter

Connects a SCSI controller to the I/O bus of the host. A host adapter may be integrated on the motherboard of the system, or it may be implemented as a separate board.

SCSI ID

A device's unique address on the SCSI bus is referred to as its ID, or identification.

SCSI Interface Controller

SCSI Interface Module

SCSI Manager

The SCSI Manager is part of the Macintosh Operating System that provides the interface between a program such as a driver or formatter and the actual hardware SCSI port.

SCSI Messages

Communication between the initiator and target for the purpose of interface management. A message can be sent in both directions: message-out from initiator to target, or message-in from target to initiator.

There are three types of message formats:

- single-byte
- two-byte
- extended (three-byte or longer)

SCSI System Cable

Attaches the first SCSI device on the bus to the computer.

Macintosh versions have a male 25-pin connector to connect to the computer and a 50-pin connector to plug into the SCSI device. This cable is often referred to as a 25-50 cable.

PC versions have a male 50-pin high-density connector to connect to the SCSI host adapter, and a 50-pin connector to plug into the SCSI device.

SCSI-SCSI Array Controller

A hardware-based disk array. The drives are connected to a RAID controller board installed inside the disk array chassis. The host computer recognizes the RAID controller board as the SCSI storage device, rather than the drives connected to it. Read and write commands sent from the computer are processed by the RAID controller board, which in turn sends the appropriate read and write commands to the drives.

SCSI-2

SCSI-2 is an upgrade to the SCSI-1 standard that builds on the SCSI specification in the following ways:

- Defines extensions to the SCSI-1 specification
- Provides more complete standardization of SCSI-1 command sets
- Describes the necessary mechanical, electrical, and functional qualities that will allow for interoperability of devices meeting the new standard

To meet these demands, SCSI-2 devices require more intelligence and firmware than their SCSI-1 counterparts.

SCSI-3

SCSI-3's main target is extending SCSI-2's functionality so that it is suitable for much higher performance rates, while maintaining backward compatibility with present SCSI.

The SCSI-3 specification has numerous goals, including better cabling schemes for Fast and Wide SCSI. Some of these cabling schemes may be standardized before the SCSI-3 specification is released.

Sector Skew

The sector offset from one platter to another in a hard drive.

Sectors, Alternate

Sectors set aside to replace bad blocks. Also called "spares."

Sectors

Sectors are the smallest subdivisions of tracks, and usually contain exactly 512 bytes of data.

Sector Header

The first group of information fields in a sector format. The header is comprised of the following:

- A field for synchronizing the data separator
- The address field, which contains the cylinder, head, and sector numbers
- The cyclic redundancy code checksum, which is used to check whether the address was read properly

Selection Phase

The bus phase in which an initiator selects a target device.

Seek Time

The time it takes the read/write head to move back and forth in search of the appropriate track. Seek time does not include latency or command overhead. (See Access Time.)

Semiconductor

An element or compound whose normal conductivity is between an insulator and a conductor, but whose resistance to an electrical current can vary depending upon its level of impurities.

Sense Data

Sense data is data returned by the Request Sense command. This data is used to diagnose the error that occurred on the proceeding command.

Sense Key

Error codes contained in sense data that indicate a particular classification of error.

Sense Request

This command retrieves sense data.

Sequential Access Device

Any device that must pass through unwanted blocks of data to access the targeted block, and can only access one block at a time. For example, a tape drive is a sequential access device.

Sequential Test

A test that is useful for finding media errors.

Serial Architecture

In a serial architecture, data is transmitted one bit at a time.

Serial Data Transfer

Data bits travel single-file along one wire in the cable.

Serial Port

A port that passes along data in sequence, one bit at a time, as opposed to a parallel port, which passes data along in groups of eight, sixteen, or thirty-two.

Serial Storage Architecture

A powerful high-speed serial interface designed to connect high-capacity data storage devices, subsystems, servers and workstations. Only four signal wires are required, compared to 68 for the closest SCSI equivalent. SSA interfaces require no address switches and no discrete terminators.

Server

See Network Server.

Servo

Information on a disk used for guiding the head's positioning over data.

See also Voice Coil Actuator.

Servo Positioning Platter

A disk dedicated exclusively to storing and maintaining servo positioning information that guides drive heads to accurate positions over requested data.

Session

A group of data containing a Lead In area, a Data area and a Lead Out area. A session can be recorded in one sitting or incrementally, depending on the formatting software's capability. Each session carries about 15 MB of overhead for the Lead In and Lead Out areas.

On a disc, a session is one contiguous spiraling string of data. There may be more than one session on a disc.

Shock Rating

A rating used to judge the ruggedness of a drive.

Short Stroking

Using only half of a higher-capacity drive to achieve faster seek times by requiring the drive to seek across only half the platter.

Signal Noise

Unwanted electrical signals that interfere with a communications channel. These can come from many sources, including fluorescent lights, electric motors, and electric or magnetic fields.

Signal Resonance

Interference with a communications signal by another signal oscillating at the same frequency. This disturbs signal integrity, making it difficult for the CPU to interpret commands and messages.

SIM

SCSI Interface Module. Part of the CAM specification. The SIM function processes SCSI requests and manages the hardware-independent interface to the HBA.

SIM services:

- Monitor I/O behavior and perform error recovery if needed
- Manage data transfer hardware, such as DMA circuitry
- Queue multiple operations for single or multiple LUNs, "freezing" the queuing of requests as necessary to perform queue recovery
- Post results back to the initiating device driver
- Manage the selection, disconnection, reconnection, and data pointers of the SCSI HBA protocol

Single Connector Attachment

See SCA.

Single-Ended

An electrical signal configuration where information is sent through one wire in a cable. The information is interpreted by the change in the voltage of the signal. Single-ended interfaces allow cable lengths of up to 6 meters.

Compare with differential.

Single-Session Recording

In CD recording, where the data is written to disc in one session.

Slave

When two devices or systems are in such a relationship that one of them has control over the other:

- The controlling device is the master.
- The controlled device is the slave.

SLED

Single Large Expensive Drives. An alternative to RAID.

Sleep Mode

A safety feature available on some computer models that parks the drive head after a certain period of inactivity.

Slew-Rate Control

Used to control rise/fall times of signals.

Slider

A rigid block of material upon which a disk head is mounted. It provides lift, stability and mechanical strength to the head assembly.

SMART

Self-Monitoring, Analysis and Reporting Technology. SMART helps protect user data from predictable degradation in drive performance.

SMD-X

Storage Module Device (SMD-E and SMD-H). Until SCSI's rise to prominence, SMD was the preferred interface for drives used with high-end server applications.

Soft Reset

The Reset condition kicks every device off the bus. It is caused when a SCSI device asserts the Reset control signal. The Soft Reset option will:

- Try to complete commands that were in process
- Hold on to all SCSI device reservations
- Maintain the SCSI device operating mode

The Soft Reset option has the advantage of allowing the initiator to reset the bus without affecting other initiators in a multiple-host system.

Compare with Hard Reset.

Software-Based Disk Array

A RAID configuration that is created and maintained through software.

Software Disk Cache

A cache that resides in the CPU's RAM. It is used for storing the most frequently accessed disk information. A software disk cache speeds data retrieval but limits the amount of RAM available for the program itself. It is usually configurable. Typically it can be enabled/disabled and adjusted in size. It also can be increased through the installation of additional memory.

Spacial Re-Use

A function provided in Serial Storage Architecture that allows data to be transferred concurrently at high speeds between many pairs of serially connected peripherals, without the need to route the data through the processor.

Spindle

The shaft that platters are mounted on.

Spindle Synchronization

In an array of disk drives, a feature that ensures all spindles are spinning in unison and at the same rate of speed. Each platter of each drive will be in precisely the right position relative to the other drives. This nearly eliminates latency, because the head on drive B will be over the appropriate sector of its platter just as the head on drive A finishes reading from or writing to the appropriate sector on its platter.

Sputtering

One of the techniques used to apply the reflective metal layer to CD media or the magnetic material to a hard disk or floppy diskette. The substrate disc is suspended in a vacuum along with a mass of the material to be deposited. This mass is bombarded with an ion stream, which dislodges atoms. The atoms are attracted and cling to the substrate, resulting in a thin, consistent metallic coating.

SSA

See Serial Storage Architecture.

SSA IA

Serial Storage Architecture Industry Association. It was formed in 1995 to promote the acceptance of the SSA standard within the industry. Its membership includes more than 25 manufacturers of systems and peripheral products.

Stepper Motor

An older model of head actuator that moves the head in discrete steps. It is a type of rotational pivot used in a floppy drive. It operates somewhat like a car's transmission, converting an incremental rotary movement into linear travel.

ST-506

In 1983, Al Shugart's Seagate Technologies introduced the ST-506 as a 5.25-inch, 5 MB hard drive implemented on the IBM XT. It became the most popular of the low-capacity MFM drives.

ST-412

Seagate's successor drive to the ST-506. It provided 12 MB of capacity.

Stamping

In CD production, manufacturing data into a disc (as opposed to writing data to a writable disc).

Status Phase

A Bus Phase in which the target sends a byte of information to the initiator that indicates the success or failure of a command (or a series of linked commands).

The Status Phase is critical for error detection and defect management.

Step Pulse

A drive feature that moves the head one track over, and speeds access time by quickly positioning the head over the correct track.

Stiction

Short for static friction. It happens when the heads of the drive are stuck to the platters of the drive. When you try to power up the drive, the heads cannot break free. Stiction is usually caused by improper lubricants on the drive platter.

Storage Peripherals

Devices attached to the host computer with cables that store user data.

Striping

See Data Striping.

Stub

A small length of a cable with connectors. It is used for connecting an internal device, such as a hard drive, to the internal SCSI port.

Subsystem

A subset of the entire computer system. A subsystem can include drive arrays and controllers on add-in boards that relieve the CPU of some of its tasks.

Surge Suppressor

An intermediating strip of electrical outlets that regulates the flow of power to a system, filtering out power surges and preventing costly damage to system components.

Sustained Data Transfer Rate

The average data transfer rate over time. It includes burst from the cache (optimal) and cross-cylinder accesses (suboptimal).

Synchronization

Causing to agree exactly in time or rate.

Synchronization Bytes

Magnetic data that marks location and time on a disk platter. These bytes are added during the original low-level formatting process of an MFM drive.

Tagged Command Queuing

Part of the SCSI-2 specification, Tagged Command Queuing allows each LUN to queue up to 256 I/O processes per initiator. This frees the initiator from having to ask for a new command each time it finishes an operation.

TAO

See Track-at-Once.

Tape Drive

A type of storage, similar to an audio tape recorder, that stores data on a magnetic tape. Tape drives are usually used for data back-up.

Target

A SCSI device, usually the peripheral, that carries out the initiator's request.

TB

See Terabyte.

T-Cal

See Thermal Recalibration.

Terabyte

A value equal to 10^{12}. It is written out as 1,000,000,000,000.

Termination

Electrical connection at each end of the SCSI bus composed of a set of resistors or other components. It is used to provide closure to the bus and reduce reflections or ringing.

Terminators for single-ended and differential interfaces are different and are not interchangeable.

Termination Power

The power supplied to a bus terminator.

Thermal Recalibration

The process of recalculating the positions of data on a hard disk platter as those positions shift due to the platter's expansion under the heat of operation.

TIB

See Transfer Information Block.

Time-Out

SCSI devices operate under a definable time period, beyond which they will "time-out" and release the bus.

Timing Mechanism

A mechanism that correlates a platter's constant speed with the distance traveled, yielding a precise calculation of the head's position over the platter.

TPI

Tracks per inch.

TPWR

See Termination Power.

Track

Invisible "grooves," in the form of concentric circles that store data on a platter. On a hard disk, each track is a single line of magnetic domains. On a CD-ROM disc, each track is a line of pits and lands.

Track Buffering

When data is requested from a particular sector, the controller will read the entire track and store it in its RAM.

Track-at-Once

A method of writing to a CD where the user can copy one track of data at a time. Up to—but no more than—99 tracks of data can be stored on a disc, space permitting. TAO recording can be used with either single-session or multisession recording. The finalized disc is 100 percent backward compatible with CD-ROM drives.

Track-to-Track Seek Time

The time it takes a drive head to move from one track to another. This usually falls in the 2 ms range.

Transfer Information Block

A block of information about a pending data transfer, used to prevent data transfer hiccups when the size of the transfer outruns the size of the track buffer.

Transformer

A device used to transfer electric energy from one circuit to another.

Transistor

A digital, solid-state miniaturized circuit used to modulate or control the flow of an electric current.

Transparent

Activity that takes place in the background, making all but the result invisible to a user.

Trap

A command trigger that causes automatic transfer of control to a trap-handler program.

Travan

A subset of the mini-cartridge format QIC (quarter-inch cartridge). At .315 inches, Travan is slightly wider than standard QIC. It allows a 750 foot tape length, which translates to larger capacity—up to 10 GB for proposed TR-5—and data transfer rates up to 1.2 MB/s.

UDF

See Universal Disk Format.

Ultra SCSI

This is the same as Fast-20 SCSI. It delivers twice the performance of regular SCSI.

See also Fast SCSI.

Uninterruptible Power Supply

An intermediary device connected to a power source and a computer. When there is a power failure, the UPS uses a battery and power circuits to produce the voltage required to keep the computer running. Depending upon the size of the battery and the power requirements of the computer, a UPS can power a computer anywhere from a few minutes to several hours.

Universal Disk Format

An ISO 13346 standard for formatting data on disks. This standard has been spearheaded by the Optical Storage Technology Association (OSTA). It would allow disks to be read/written on any platform, ensuring full data interchange.

Universal Serial Bus

A 12 Mb/s interface supporting up to 63 peripheral devices. USB is intended to support low-speed peripherals such as keyboards and pointing devices, and is not suitable for mass storage or video applications. USB supports automatic configuration ("plug-and-play") and hot-plugging.

UPS

See Uninterruptible Power Supply.

USB

See Universal Serial Bus.

Vapor Deposition

A technique for applying a chrome-like covering onto high-speed, high-capacity hard drives.

Variable Zone Recording

A method of encoding that allows the outer tracks of the platter to hold more sectors than the inner tracks. Similar to notch.

Vendor-Unique Commands

Commands left undefined within a standard, that act as place-holders for custom commands that will be developed by individual vendors.

VESA

Video Electronic Standards Association. See VESA Local Bus.

VESA Local Bus (VLB)

Video Electronic Standards Association Local Bus. It was designed to interface the Intel 80486 high speed processor bus to a local high-speed expansion bus. It ran at the processor speed and provided for high-speed, 32-bit data transfers.

Virtual Memory

A technique whereby a computer offloads some of the data/program from its primary memory onto disk, giving the impression that primary memory can continue to accept/store virtually unlimited amounts of data.

VLB

See VESA Local Bus.

VLSI

Very-Large-Scale Integration. A chip with 20- to 900-thousand logic gates per chip. Transistors form logic gates that control the flow of electrons through chips.

Voice Coil Actuator

A type of actuator that moves the read/write head in increments of infinitely-controllable size. Uses servo information for positioning.

Volume

Also known as a partition. Represented by an icon on the Desktop and used to store files and folders of information.

Volume Bit Map

A directory structure that keeps track of allocation blocks that are in use and that are free. It is used to determine where to put data that needs space and where to free up space when a file is deleted.

Volume Information Block

A master directory block that contains important information on the volume, including:

- Its name and type
- The number of files and folders on the volume
- The allocation block size
- Pointers to the location of files

There is a backup copy of this near the end of the disk.

Warm Spare

A replacement drive for a RAID system that requires the system to go off-line but not power-down in order to replace components.

Watermark

A reference point. In HSM ToolKit, a watermark is a user-defined percentage of disk capacity. When the watermark is reached, HSM ToolKit is triggered to migrate files to free up some disk space.

Wedged Servo

See Embedded Servo.

White Book

The standard specification for Video CD. JVC, Matsushita, Sony and Philips coauthored this specification. It is also known as the "Video CD Standard."

Wide SCSI

A SCSI-2 option that makes possible 16- or 32-bit wide data transfers and consequently much faster data transfer rates. In order to handle the extra width, an additional 29 signals are necessary. It requires a 68-pin cable connector.

Winchester 30/30

Considered to be the first true hard drive technology. It was developed in 1973 by IBM. It was named after the Winchester 30/30 rifle because the hard drive used two 30 MB disks, one fixed and one removable.

Winchester Drive

A fixed disk drive in which a sealed data module houses the access arm and the magnetic data disk. Most modern hard drives use Winchester technology.

Wired-or Signal

Or "Or-tied." A control signal that requires simultaneous control signals from more than one device to drive a bus phase true or positive, preventing electrical conflict. No devices drive the signal to a false state. Instead, the terminators pull the signal false whenever it is not driven.

Word

Used to denote the number of bits that constitute a common unit of information in a particular computer system.

WORM Drive

A CD-Recordable drive that writes to and reads from compact discs.

See also Write-Once, Read-Many.

Write-Back Caching

Write-back caching keeps track of what information in the cache has been modified by the microprocessor. This is done by marking modified information with a "dirty bit." When displaced from the cache, all the information with dirty bits is written to primary memory. It's likely that the term "dirty bit" was coined to denote a tag that marked information that needed to be "cleaned out" (written) to the disk or to memory.

Write Caching

Cache method by which the controller transfers a write request to its own cache, tells the CPU that the task is complete, and then completes the write at a later time. This speeds operations because the controller would not ordinarily tell the CPU it had finished the command until it actually had, and the CPU would have to wait for notification before going on to the next command.

Write-Once, Read Many (WORM)

Generic term for a type of drive (WORM drive) that uses media that can be written to only once, but that can be read many times. Different devices use different techniques for preventing data from being erased. Some drives use series of software flags and special data bits that tell the firmware of the drive not to write to certain data blocks. Others physically change the media so it cannot be rewritten. Examples of WORM drives include multifunction magneto-optical drives, phase change optical drives, and CD-Recordable drives.

Write-Through Cache

A variation of write caching, in which data destined for the drive is written to the disk but also stored in the cache. If this data is needed again, it can be read from the cache instead of going to disk. This is often combined with read caching to accelerate disk performance.

XOR

"XOR" stands for "exclusive or," a function of Boolean logic used in creating parity data. The XOR function sets a parity bit to a 1 if and only if either (but not both) of the compared data bits is 1.

XOR Engine

A custom hardware engine that speeds up generation of parity in RAID 4 and 5 systems, which allows a RAID drive to be recovered in the event of a failure. XOR engines are usually used on higher end RAID subsystems. Other RAID subsystems rely on an on-board processor to do the XOR calculation.

XPT

SCSI-2 CAM (Common Access Method) Transport. It is a layer of software that peripheral drivers and application programs use to initiate the execution of CAM functions.

Yellow Book

Standard specification for CD-ROM. It allows for the presence of data tracks on a CD. It builds on the Red Book Standard. The Yellow Book standard specifies that CD-ROM must encode the first track as data. In addition to the two layers of error correction outlined in the Red Book, data is further protected by a third layer of error detection and correction. When a disc conforms to Yellow Book standard, it will usually say "data storage" beneath the disc logo.

Zip Drive

A drive with a 3.5" cartridge containing a flexible disk that spins within a cushion of filtered air.

Index

Bus Mastering 190
Bus Phases 126, 179
   and control signals 136
   bus free 152
   data 131
   message out 152
   selection 131
Buses 261–282
   Apple Desktop Bus 220
   arbitration 169, 205
   block multiplexer 118
   bus clock 262
   bus mastering 262
   bus reset 130, 131, 132
   CardBus 282
   data bus lines 133, 138
   EISA 266
   FIFO 264
   hard reset 132
   ISA 238, 264–265
   MicroChannel 236, 265
   Move16 264
   NuBus 261–264, 273, 276
   OEM channel 118, 122
   PCI 226, 254, 267–281
   PCI Mezzanine 281
   PCI on Macintosh 271
   S-Bus 226
   SCSI bus 122, 123, 130, 133, 143, 169
   termination 146
   VESA 254
   VESA Local Bus (VLB) 266–267
Byte 122
Byte-Based Striping 70

C

Cables 140–151, 225, 235
   ACK 140
   cable extender 141, 143
   chip requirements 145
   daisy chain 140, 148
   differential 145
   Enhanced IDE 254
   fiber optic 227, 228

   GND 140
   HDI-30 178
   IDE 237
   impedance 140, 148, 151
   improper termination 148
   length limitations 145
   parity 140
   peripheral interface cable 141
   recommendations 140
   REQ 140
   ribbon cables 140
   SCSI Disk Adapter 178
   SCSI System cable 141
   SSA 229
   stubs 143
Cache 34–40
   cache algorithm 38
   CPU cache 35, 36
   data transfer rates 35
   hard drive cache 35, 37
   hardware caching controller 40
   Level 2 cache 36
   prefetch 38
   RAM 36
   RAM drives 40
   read caching 38
   read-ahead buffer 38
   software disk cache 35, 36
   track buffer 38
   write caching 39
   write-back cache 266
   write-through cache 39
CAM 180, 189, 208–209, 237
Capacitor 177
Catalog Tree 187
CD Formats
   CD Extra 102
   CD-Bridge 101
   CD-DA 101
   CD-G 101
   CD-i 101
   CD-R 102
   CD-ROM 101
   CD-ROM XA 101
CD Mastering 98

UNIX 226, 255
UPS 39, 48
USB 217, 219

V

Vapor Deposition 19
Variable Zone Recording 26, 234
Volume Bit Map 187
Volume Information Block 187
Volume Limits
    allocation block size 187
    Macintosh 187

W

Western Digital 119, 235, 237, 252
White Book 101
Win32 189
Winchester 7
Windows 190, 226, 249, 255, 256,
    258, 276, 286, 293
Write Caching 39
Write-Through Cache 39
Writing 13, 17
    ablative WORM 106
    CD-R 99
    CD-ROM 93

data mapping 185
encoding 26
floptical 92
interleaving 30
magneto-optical 90
phase change optical 92
scatter/gather 254
sector skew 31
variable zone recording 26

X

Xebec 119
XOR 64, 73, 77
XPT 180, 208
Xyratex 227

Y

Yellow Book 101

Z

Ziff-Davis 293
Zones 26